Tom Cur

654-4868

EXAM 10, 11, 12, 13, 14, 15, 16
Some of ch. 5
Do prob. in 15 + 16

PROBABILITY
AND
STATISTICS
FOR
ENGINEERS

Prentice-Hall Mathematics Series
DR. ALBERT A. BENNETT, EDITOR

PROBABILITY
AND
STATISTICS
FOR
ENGINEERS

IRWIN MILLER AND **JOHN E. FREUND**

ARTHUR D. LITTLE, INC.

PROFESSOR OF MATHEMATICS
ARIZONA STATE UNIVERSITY

PRENTICE-HALL, INC., ENGLEWOOD CLIFFS, NEW JERSEY

PRENTICE-HALL INTERNATIONAL, INC. *London*
PRENTICE-HALL OF AUSTRALIA, PTY., LTD. *Sydney*
PRENTICE-HALL OF CANADA, LTD. *Toronto*
PRENTICE-HALL OF INDIA (PRIVATE) LTD., *New Delhi*
PRENTICE-HALL OF JAPAN, INC. *Tokyo*

Library of Congress Catalog Card Number 65–10075

Current printing (last digit):
13 12 11 10 9 8 7 6 5 4

PRINTED IN THE UNITED STATES OF AMERICA, *C71166*

PREFACE

This book has been written for an introductory course in probability and statistics for students of engineering and the physical sciences. It has been tested extensively in courses for university students as well as through in-plant training of practicing engineers. The authors have found that the material in the book can be covered in a two-semester or three-quarter course consisting of three lectures a week. However, through a choice of topics the book also lends itself as a text for shorter courses with emphasis upon either theory or applications.

Chapters 2, 3, 4, and 7 provide a brief, though rigorous, introduction to the theory of statistics, and together with some of the material in Chapters 5 and 16, they are suitable for an introductory semester (or quarter) course on the mathematics of probability and statistics. Chapters 6, 8, 9, 10, and 11 contain conventional material on the elementary methods of statistical inference, including a treatment of short-cut and nonparametric methods. Chapters 12, 13, and 14 comprise an introduction to some of the standard, though more advanced, topics of experimental statistics, while Chapters 5, 15, and 16 deal with special applications, some very new, which have become increasingly important in recent years.

v

The mathematical background expected of the reader is a year course in calculus; actually, calculus is required mainly for Chapters 4 and 7 dealing with basic distribution theory in the continuous case, for Chapters 5 and 16 dealing with special applications (random processes, reliability, etc.), and for the least-squares methods of Chapters 12 and 13. The treatment of probability in Chapter 2 is modern in the sense that it is based on the elementary theory of sets.

The authors would like to express their appreciation and indebtedness to the D. Van Nostrand Company for permission to reproduce the material in Table II; to the late Sir Ronald A. Fisher, F.R.S., Cambridge, and to Messrs. Oliver and Boyd, Ltd., Edinburgh, for permission to reprint Table IV from their book, *Statistical Methods for Research Workers;* to Professor E. S. Pearson and the *Biometrika* trustees for permission to reproduce the material in Tables V, VI, and VIII; to Donald B. Owen and Addison-Wesley, Inc., for permission to reproduce part of the Table of Random Numbers from their *Handbook of Statistical Tables;* to Frank J. Massey, Jr., and the *Journal of the American Statistical Association* for permission to reproduce the material in Table IX; to D. B. Duncan, H. L. Harter, and *Biometrics* for permission to reproduce Table X; to the American Society for Testing and Materials for permission to reproduce Table XI; and to the McGraw-Hill Book Company for permission to reproduce the material in Table XII.

The authors would also like to express their appreciation to the editorial staff of Prentice-Hall, Inc., for their courteous cooperation in the production of this book, to the various secretaries who helped in the typing of the manuscript, and above all to their wives for not complaining too much about the demands made on their husbands throughout the writing of this book.

IRWIN MILLER AND JOHN E. FREUND

CONTENTS

vii

viii

ix

PROBABILITY
AND
STATISTICS
FOR
ENGINEERS

1 | INTRODUCTION

1.1 Modern Statistics

The origin of statistics is usually traced to two very dissimilar human interests, games of chance and what is now called political science. Mid-eighteenth century studies in probability led to the mathematical treatment of errors of measurement, and the resulting "laws of error" led to the theory which today forms the basis of mathematical statistics. In the same century, interest in the analysis of political units led to what is now called *descriptive statistics*. At first, descriptive statistics consisted merely of the presentation of data in tables and charts; later it grew to include also the summarization of data by means of numerical descriptions.

In recent decades, the growth of statistics has made itself felt in almost every major phase of human activity, and the most important feature of its growth has been the shift in emphasis from descriptive statistics to the methods of *statistical inference, or inductive statistics*. Statistical inference concerns generalizations based on sample data; it applies to such problems

1

as *estimating* the average fuel consumption of a missile engine on the basis of some trial runs, *testing* a manufacturer's claim on the basis of measurements performed on samples of his product, and *predicting* the hardness of a metal on the basis of records pertaining to the past performance of a production process.

Statistical inference involves generalizations which actually go beyond the information contained in a set of data. In making such inductive inferences one must proceed with extreme caution. One must decide carefully how far one can go in generalizing from a given set of data, whether such generalizations are at all reasonable or justifiable, whether it might be wise to wait until there are more data, and so forth. Indeed, some of the most important problems of statistical inference concern the appraisal of the risks and the consequences to which one might be exposed by making generalizations from sample data. This includes an appraisal of the probabilities of making wrong decisions, the chances of making incorrect predictions, and the possibility of obtaining estimates which do not lie within permissible limits.

In recent years, attempts have been made to treat all these problems within the framework of a unified theory called *decision theory*. Although this theory has many conceptual as well as theoretical advantages, it poses some problems of application that are difficult to overcome. To understand these problems, one must realize that *no matter how objectively an experiment or an investigation is planned, it is impossible to eliminate all elements of subjectivity*. It is at least partly a subjective decision whether to base an experiment (say, the determination of a specific heat) on 5 measurements, on 12 measurements, or on 25 or more. Also, subjective factors invariably enter the design of equipment, the hiring of personnel, and even one's deciding *how* to formulate a hypothesis and the alternative against which it is to be tested. (This important problem will be discussed in some detail in Chapter 8.) An element of subjectivity enters even when we define such terms as "good" or "best" in connection with the description of decision criteria—for instance, in Chapter 12 we shall ask for a straight line which "best" fits a given set of paired data. Above all, subjective judgments are virtually unavoidable when one is asked to put "cash values" on the various risks to which one is exposed. In other words, it is impossible to be completely objective in specifying "rewards" for being right (or close) and "penalties" for being wrong (or not close enough). After all, if a scientist is asked to judge the safety of a piece of equipment, how can he possibly put a cash value on the possibility that he might make an error, when such an error may lead to the loss of human lives?

Whether or not statistical inference is viewed within the broader framework of decision theory, it depends heavily on the theory of probability. We shall approach the subject of statistics as a science, developing each statistical idea insofar as possible from its probabilistic foundation, and applying each idea to problems of physical or engineering science as soon as it has been developed. The methods we shall use in stating and solving these problems might be called the *classical approach,* because they do not *formally* take into account all the subjective factors mentioned in the preceding paragraph. However, we shall endeavor continually to make the reader aware that such subjective factors do exist, and to indicate whenever possible what role they might play in making the final decision. Subjectivity plays an important role in the choice among statistical methods or formulas to be used in a given situation, in deciding on the size of a sample, in specifying the probabilities with which we are willing to risk errors, and so forth. This "bread-and-butter" approach to statistics presents the subject in the form in which it has so successfully contributed to engineering science, as well as to the natural and social sciences, in the last twenty years.

1.2 Statistics and Engineering

There are few areas where the impact of the recent growth of statistics has been felt more strongly than in engineering and industrial management. Indeed, it would be difficult to overestimate the contributions statistics has made to problems of production, to the effective use of materials and manpower, to basic research, and to the development of new products. As in the other sciences, statistics has become a vital tool to the engineer; in fact, some knowledge of statistics has become a necessity without which he cannot possibly appreciate, understand, or apply much of the work done in his field.

In this text, our attention will be directed largely towards engineering applications, but we shall not hesitate to refer also to other areas, to impress upon the reader the great generality of most statistical techniques. Thus, the reader will find that the statistical method which is used to estimate the coefficient of thermal expansion of a metal serves also to estimate the average time it takes a secretary to perform a given task, the average length of an adult iguana, or the average I.Q. of an immigrant arriving in the United States. Similarly, the statistical method which is used to compare the performance of two engines serves also to compare the effectiveness of two teaching methods, the merits of two fertilizers, or the audience response to two different kinds of television programs.

In spite of the generality of most statistical techniques, there are also instances where the requirements of different fields have led to the development of special techniques. Thus, problems of economic forecasting led to special methods used in the analysis of series of business data; the medical problem of determining critical dosages led to what is called probit analysis;

problems in psychological testing led to factor analysis, and so forth. So far as engineering is concerned, we shall introduce the reader to three areas which have required the development of special techniques. Chapter 5 contains a brief introduction to *operations research,* a new technology which is characterized by the application of scientific techniques (including probability theory and statistics) to problems involving the operations of a "system" looked upon as a whole. Thus, it applies to the conduct of a war, the management of a firm, the manufacture of a product, and so forth. Of course, it must be understood that this special chapter and the two special chapters mentioned in the next paragraph are mere introductions; entire books have been devoted to each of these areas.

In Chapter 15 we shall introduce the reader to special methods used in problems of *quality assurance,* including the problem of controlling (establishing and maintaining) quality in mass production, the problem of establishing tolerance limits, and problems of sampling inspection. Finally, in Chapter 16 we shall present special techniques which have been developed to meet the reliability needs of the highly complex products of space-age technology.

2 | PROBABILITY

2.1 Sample Spaces

In statistics it is customary to refer to any process of observation as an *experiment*. Thus, an experiment may consist of the simple process of noting whether a soldered connection is broken or intact; it may consist of determining what proportion of a sample of housewives prefers Brand X to Brand Y; or it may consist of the very complicated process of finding the mass of an electron. The results of any such observations, whether they be simple "yes" or "no" answers, instrument readings, or whatever, are called the *outcomes* of the respective experiments. The totality of the possible outcomes of an experiment is called the *sample space* of the experiment and it will be denoted by the letter S.

When dealing with problems in which uncertainties are connected with the various outcomes, it is convenient to think of the outcomes of an experiment, the *elements* of the sample space, as points in a space of one or more dimensions. For example, if an experiment consists of examining a single solder joint, it may be intact (denoted by the number 0) or it may be broken (denoted by the number 1) and the sample space is one-dimensional, as shown in Figure 2.1. If a circuit has two solder joints there are four possible outcomes, as shown in the two-dimensional sample space of Figure 2.2. Here each coordinate is 0 or 1 depending on whether the corresponding joint is intact or broken. In general, if a circuit has n solder joints, there are 2^n possible outcomes which may be regarded as that many points in an n-dimensional sample space. It is of interest to note that the sample spaces used here in connection with the inspection of solder joints could also serve to describe the results of other experiments; for example the number of heads obtained in n flips of a coin, with 0 denoting "tail" and 1 denoting "head."

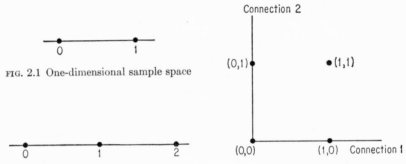

FIG. 2.1 One-dimensional sample space

FIG. 2.3 One-dimensional sample space

FIG. 2.2 Two-dimensional sample space

The geometrical configuration one can use to represent the outcomes of an experiment is not necessarily unique. For instance, we could have regarded the outcomes of the solder-joint experiment to be the total number of broken joints and, if the circuit has 2 solder joints, the outcomes are 0, 1, or 2, as depicted in the one-dimensional sample space of Figure 2.3. Note that the point 1 in Figure 2.3 corresponds to the *two* points $(1, 0)$ and $(0, 1)$ in Figure 2.2. (Similarly, for n solder joints the point which represents 1 broken joint in a diagram analogous to Figure 2.3 corresponds to the n points $(1, 0, 0, \ldots, 0)$, $(0, 1, 0, \ldots, 0)$, $\ldots$, $(0, 0, \ldots, 0, 1)$ in a diagram analogous to Figure 2.2.) Generally, it is desirable to use sample spaces whose elements cannot be further "subdivided"; that is, the individual elements of a sample space should not represent two or more outcomes which are distinguishable in some fashion. Thus, sample spaces like those of Figures 2.1 and 2.2 should be used in preference to sample spaces like the one of Figure 2.3.

It is often convenient to classify sample spaces according to the *number of elements* which they contain. Thus, the sample spaces of Figures 2.1, 2.2, and 2.3 have 2, 4, and 3 elements, respectively, and they are all referred to as *finite* sample spaces. Other examples of finite sample spaces are the one used to represent a roll of a pair of dice (it has 36 elements); the one used to represent the election of a president and a vice-president from among the 25 members of a club (it has 600 elements); and the one used to represent the classification of five television sets as superior, average, or inferior (it has $3^5 = 243$ elements, as will be explained below).

To consider an example where a finite sample space does not suffice, suppose that a person inspects solder joints and that we are interested in the number he has to inspect before he observes the first broken joint. It could be the first, the second, . . . , the hundredth, . . . , and for all we know he might have to inspect a million or more before he finds a broken joint. Not knowing how far we might have to go, it is appropriate in an example like this to consider the sample space to be the whole set of natural numbers. The number of elements in this sample space is *countably infinite*.

To go one step further, if we were to measure the resistance of a solder joint in ohms, the sample space would consist of points on a continuous scale (a certain interval on the line of real numbers). The elements of this sample space cannot be counted, that is, they cannot be put into one-to-one correspondence with the natural numbers. In general, a sample space is said to be *discrete* if it has finitely many or a countable infinity of elements. If the elements (points) of a sample space constitute a continuum, for example, all the points on a line, all the points on a line segment, all the points in a plane, and so forth, the sample space is said to be *continuous*. In the remainder of this chapter we shall consider only discrete and mainly finite sample spaces.

At times it can be quite difficult, or at least tedious, to determine the number of elements in a finite sample space by direct enumeration. To illustrate a method that can often be used to simplify this task, consider the following problem concerning the firing of a missile which consists of three subsystems: propulsion, guidance, and airframe. Suppose that P_1, P_2, and P_3 represent the propulsion system's performance being perfect, good, or inferior, that G_1 and G_2 represent the missile's responding or not responding to guidance, and that A_1, A_2, and A_3 represent the airframe's remaining intact, one or more of the control surfaces becoming defective, or a major airframe breakdown. The possible outcomes of a missile firing may then be visualized by means of the "tree" diagram of Figure 2.4. Following (from left to right) a given path along the tree we obtain a given outcome of the firing, that is, a particular element of the sample space of the experiment. Evidently, the tree has 18 paths and the sample space of the experiment, thus, has 18 elements. We could also have determined the number of elements of this sample space by noting that there are three "P-branches," that each P-branch forks into two "G-branches," and that each G-branch forks into three "A-branches." Thus, there are $3 \cdot 2 \cdot 3 = 18$

combinations of branches, or paths. This result is generalized by the following theorem:

> THEOREM 2.1. *If sets $A_1, A_2, \ldots, A_k$ contain, respectively, $n_1, n_2, \ldots, n_k$ elements, there are $n_1 \cdot n_2 \cdot \ldots \cdot n_k$ ways of selecting first an element from A_1, then an element from $A_2, \ldots$, and finally an element from A_k.*

This theorem can be verified by constructing a tree diagram similar to that of Figure 2.4. To illustrate the use of this theorem, consider again

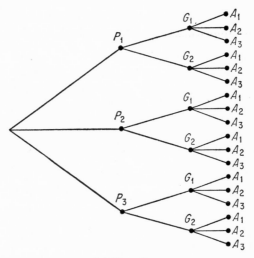

FIG. 2.4 Tree diagram

two of the examples on page 7. A club with a membership of 25 can elect a president in 25 ways; subsequently it can elect a vice-president in 24 ways, and the whole selection can be made in $25 \cdot 24 = 600$ ways. So far as the classification of the television sets is concerned, each of the five sets can be judged superior, average, or inferior, and there are altogether $3 \cdot 3 \cdot 3 \cdot 3 \cdot 3 = 3^5 = 243$ ways in which the classification can be made. Note that, if we had been interested only in knowing how many of the television sets fit each description, the sample space would have contained only 21 elements (see Exercise 5 on page 12).

2.2 Events

Probabilities are always associated with the occurrence or the nonoccurrence of events, such as the event that three defectives are found in a sample of 50 ball bearings, the event that a tire will last at least

20,000 miles before it must be recapped, the event that a switchboard has 8 incoming calls during a certain period of time, and so forth. Thus, in connection with probabilities, we always refer to an individual outcome or to a set of outcomes of an experiment as an event. (The event of getting exactly 0 heads in 5 tosses of a coin pertains to an individual outcome while the event of getting exactly 1 head pertains to a set of five outcomes.) In other words, *we shall think of an event as a subset of an appropriate sample space.* To illustrate this further, suppose that an assembly consists of two subassemblies, with the first containing 4 components and the second containing 3. If we are concerned only with the total number of defective components in each subassembly (not with what particular components have failed) the number of elements in the sample space is $5 \cdot 4 = 20$ and the corresponding two-dimensional sample space is shown in Figure 2.5.

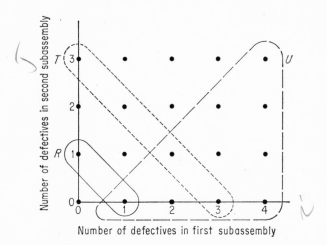

FIG. 2.5 Events in a sample space

Now suppose we let R stand for the event that the whole assembly has exactly 1 defective component, we let T stand for the event that it has exactly 3 defective components, and we let U stand for the event that the first subassembly has more defective components than the second. The elements of the sample space which correspond to these events are indicated, respectively, by means of the solid, dotted, and dashed curves of Figure 2.5. Note that events R and T have no elements in common—they are *mutually exclusive* events.

In many problems of probability we are interested in events which are actually combinations of two or more events. In our illustration we may be interested, for example, in the event that the whole assembly contains 1 *or* 3 defectives or in the event that the whole assembly contains 3 defectives while (at the same time) the first subassembly has more defective components than the second. To handle situations like these, let us now define the *union* and the *intersection* of two sets. Formally, if A and B are any two events in S, their *union* $A \cup B$ is the subset of S which contains all elements that are either in A, in B, or in both. The *intersection* $A \cap B$ is the subset of S which contains all elements that are in both A and B. Returning now to the example depicted in Figure 2.5, it can be seen that $R \cup T$ contains the elements

$$(0, 1), \quad (0, 3), \quad (1, 0), \quad (1, 2), \quad (2, 1), \quad (3, 0)$$

while $R \cap T$ has no elements at all. Following the practice of denoting the *empty set*, or *null set*, by the symbol $\varnothing$, we can write $R \cap T = \varnothing$—which, incidentally, is a mathematical way of expressing the fact that R and T are mutually exclusive. Note also that $R \cap U$ has the single element $(1, 0)$ and $T \cap U$ contains the elements $(2, 1)$ and $(3, 0)$.

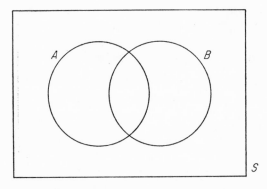

FIG. 2.6 Venn diagram

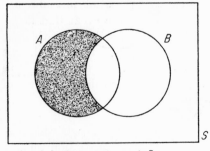

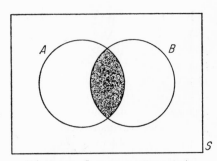

(a) *A* is a subset of *B*   (b) *A* and *B* are mutually exclusive

FIGURE 2.7

Finally, note that the elements $(0, 0)$, $(0, 1)$, $(1, 1)$, $(0, 2)$, $(1, 2)$, $(2, 2)$, $(0, 3)$, $(1, 3)$, $(2, 3)$, and $(3, 3)$ belong to S but not to U. The subset consisting of these 10 elements is called the *complement* of U with respect to S and it is denoted U'. In general, the complement A' of a set A belonging to some sample space S is the set which consists of all elements of S none of which is an element of A. Observe that the complement of S with respect to itself is the null set, that is, $S' = \varnothing$.

Sample spaces and events, particularly relationships between events, are often depicted by means of *Venn diagrams* like those of Figures 2.6, 2.7, and 2.8. Here the sample space S is represented by a rectangle while subsets or events are represented by circles, parts of circles, or combinations thereof.

For instance, Figure 2.7(a) depicts the relation "A is a subset of B," with the black coloring indicating that the corresponding set is empty, while Figure 2.7(b) depicts the relation that "A and B are mutually exclusive." The set operations $\cap$ and $\cup$ are represented in Venn diagrams as shown in Figure 2.8. The set operations which we have introduced together with appropriate axioms lead to the algebra of sets, or Boolean algebra as it is also called. We shall not go into a formal study of this subject in this book, justifying instead whatever theorems are needed with aid of Venn diagrams. As an example, let us demonstrate that

$$(A \cup B)' = A' \cap B'$$

which expresses the fact that the complement of the union of two sets equals the intersection of their respective complements. To begin with, note that the shaded region of Figure 2.9(a) represents the set $(A \cup B)'$ (compare this diagram with Figure 2.8(b)). The crosshatched region of

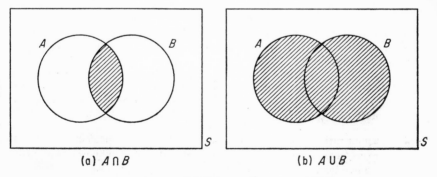

(a) $A \cap B$ (b) $A \cup B$

FIG. 2.8 Set operations

Figure 2.9(b) was obtained by shading the region representing A' with lines going in one direction and that representing B' with lines going in another direction. Thus, the crosshatched region represents the intersection of A'

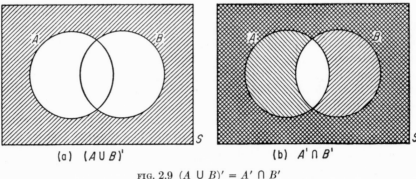

(a) $(A \cup B)'$ (b) $A' \cap B'$

FIG. 2.9 $(A \cup B)' = A' \cap B'$

and B', and it can be seen that it is identical with the shaded region of Figure 2.9(a).

EXERCISES

1. A tire manufacturer wishes to test four different tread designs on three different kinds of road surfaces and at five different speeds. How many different test runs are required?

2. An experimenter has four different protective coatings to apply to both sides of a sheet of steel. In how many ways can he coat both sides of the sheet of steel if

    (a) both sides must be coated with the same material,

    (b) the two sides can but need not be coated with the same material,

    (c) both sides cannot be coated with the same material.

3. An experiment consists of rolling a die and then flipping a coin if and only if the die came up 1, 3, or 5. Draw a tree diagram and count the number of possible outcomes.

4. Construct a tree diagram to determine the number of ways that a coin can be flipped four times in succession such that throughout the series of flips the number of heads is always greater than or equal to the number of tails.

5. By enumerating all possible outcomes, verify the statement on page 8 that there are 21 distinct outcomes if we are interested only in knowing how many of the five television sets fit each of the three descriptions.

6. In each of the following experiments decide whether it would be appropriate to use a sample space which is finite, countably infinite, or continuous:

    (a) One of twelve vice-presidents is to be chosen president of a company.

(b) An experiment is conducted to measure the coefficient of expansion of certain refractory bricks.

(c) Measurements of radiation intensity are made with a Geiger counter.

(d) A policeman measures the alcohol content of a driver's blood.

(e) A coin is flipped until the first head appears.

(f) A traffic survey is made to estimate the number of cars in the county with defective headlights.

7. Among six applicants for a job Mr. Andrews is married, does not play golf, and is not a home owner, Mr. Bailey is single, does not play golf, and is a home owner, Mr. Clark is married, plays golf, and is a home owner, Mr. Dodds is single, plays golf, and is not a home owner, Mr. Edwards is married, does not play golf, and is a home owner, and Mr. Fox is single, plays golf, and is a home owner. One of these applicants is to get the job and the event that the job is given to a golf player, for example, is denoted {Clark, Dodds, Fox}. Indicate in a similar manner sets denoting the events that

(a) the position is given to a home owner,

(b) the position is given to a married golf player,

(c) the position is given to an unmarried person who is not a home owner,

(d) the position is given to a man who is either married or a single golf player.

8. Referring to Exercise 7, indicate

(a) the complement of the set given in part (a),

(b) the union of the sets of parts (a) and (b),

(c) the intersection of the sets of parts (a) and (d),

(d) the intersection of the sets of parts (b) and (c).

9. A manufacturer buys parts from four different vendors numbered 1, 2, 3, and 4. Referring to orders placed on two successive days, (1, 4) denotes the event that on the first day the order was given to vendor 1 and on the second day it was given to vendor 4. Letting A represent the event that vendor 1 gets at least one of these two orders, B the event that the same vendor gets both orders, and C the event that vendors 1 and 3 do not get either order, list the elements of

(a) the entire sample space,   (e) A'

(b) A,   (f) $B \cup C$,

(c) B,   (g) $A \cap B$,

(d) C,   (h) $A \cap C$.

10. Use Venn diagrams to verify that

(a) $(A \cap B)' = A' \cup B'$,

(b) $A \cup (A \cap B) = A$,

(c) $(A \cap B) \cup (A \cap B') = A$,

(d) $A \cup B = (A \cap B) \cup (A \cap B') \cup (A' \cap B)$,

(e) $A \cup (B \cap C) = (A \cup B) \cap (A \cup C)$.

2.3 Probability

In this section we shall define probability using the concept of a *set function*, an *additive set function* to be exact. Since the reader is probably most familiar with functions for which the elements of the domain and the range are numbers, let us first consider a very simple example where the elements of the domain are sets while the elements of the range are real numbers. In other words, we shall study a function, a correspondence, which assigns real numbers to the subsets of a given set (to the subsets of a sample space if we are concerned with the outcomes of a given experiment). The set function which we shall consider is the one which assigns to each subset A of a given finite set the *number of elements* in A, written $N(A)$. Suppose, then, that a company has 50 employees who are classified according to their marital status (married M and not married M') and according to whether they are college graduates or not (G or G'). The distribution of these 50 employees among the various categories is as shown in the Venn diagram of Figure 2.10 and, using this

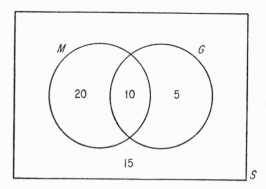

FIG. 2.10 Distribution of elements in S

diagram, we can now determine the value $N(A)$ for any one of the 16 subsets (categories) into which the employees can be classified. (In Exercise 1 on page 22 the reader will be asked to verify that there are, indeed, 16 subsets including the set S of all 50 employees and the empty set $\varnothing$.) The numbers in Figure 2.10 are the number of married employees who are not college graduates, the number of married employees who are college graduates, the number of unmarried employees who are college graduates, and the number of unmarried employees who are not college graduates, that is,

$$N(M \cap G') = 20, \quad N(M \cap G) = 10, \quad N(M' \cap G) = 5,$$
$$N(M' \cap G') = 15$$

To find the number of employees that are married, we have only to add the number of married employees who are college graduates to the number of married employees who are not college graduates, and we obtain

$$N(M) = N(M \cap G) + N(M \cap G') = 10 + 20 = 30$$

Similarly, we find that the number of employees who are college graduates is

$$N(G) = N(M \cap G) + N(M' \cap G) = 10 + 5 = 15$$

and since $N(S) = 50$, where S is the set of all 50 employees, we obtain by subtraction

$$N(M') = 50 - 30 = 20 \quad \text{and} \quad N(G') = 50 - 15 = 35$$

The set function which we have introduced in this example is said to be *additive*, meaning that the number which it assigns to the union of two subsets which have no elements in common equals the *sum* of the numbers assigned to the individual subsets.* It was this property which enabled us to calculate the number of married employees by adding the number of married employees who are college graduates to the number of married employees who are not college graduates. Note that this property only applies to subsets which have no elements in common, called *disjoint* subsets; as we indicated on page 9, events that correspond to disjoint subsets are called *mutually exclusive events*. When dealing with two subsets A and B which may have some elements in common we have the more general formula

$$N(A \cup B) = N(A) + N(B) - N(A \cap B)$$

which, applied to our example, gives

$$N(M \cup G) = N(M) + N(G) - N(M \cap G) = 30 + 15 - 10 = 35$$

for the number of employees who are married, college graduates, or both. Note that we subtracted the number of married college graduates because they were counted twice, once among the married employees and once among the employees who are college graduates.

Using the concept of an additive set function, let us now define what we

---

* A simple example of a set function which is *not* additive is the one which assigns to every subset the square of the number of elements which it contains.

mean by the *probability of an event*. Given a finite sample space S and an event A in S, we define $P(A)$, the probability of A, to be a value of an additive set function **P**, called a *probability function*. For a set function **P** to be a probability function, it must satisfy the following three conditions:

AXIOM 1. $0 \leq P(A) \leq 1$ *for each event A in S.*

AXIOM 2. $P(S) = 1$.

AXIOM 3. *If A and B are any mutually exclusive events in S, then* $P(A \cup B) = P(A) + P(B)$.

The first axiom states that the probability function assigns to every event A in S some real number from 0 to 1, inclusive. The second axiom states that the sample space as a whole is assigned the number 1 and it expresses the idea that the probability of a certain event, an event which must happen, is equal to 1. The third axiom states that the probability function must be additive, and with the use of mathematical induction it can be extended to include any finite number of mutually exclusive events. In other words, it can be shown that

$$P(A_1 \cup A_2 \cup \ldots \cup A_n) = P(A_1) + P(A_2) + \ldots + P(A_n)$$

where $A_1, A_2, \ldots, A_n$ are any mutually exclusive events in S. (How this third property must be modified when S is not finite will be discussed in Section 2.7.)

The three properties which we have listed are axioms for a theory of probability and they require no proof. However, if the resulting theory is to be applied to the physical world, we must show somehow that the axioms are realistic, that is, we must show that they yield reasonable results. To do so, let us say a few words about the so-called *frequency interpretation* of probability. According to this widely held interpretation, a probability is looked upon as a *relative frequency, or proportion, in the long run*. Thus, if we say "the probability that a man of 50 will live to be 65 is 0.72," we mean that if present conditions prevail, 72 per cent of all men aged 50 will live to be 65, and if we say "the probability that a person entering a super-market will buy a given product is 0.25," we mean that in the long run 25 per cent of all persons entering the supermarket will buy the given product. Note that if we say "the probability of getting heads with a balanced coin is 0.50," we mean that in the long run we will get 50 per cent heads and 50 per cent tails. However, it does *not* mean that we must necessarily get 10 heads and 10 tails in 20 flips or 50 heads and 50 tails in 100, but if a balanced coin is flipped a very large number of times we can almost always expect to get very close to 50 per cent heads and 50 per cent tails.

To demonstrate that the three axioms of probability are consistent with the frequency interpretation, we need only observe that the proportion of the time an event occurs cannot be negative or exceed 1 and that one outcome or another must occur 100 per cent of the time, that is, with a probability of 1. Also, if A and B are mutually exclusive events, the proportion of the time that either one or the other occurs is the *sum* of the proportions of the time that they occur. If the proportion of voters favoring a piece of legislation is 0.42 and the proportion undecided is 0.19, then 0.61 is the proportion of the voters who are either for the legislation or undecided.

Before giving some examples of probability functions, it is important to stress the point that *the three axioms do not tell us how to assign probabilities to the various outcomes of an experiment, they merely restrict the ways in which it can be done.* In actual practice, probabilities are assigned either on the basis of estimates obtained from past experience, on the basis of a careful analysis of conditions underlying the experiment, or on the basis of assumptions—say, the common assumption that various outcomes are equiprobable.

The following are three examples of *permissible* ways of assigning probabilities in an experiment where there are three possible and mutually exclusive outcomes A, B, and C:

(a) $P(A) = 1/3,$ $P(B) = 1/3,$ $P(C) = 1/3$

(b) $P(A) = 0.57,$ $P(B) = 0.24,$ $P(C) = 0.19$

(c) $P(A) = 24/27,$ $P(B) = 2/27,$ $P(C) = 1/27$

However,

(d) $P(A) = 0.64,$ $P(B) = 0.38,$ $P(C) = -0.02$

(e) $P(A) = 0.35,$ $P(B) = 0.52,$ $P(C) = 0.26$

are not permissible because they violate, respectively, Axioms 1 and 2 on page 16.

If a sample space has n outcomes, it can be shown that it contains 2^n subsets, including the sample space as a whole and the null set $\varnothing$. Thus, if $n = 20$ there are over a million events in S, and the problem of specifying a probability for each event becomes very complicated. Fortunately, this task can be simplified considerably by the use of the following theorem:

THEOREM 2.2. *If A is an event in S, then $P(A)$ equals the sum of the probabilities of the individual outcomes comprising A.*

To prove this theorem, let $E_1, E_2, \ldots, E_n$ be the n outcomes comprising A, so that we can write $A = E_1 \cup E_2 \cup \ldots \cup E_n$. Since the E's are individual outcomes they are mutually exclusive, and by the extension of Axiom 3 on page 16 we have

$$P(A) = P(E_1 \cup E_2 \cup \ldots \cup E_n)$$
$$= P(E_1) + P(E_2) + \ldots + P(E_n)$$

which completes the proof.

To illustrate the use of this theorem, let us return to the missile example introduced on page 7. The 18 possible outcomes together with a set of appropriate probabilities are shown in the accompanying table. (The probabilities assigned to the 18 outcomes were chosen arbitrarily in this example, but in such a way that the axioms of probability are satisfied. In practice such probabilities might be estimates based on past experience and, perhaps, suitable assumptions, see page 28.)

Outcome	Probability	Outcome	Probability
$P_1 \cap G_1 \cap A_1$	0.336	$P_2 \cap G_2 \cap A_1$	0.042
$P_1 \cap G_1 \cap A_2$	0.096	$P_2 \cap G_2 \cap A_2$	0.012
$P_1 \cap G_1 \cap A_3$	0.048	$P_2 \cap G_2 \cap A_3$	0.006
$P_1 \cap G_2 \cap A_1$	0.084	$P_3 \cap G_1 \cap A_1$	0.056
$P_1 \cap G_2 \cap A_2$	0.024	$P_3 \cap G_1 \cap A_2$	0.016
$P_1 \cap G_2 \cap A_3$	0.012	$P_3 \cap G_1 \cap A_3$	0.008
$P_2 \cap G_1 \cap A_1$	0.168	$P_3 \cap G_2 \cap A_1$	0.014
$P_2 \cap G_1 \cap A_2$	0.048	$P_3 \cap G_2 \cap A_2$	0.004
$P_2 \cap G_1 \cap A_3$	0.024	$P_3 \cap G_2 \cap A_3$	0.002

From this table, we compute $P(G_1)$, the probability that the missile responds to guidance, by adding the probabilities of the 9 outcomes comprising the event G_1, obtaining

$$P(G_1) = 0.336 + 0.096 + 0.048 + 0.168 + 0.048 + 0.024$$
$$+ 0.056 + 0.016 + 0.008 = 0.800$$

Using Theorem 2.2 we similarly find that

$$P(A_1) = 0.336 + 0.084 + 0.168 + 0.042 + 0.056 + 0.014 = 0.700$$
$$P(P_1) = 0.336 + 0.096 + 0.048 + 0.084 + 0.024 + 0.012 = 0.600$$
$$P(P_1 \cap G_1) = 0.336 + 0.096 + 0.048 = 0.480$$

the last value being the probability that the missile's propulsion system performs perfectly *and* the missile responds to guidance. To find the probability that two or more of the component systems operate imperfectly, we have only to add the probabilities of all outcomes having two or three subscripts not equal to 1, getting 0.212.

To consider another illustration, let us refer again to the example on page 14 and let us suppose that 1 of the 50 employees is to be elected by lot to a labor-management committee. Assuming that each employee, thus, has a probability of 1/50 of being elected, it can easily be verified by using Theorem 2.2 that the probability that a married employee is elected is $P(M) = 3/5$, the probability that an employee who is a college graduate is elected is $P(G) = 3/10$, and the probability that the employee who is elected is married, a college graduate, or both is $P(M \cup G) = 7/10$. (Using Theorem 2.2, each of these probabilities was obtained by adding 1/50 as many times as there are individual outcomes in the respective events.)

In this last example we could have used to advantage the following theorem which applies to experiments where the individual outcomes are all equiprobable:

THEOREM 2.3. *If an experiment has n possible outcomes which are equiprobable and if s of these are labeled "success," then the probability of a "success" is s/n.*

This theorem follows immediately from Theorem 2.2 and the generalization of the third axiom of probability given on page 16. We would, thus, have found that the probability that a married employee is elected is

$$P(M) = \frac{N(M)}{N(S)} = \frac{30}{50} = 3/5$$

and that the probability that an employee who is a married college graduate is elected is

$$P(M \cap G) = \frac{N(M \cap G)}{N(S)} = \frac{10}{50} = 1/5$$

Theorem 2.3 is particularly useful in problems dealing with games of chance, where it is assumed that if a deck of cards is properly shuffled each card has the same chance of being selected, if a coin is properly flipped each face has the same chance of coming up, and if a die is properly rolled each face is as likely to come up as any other. We thus find that the probability of drawing a queen from an ordinary deck of 52 playing cards is 4/52, the probability of getting heads with a balanced coin is 1/2, and the probability of rolling an even number with a die is 3/6.

2.4 Some Elementary Theorems

Using the axioms of probability, it is possible to derive many theorems which play an important role in applications. First let us show that

THEOREM 2.4. *If A is any event in S, then $P(A') = 1 - P(A)$*

which expresses the fact that if it rains 34 per cent of the time it does not rain 66 per cent of the time, if 13 per cent of the students fail a certain course then 87 per cent do not, and if someone wins at a given game 43 per cent of the time he loses or ties 57 per cent of the time. To prove this theorem observe that A and A' are mutually exclusive by definition, and that $A \cup A' = S$ (that is, among them, A and A' contain all of the elements of S). Hence, we have

$$P(A \cup A') = P(A) + P(A')$$

according to Axiom 3,

$$P(A \cup A') = P(S) = 1$$

according to Axiom 2, and it follows that

$$P(A) + P(A') = 1$$

which completes the proof of Theorem 2.4. As a special case we find that $P(\varnothing) = 1 - P(S) = 1 - 1 = 0$, since the empty set $\varnothing$ is the complement of S. Referring to the example on page 18, we thus find the probability that the missile's propulsion system does *not* perform perfectly is $1 - P(P_1) = 1 - 0.600 = 0.400$ and the probability that *at most one* of the subsystems operates imperfectly is $1 - 0.212 = 0.788$.

On page 16 we observed that Axiom 3 can be extended to include more than two mutually exclusive events. Another useful and important extension of this axiom allows us to find the probability of the union of any two events in S regardless of whether they are mutually exclusive. To motivate the theorem which follows, consider again the example on page 14, the one dealing with the 50 employees, where we obtained the *number* of employees who are married, college graduates, or both, by writing

$$N(M \cup G) = N(M) + N(G) - N(M \cap G)$$
$$= 30 + 15 - 10$$
$$= 35$$

As we pointed out at the time, we had to subtract the number of employees who are married college graduates because they were counted twice, once among the employees who are married and once among those who are college graduates. Dividing each of the above figures by 50, the total number of employees, we could similarly have argued that the *proportion* of employees who are married, college graduates, or both, equals the *proportion* of employees who are married *plus* the *proportion* of employees who are college graduates *minus* the *proportion* of employees who are married college graduates. In line with this intuitive justification let us now prove the following theorem, usually called the *general law of addition:*

THEOREM 2.5. *If A and B are any events in S, then*

$$P(A \cup B) = P(A) + P(B) - P(A \cap B)$$

To prove this theorem, note first from the Venn diagram of Figure 2.11 that

$$A \cup B = (A \cap B) \cup (A \cap B') \cup (A' \cap B)$$

and also that

$$A = (A \cap B) \cup (A \cap B')$$
$$B = (A \cap B) \cup (A' \cap B)$$

(The reader was asked to verify these important relations in parts (c) and (d) of Exercise 10 on page 14.) Since $A \cap B$, $A \cap B'$, and $A' \cap B$ are evidently mutually exclusive, the extension of Axiom 3 on page 16 yields

$$P(A \cup B) = P(A \cap B) + P(A \cap B') + P(A' \cap B)$$

and after adding and subtracting $P(A \cap B)$ we obtain

$$P(A \cup B) = [P(A \cap B) + P(A \cap B')] + [P(A \cap B)$$
$$+ P(A' \cap B)] - P(A \cap B)$$
$$= P(A) + P(B) - P(A \cap B)$$

When A and B are mutually exclusive, Theorem 2.5 reduces to Axiom 3, since in that case $P(A \cap B) = 0$. For this reason, we often refer to Axiom 3 as the *special law of addition* whereas Theorem 2.5 is called the *general law of addition*. To illustrate the use of this theorem, let us refer again to the

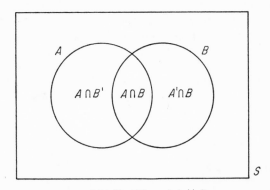

FIG. 2.11 Partition of $A \cup B$

missile example on page 7 and let us determine the probability $P(P_1 \cup G_1)$, namely, the probability that the missile's propulsion system works perfectly, that the missile responds to guidance, or both. We could obtain this probability from the table on page 18, adding the probabilities of all those outcomes where at least one of the letters P or G has the subscript 1. On the other hand, using Theorem 2.5 and the probabilities which we already obtained on page 18, we get

$$P(P_1 \cup G_1) = 0.600 + 0.800 - 0.480$$
$$= 0.920$$

It is instructive to note that if we had made the mistake of using the special law of addition in this example, we would have gotten the absurd result that the desired probability equals 1.400.

EXERCISES

1. List the 16 subsets into which the 50 employees of the example on page 14 can be classified.

2. Referring to Figure 2.10, find
   (a) $N(M \cup G')$,
   (b) $N(M' \cup G)$,
   (c) $N[(M \cap G)']$.

3. Among 100 engineering students 15 are studying to be chemical engineers, 60 are undergraduates, and 5 are undergraduates studying to be chemical engineers. How many of these students
   (a) are not studying to be chemical engineers,
   (b) are not undergraduates,
   (c) are studying to be chemical engineers, are undergraduates, or both,
   (d) are undergraduates not studying to be chemical engineers,
   (e) are nonundergraduates studying to be chemical engineers,
   (f) are nonundergraduates not studying to be chemical engineers.

4. A dealer's stock of 75 cars includes cars with power steering (A), compacts (B), and cars with automatic transmissions (C). Using the information given in Figure 2.12, find
   (a) $N(A)$,
   (b) $N(B)$,
   (c) $N(C)$,
   (d) $N(A \cap B)$,
   (e) $N(A \cap C)$,
   (f) $N(A \cap B \cap C)$,
   (g) $N(A \cup B)$,
   (h) $N(B \cup C)$,
   (i) $N(A' \cup B' \cup C)$,
   (j) $N[B \cap (A \cup C)]$.

5. An experiment has exactly four distinct outcomes: A, B, C, and D. Check whether the following assignments of probabilities are permissible:
   (a) $P(A) = 0.36$, $P(B) = 0.18$, $P(C) = 0.21$, $P(D) = 0.25$,
   (b) $P(A) = 0.29$, $P(B) = 0.35$, $P(C) = 0.18$, $P(D) = 0.15$,
   (c) $P(A) = 0.42$, $P(B) = 0.17$, $P(C) = -0.08$, $P(D) = 0.49$,
   (d) $P(A) = 17/80$, $P(B) = 11/40$, $P(C) = 1/2$, $P(D) = 1/80$.

6. Referring to the sample space illustrated in Figure 2.5, denote by (i, j) the outcome that there are i defective components in the first subassembly and j defective components in the second subassembly ($i = 0, 1, 2, 3, 4; j = 0, 1,$

2, 3). Assuming that the probability of outcome $(0, 0)$ is $1/2$ and the probabilities of the remaining outcomes are inversely proportional to $i + j$, the total number of defective components in the whole assembly, find the probability of each outcome in the sample space.

7. Referring to the results of Exercise 6, find the following probabilities:

(a) the first subassembly has at most one defective component,

(b) the second subassembly has at least two defective components,

(c) the entire assembly has at most one defective component,

(d) the second subassembly has more defective components than the first subassembly.

8. In the example on page 18 it was assumed that each of the 50 employees had the same chance of being elected to a labor-management committee. If, instead, a college graduate has twice the probability of being elected as a non-college graduate, find (a) $P(M)$, (b) $P(G)$, (c) $P(M \cap G)$, and (d) $P(M \cup G)$.

9. Referring to the table on page 18, find

(a) $P(P_2)$,

(b) $P(P_3)$,

(c) $P(A_2)$,

(d) $P(P_2 \cap A_2)$,

(e) $P(P_2 \cup A_2)$,

(f) $P(P_3 \cup A_1)$.

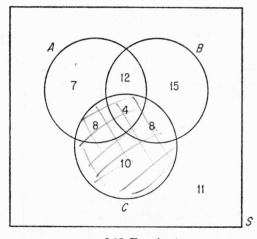

FIG. 2.12 Exercise 4

10. What is the probability of rolling (a) 7 (b) 11, (c) 7 or 11, (d) 2 or 3 or 12, with a pair of balanced dice?

11. What is the probability of drawing (a) a black queen, (b) a red card, (c) 5, 6, or 7, (d) a black ace or a red king, from a well-shuffled standard deck of 52 playing cards?

12. A lottery sells tickets numbered from 1 to 10,000. What is the probability that the number drawn is divisible by 20?

13. Referring to Exercise 4, suppose that one of the cars on the dealer's lot was damaged in a windstorm. Assuming equal probabilities, find the probability that

   (a) the damaged car is a compact

   (b) the damaged car has power steering

   (c) the damaged car is a compact without automatic transmission

   (d) the damaged car is not a compact but has an automatic transmission and power steering

14. If A and B are mutually exclusive events, $P(A) = 0.20$, and $P(B) = 0.55$, find

   (a) $P(A')$,

   (b) $P(A \cup B)$,

   (c) $P(A \cap B)$,

   (d) $P(A' \cap B')$.

15. Given $P(A) = 0.30$, $P(B) = 0.78$, and $P(A \cap B) = 0.16$, find

   (a) $P(A \cup B)$,

   (b) $P(A \cap B')$,

   (c) $P(A' \cup B')$,

   (d) $P(A' \cap B)$.

16. The probability that at least one of three events A, B, and C will occur is given by

$$P(A \cup B \cup C) = P(A) + P(B) + P(C) - P(A \cap B) - P(A \cap C) - P(B \cap C) + P(A \cap B \cap C)$$

Verify this formula with the probabilities shown in Figure 2.13.

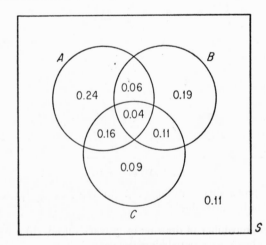

FIG. 2.13 Exercise 16

17. In controlling the quality of mass-produced glass bricks, the probability that an inspector will get one which is cracked is 0.0025, the probability that he will get one with air bubbles is 0.0020, the probability that he will get one with discoloration is 0.0020, the probability that he will get one which has an air bubble and is cracked is 0.0006, the probability that he will get one which is cracked and discolored is 0.0005, the probability that he will get one which has air bubbles and is discolored is 0.0004, and the probability that he will get a glass brick with all three of these imperfections is 0.0001. What is the probability that he will get a glass brick with at least one of these imperfections?

18. Show that (a) $P(A) \geq P(A \cap B)$, and (b) $P(A) \leq P(A \cup B)$. [*Hint:* Refer to parts (c) and (d) of Exercise 10 on page 14.]

19. Given that A, B, and C are mutually exclusive events, explain why each of the following is not a permissible assignment of probabilities:

(a) $P(A) = 0.4$, $P(B) = 0.4$, $P(A \cup C) = 0.2$,

(b) $P(A) = 0.7$, $P(B) = 0.1$, $P(B \cap C) = 0.3$,

(c) $P(A) = 0.6$, $P(A \cap B') = 0.5$.

2.5 Conditional Probability

As we have defined probability, it is meaningful to ask for the probability of an event only if we refer to a given sample space S. To ask for the probability that an engineer has a salary of \$10,000 or more is meaningless unless we specify whether we are referring to the entire United States, a particular industry, a given plant, etc., and unless we specify how the selection is to be made. Thus, when we use the symbol $P(A)$ for the probability of A, we really mean the probability of A *given some sample space S.* Since the choice of S is by no means always evident, and since there are problems in which we are interested in the probabilities of A with respect to more sample spaces than one, the notation $P(A \mid S)$ is used to make it clear that we are referring to the particular sample space S. We read $P(A \mid S)$ as "the *conditional probability* of A relative to S" and every probability is, thus, a conditional probability. Of course, we use the simplified notation $P(A)$ whenever the choice of S is clearly understood.

To illustrate some of the ideas connected with conditional probabilities, let us again consider the set of 50 persons among whom some are married and some are college graduates as shown in Figure 2.10. Assuming equal probabilities, we saw on page 19 that the probability that a college graduate is elected to the labor-management committee is $P(G) = 3/10$; let us now see if this probability changes when it is known that a married person has been elected. To find $P(G \mid M)$ we have only to look at the reduced sample space M of Figure 2.14, and to assume that each of the 30 married employ-

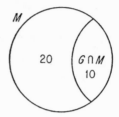

FIG. 2.14 Reduced sample space

ees, among whom 10 are college graduates, has the same probability of being elected. Using Theorem 2.3 we, thus, get

$$P(G \mid M) = \frac{N(G \cap M)}{N(M)} = \frac{10}{30} = \frac{1}{3}$$

Note that if we divide the numerator and the denominator of the last expression by $N(S)$, we get

$$P(G \mid M) = \frac{\dfrac{N(G \cap M)}{N(S)}}{\dfrac{N(M)}{N(S)}} = \frac{P(G \cap M)}{P(M)}$$

and it can be seen that the desired conditional probability is the *ratio* of the probability that the person elected is a college graduate who belongs to the reduced sample space M to the probability that he belongs to M.

Looking at this example in another way, note that with respect to the whole sample space S we have

$$P(G \cap M) = \frac{N(G \cap M)}{50} = \frac{1}{5}$$

$$P(G' \cap M) = \frac{N(G' \cap M)}{50} = \frac{2}{5}$$

assuming, as before, that each of the 50 employees has the same probability of being elected to the committee. Thus, the probabilities that the person elected is or is not a college graduate, given that he is married, should be in the ratio 1:2. Since all probabilities in the reduced sample space must add up to 1, we have

$$P(G \mid M) = \frac{1}{3} \quad \text{and} \quad P(G' \mid M) = \frac{2}{3}$$

which agrees with the result obtained before. This also explains why we had to divide by $P(M)$ when we wrote

$$P(G \mid M) = \frac{P(G \cap M)}{P(M)}$$

on page 26. Division by $P(M)$, or multiplication by $\frac{1}{P(M)}$, takes care of the *proportionality factor* which makes the sum of the probabilities over the reduced sample space equal to 1. Following these observations, let us now make the following formal definition:

If A and B are any events in S and $P(B) \neq 0$, the conditional probability of A relative to B is given by

$$P(A \mid B) = \frac{P(A \cap B)}{P(B)}$$

To illustrate this definition, suppose that an order is to be shipped from the East Coast to Los Angeles by way of Chicago. From past experience it is estimated that the probability that such an order will arrive in Chicago on time is 0.80, and the probability that it will be late arriving in Chicago and on time arriving in Los Angeles is 0.10. Supposing that an inquiry shows that the order arrived late in Chicago, we want to determine the probability that it will nevertheless arrive on time in Los Angeles. If L represents the order's arriving on time in Los Angeles, and C represents its arriving late in Chicago, we have $P(C) = 1 - 0.80 = 0.20$, $P(L \cap C) = 0.10$, and, hence,

$$P(L \mid C) = \frac{0.10}{0.20} = 0.50$$

An immediate consequence of our definition of conditional probability is given by the following theorem, usually called the *general law of multiplication:*

THEOREM 2.6. *If A and B are any events in S, then*

$$P(A \cap B) = P(A) \cdot P(B \mid A) \qquad \text{if } P(A) \neq 0$$
$$= P(B) \cdot P(A \mid B) \qquad \text{if } P(B) \neq 0$$

The second of these relations follows from the definition of conditional probability, multiplying both sides by $P(B)$; the first is obtained by interchanging the letters A and B in the definition of conditional probability and then multiplying both sides by $P(A)$. Note that the definition of $P(B \mid A)$ and $P(A \mid B)$ assumes that $P(A) \neq 0$ and $P(B) \neq 0$, respectively.

To illustrate the use of Theorem 2.6, suppose we want to determine the probability of getting two defective light bulbs in succession from a shipment of 500 light bulbs among which 25 are defective. Assuming equal probabilities for each selection, the probability that the first one is defective is $\frac{25}{500}$ and the probability that the second is defective *given that the first is defective* is $\frac{24}{499}$. Substituting these values, we find that the desired probability of getting two defective light bulbs in succession is $\frac{25}{500} \cdot \frac{24}{499} = \frac{6}{2495}$.

Returning now to the missile-firing example, for which the probabilities of the individual outcomes are given in the table on page 18, let us compute the probability that the missile will respond to guidance, given that its propulsion system works perfectly. Using the results obtained on page 18, we get

$$P(G_1 \mid P_1) = \frac{P(P_1 \cap G_1)}{P(P_1)} = \frac{0.480}{0.600} = 0.800$$

and it is of interest to note that this equals the value which we obtained earlier for $P(G_1)$. This means that the probability of the missile's responding to guidance is the same regardless of whether or not the performance of the propulsion system is perfect; we say that *the missile's response to guidance is independent of the performance of the propulsion component.* In general, if A and B are any events in a sample space S, we say that A *is independent of B* if and only if $P(A \mid B) = P(A)$. Using Theorem 2.6, it can easily be seen that *if A is independent of B then B is also independent of A;* that is, $P(A \mid B) = P(A)$ implies $P(B \mid A) = P(B)$ provided $P(A) \neq 0$, and it is customary to say simply that A *and B are independent.*

In the special case where A and B are independent, Theorem 2.6 leads to the following, which is usually called the *special law of multiplication:*

THEOREM 2.7. *If A and B are independent events, then*

$$P(A \cap B) = P(A) \cdot P(B)$$

Applying this rule we find, for example, that the probability of getting two heads in two successive flips of a balanced coin is $\frac{1}{2} \cdot \frac{1}{2} = \frac{1}{4}$ and that the probability of drawing two aces in succession from a standard deck of 52 playing cards is $\frac{4}{52} \cdot \frac{4}{52} = \frac{1}{169}$ provided the first card is replaced before the second is drawn.

The special law of multiplication is readily extended to apply to more than two independent events: *if three or more events are independent, the probability that they will all occur is given by the product of their respective probabilities.* We used this, in fact, in determining the probabilities given in the table on page 18, assuming independence and letting $P(P_1) = 0.60$, $P(P_2) = 0.30$, $P(P_3) = 0.10$, $P(G_1) = 0.80$, $P(G_2) = 0.20$, $P(A_1) = 0.70$, $P(A_2) = 0.20$, and $P(A_3) = 0.10$. Substituting these values we obtained

$$P(P_1 \cap G_1 \cap A_1) = P(P_1) \cdot P(G_1) \cdot P(A_1) = (0.60)(0.80)(0.70) = 0.336$$
$$P(P_3 \cap G_2 \cap A_2) = P(P_3) \cdot P(G_2) \cdot P(A_2) = (0.10)(0.20)(0.20) = 0.004$$

and the other 16 probabilities on page 18.

2.6 The Rule of Bayes

The general law of multiplication is useful in solving many problems in which the ultimate outcome of an experiment depends on the outcomes of various intermediate stages. Suppose, for example, that we are interested in the performance of voltage regulators received by a plant from two different suppliers, B_1 and B_2, in the proportion 3 to 1. In other words, the probability that any one voltage regulator received by the plant comes from supplier B_1 is $3/4$ and the probability that it comes from supplier B_2 is $1/4$. Suppose, furthermore, that 95 per cent of the voltage regulators supplied by B_1 and 80 per cent of those supplied by B_2 perform according to specifications. What we would like to know is the probability of the event A that any one voltage regulator received by the plant will perform according to specifications.

Using the fact that $A = (A \cap B_1) \cup (A \cap B_2)$ and that $(A \cap B_1)$ and $(A \cap B_2)$ are mutually exclusive (see Figure 2.11, letting B_1 and B_2 take the place of B and B'), the special law of addition yields

$$P(A) = P(A \cap B_1) + P(A \cap B_2)$$

If we then apply the general law of multiplication to $P(A \cap B_1)$ and $P(A \cap B_2)$, we obtain

$$P(A) = P(B_1) \cdot P(A \mid B_1) + P(B_2) \cdot P(A \mid B_2)$$

Substituting the given probabilities $P(B_1) = 3/4, P(B_2) = 1/4, P(A \mid B_1) = 0.95$, and $P(A \mid B_2) = 0.80$, we get

$$P(A) = \tfrac{3}{4}(0.95) + \tfrac{1}{4}(0.80) = 0.9125$$

for the desired probability that any one voltage regulator received by the plant will perform according to specifications.

In this particular example there were two alternatives at the intermediate stage, suppliers B_1 and B_2. In general, if there are n mutually exclusive alternatives $B_1, B_2, \ldots, B_n$ at the intermediate stage, we can find the probability of the final outcome, event A, by means of the formula[*]

$$\blacklozenge \qquad P(A) = \sum_{i=1}^{n} P(B_i) \cdot P(A \mid B_i) \qquad \blacklozenge$$

---

[*] The symbols $\blacklozenge$ are used to set off important formulas or expressions which are not otherwise distinguished as parts of theorems or definitions.

sometimes called the *rule of elimination*. We can visualize this situation by constructing a "tree" like the one shown in Figure 2.15, where the probability of the final outcome A is given by the sum of the products of the probabilities corresponding to each individual branch. To illustrate, suppose that there had been three suppliers in our example and that the required probabilities are shown in Figure 2.16. Then, the probability

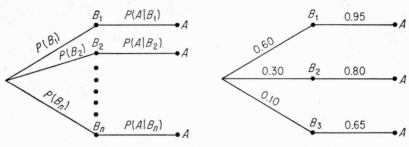

FIG. 2.15 Rule of elimination   FIG. 2.16 Rule of elimination

that any one voltage regulator received by the plant will perform according to specifications is

$$P(A) = (0.60)(0.95) + (0.30)(0.80) + (0.10)(0.65)$$
$$= 0.875$$

To consider a problem which is closely related to the one we have just discussed, suppose we want to know the probability that a particular voltage regulator came from supplier B_3, *when it is known that it performs according to specifications*. Referring to Figure 2.16, we shall use the same information as before, but now we must find $P(B_3 \mid A)$ instead of $P(A)$. To solve this problem we write

$$P(B_3 \mid A) = \frac{P(A \cap B_3)}{P(A)}$$

and then substitute

$$P(A \cap B_3) = P(B_3) \cdot P(A \mid B_3)$$

and
$$P(A) = \sum_{i=1}^{3} P(B_i) \cdot P(A \mid B_i)$$

respectively, into the numerator and the denominator in accordance with the general law of multiplication and the rule of elimination. We thus obtain the formula

$$P(B_3 \mid A) = \frac{P(B_3) \cdot P(A \mid B_3)}{\sum\limits_{i=1}^{3} P(B_i) \cdot P(A \mid B_i)}$$

which expresses the required probability in terms of given probabilities. Substituting the values from Figure 2.16, we finally obtain

$$P(B_3 \mid A) = \frac{(0.10)(0.65)}{(0.60)(0.95) + (0.30)(0.80) + (0.10)(0.65)}$$

$$= 0.074$$

Note that the probability that a voltage regulator is supplied by B_3 decreases from 0.10 to 0.074 once it is known that it performs according to specifications.

The method used to solve this last example can be generalized to yield the following formula, called the *rule of Bayes:*

THEOREM 2.8. *If $B_1, B_2, \ldots, B_n$ are mutually exclusive events of which one must occur, that is, $\sum\limits_{i=1}^{n} P(B_i) = 1$, then*

$$P(B_r \mid A) = \frac{P(B_r) \cdot P(A \mid B_r)}{\sum\limits_{i=1}^{n} P(B_i) \cdot P(A \mid B_i)}$$

for $r = 1, 2, \ldots,$ or n.

This rule provides a formula for finding the probability that the "effect" A was "caused" by the event B_r. For example, in our illustration we found the probability that an acceptable voltage regulator was made by supplier B_3. The probabilities $P(B_i)$ are called the "prior" or "a priori" probabilities of the "causes" B_i, and in practice it is often difficult to assign them numerical values. For many years Bayes' rule was looked upon with suspicion because it was used with the often-erroneous assumption that the prior probabilities are all equal. A good deal of the controversy once surrounding the rule of Bayes has been cleared up with the realization that the probabilities $P(B_i)$ must be determined separately in each case from the nature of the problem, preferably on the basis of past experience. We shall return to this problem with an example of *Bayesian inference* in Chapter 8.

To further illustrate the rule of Bayes, suppose that an office has four secretaries handling, respectively, 20, 60, 15, and 5 per cent of the filing of all government reports. The probabilities that they misfile such reports are, respectively, 0.05, 0.10, 0.10, and 0.05 and we want to find the probability that a misfiled report can be blamed on secretary No. 1. Substituting these values into the formula for the rule of Bayes, we obtain

$$P(B_1 \mid A) = \frac{(0.20)(0.05)}{(0.20)(0.05) + (0.60)(0.10) + (0.15)(0.10) + (0.05)(0.05)}$$

$$= 0.114$$

and it is of interest to note that although only 5 per cent of the reports handled by secretary No. 1 are misfiled, over 11 per cent of all misfiled reports are her responsibility.

EXERCISES

1. Referring to Figure 2.10, find $P(M \mid G)$ and $P(M \mid G')$; assume that originally each of the 50 employees had the same probability of being elected.

2. If in the example on page 27 it is also given that $P(L) = 0.60$, find the probability that a shipment was late arriving in Chicago, given that it arrived on time in Los Angeles.

3. Referring to Exercise 13 on page 24 and Figure 2.12, find the following probabilities:

   (a) the damaged car is a compact, given that it has power steering,

   (b) the damaged car has automatic transmission, given that it is a compact,

   (c) the damaged car has power steering or an automatic transmission, given that it is a compact,

   (d) the damaged car is a compact with automatic transmission, given that it does not have power steering,

   (e) the damaged car is not a compact, given that it has power steering and an automatic transmission,

   (f) the damaged car is not a compact, given that it has power steering, an automatic transmission, or both.

4. Referring to the probabilities of Figure 2.13, find

   (a) $P(A \mid B)$,   (e) $P(A \mid B \cup C)$,

   (b) $P(B \mid C')$,   (f) $P(A \mid B \cap C)$,

   (c) $P(A \cap B \mid C)$,   (g) $P(A \cap B \cap C \mid B \cap C)$,

   (d) $P(B \cup C \mid A')$,   (h) $P(A \cap B \cap C \mid B \cup C)$.

5. Using the results of Exercise 6 on page 22, find

   (a) the probability that the whole assembly has two defective components, given that the first subassembly has one defective component,

   (b) the probability that the first subassembly has at least two defective components, given that the whole assembly has three defective components,

   (c) the probability that the whole assembly has at least three defective components, given that the first subassembly has more defective components than the second subassembly.

6. The probability that a construction job will be finished on time is 17/20, the probability that there will be no strikes is 3/4, and the probability that the

construction job will be finished on time, given that there will be no strikes, is 14/15. Find

(a) the probability that the construction job will be finished on time and there will be no strikes,

(b) the probability that there will have been no strikes, given that the construction job will be finished on time.

7. An urn contains 40 white marbles and 10 black marbles. If two marbles are drawn at random (with equal probabilities), find the probability that they are both white if

(a) the first marble is replaced before the second is drawn,

(b) the first marble is not replaced before the second is drawn.

8. What is the probability of drawing three aces in succession from a well-shuffled standard deck of 52 playing cards, if cards are not put back into the deck immediately after they have been drawn?

9. Suppose the probability that the Los Angeles Dodgers will win the National League pennant is 0.25 and the probability that the San Francisco Giants will win it is 0.20. Furthermore, the probability that the National League team will win the World Series is 0.45, 0.55, or 0.35, depending on whether the Los Angeles Dodgers, the San Francisco Giants, or some other team wins the National League pennant. What is the probability that a National League team will win the World Series?

10. Referring to Exercise 2 above, find the probability that such an order will arrive on time in Los Angeles, given that it arrived on time in Chicago. [*Hint:* Use the rule of elimination.]

11. Referring to the illustration on page 29, find $P(B_1 \mid A)$ and $P(B_2 \mid A)$.

12. Given that a National League team wins the World Series, use the probabilities of Exercise 9 above to find the probability that the Los Angeles Dodgers won the National League pennant.

13. The probability that an airplane accident which is due to structural failure is diagnosed correctly is 0.85 and the probability that an airplane accident which is *not* due to structural failure is diagnosed incorrectly as being due to structural failure is 0.35. If 30 per cent of all airplane accidents are due to structural failures, find the probability that an airplane accident is due to structural failure, given that it has been diagnosed as being due to structural failure.

14. A race driver uses a Corvette in 50 per cent of the races he enters, a Jaguar in 30 per cent of the races, and an Alfa Romeo in 20 per cent of the races. Of 25 races he has entered with the Corvette he has won 5, of 15 races he has entered with the Jaguar he has won 4, and of 10 races he has entered with the Alfa Romeo he has won 4. Using these figures to estimate the respective probabilities, what is the probability that this race driver will win in the race for which he is entered at Le Mans?

15. Referring to Exercise 14, suppose that word has just arrived that he has won the race. What is the probability that he drove the Corvette?

 not on test

2.7 More General Sample Spaces

So far, we have discussed the theory of probability as it applies to finite sample spaces. This restriction has been made to simplify our introduction to the theory; it does not imply that there is any essential difference in applications dealing with sample spaces that are countably infinite or continuous. In this section, we shall treat several examples of such sample spaces, indicating in each case what modification of the theory is required to define probability functions.

To give an example of an experiment best described by a discrete but infinite sample space, suppose we are interested in the number of defects (such as seams or slivers) in 100 feet of wire. It is evident that the sample space is discrete, consisting of outcomes corresponding to the numbers $0, 1, 2, \ldots$. Since we cannot find a number N such that the largest number of defects per 100 feet of wire cannot exceed N *without being arbitrary*, the sample space will be regarded as being countably infinite.

To construct probability functions over an infinite sample space like the one just described, Axiom 3 must be modified as follows, to include also the union of countably many subsets:

AXIOM 3′. *If $A_1, A_2, A_3, \ldots$ is a finite or infinite sequence of mutually exclusive events in S, then*

$$P(A_1 \cup A_2 \cup A_3 \cup \ldots) = P(A_1) + P(A_2) + P(A_3) + \ldots$$

To give an example of a probability function which is consistent with Axiom 3′ as well as Axioms 1 and 2 on page 16, suppose that in the above illustration the probability that there are x defects in 100 feet of wire is given by

$$\frac{e^{-\lambda}\lambda^x}{x!}$$

for $x = 0, 1, 2, \ldots$. (The Greek letter λ, *lambda*, represents a positive constant.) Since the probabilities are all nonnegative and we shall show that their sum is 1, the given probability function is evidently consistent with Axiom 1; to show that it is also consistent with Axiom 2, we have to show that $P(S) = 1$. Making use of Axiom 3′, we get

$$P(S) = \sum_{x=0}^{\infty} \frac{e^{-\lambda}\lambda^x}{x!} = e^{-\lambda} \sum_{x=0}^{\infty} \frac{\lambda^x}{x!}$$

Since the infinite sum is the Maclaurin series expansion for e^{λ}, it follows that $P(S) = 1$. The probability function of this illustration has many important applications, and we shall meet it again in Chapters 3, 5, and 16.

The problem of defining probabilities in connection with continuous sample spaces is somewhat more complicated. To illustrate the nature of these complications, suppose that an accident occurs on a turnpike whose length is 200 miles, and that we are interested in the probability that it occurred at some given location or, perhaps, some particular stretch of the road. The outcomes of this experiment can be looked upon as a continuum of points, namely, those on the continuous interval from 0 to 200. Suppose the probability that the accident occurred on any interval of length L is $L/200$, with L measured in miles. Note that this arbitrary assignment of probability is consistent with Axioms 1 and 2, since these probabilities are all nonnegative and less than or equal to 1, and $P(S) = 200/200 = 1$. Of course, we are considering so far only events represented by intervals which form part of the line segment from 0 to 200. Using Axiom 3', we can also obtain probabilities of events which are not intervals but which can be represented by the union of finitely many or countably many intervals. Thus, for two nonoverlapping intervals of length L_1 and L_2 we have a probability of

$$\frac{L_1 + L_2}{200}$$

and for an infinite sequence of nonoverlapping intervals of length L_1, L_2, L_3, . . . , we have a probability of

$$\frac{L_1 + L_2 + L_3 + \ldots}{200}$$

Note that the probability that the accident occurred at any given point is equal to zero because we can look upon a point as an interval of zero length. However, the probability that the accident occurred in a very short interval is positive; for instance, for an interval of length 1 foot the probability is $9.5(10)^{-7}$.

In defining a probability function for the continuous case, we again use Axioms 1, 2, and 3', but we must restrict the meaning of the term "event." So far as practical considerations are concerned, this restriction is of no consequence; we simply do not assign probabilities to some rather abstruse point sets, which cannot be expressed as the unions or intersections of finitely many or countably many intervals. The probability function which we have used in the above example is, of course, a special one; it is similar in nature to the one based on equal probabilities in the discrete case. Various other probability functions defined on continuous sample spaces will be treated separately in Chapter 4.

3 | PROBABILITY DISTRIBUTIONS

3.1 Random Variables

In most experiments we are interested only in a particular numerical description (or numerical descriptions) of the outcomes. For example, in the inspection of manufactured products we may be interested only in the total number of defective items and not in the nature of the defects; in the study of the composition of an alloy we may want to know the per cent of chromium present, without caring about the other elements; in the analysis of a road test we may be interested only in the average fuel consumption over various terrains and not in any other performance characteristics.

To illustrate this idea more specifically, let us refer again to the missile firing example and the 18 outcomes listed on page 18. Suppose, however, that now we are interested only in the total number of subsystems that failed in flight. Again listing the elements of the sample space and their probabilities, but now adding a column giving the number of subsystems that failed, we obtain the following table:*

---

* It is assumed here that a subsystem fails if its performance is not perfect.

Outcome	Prob- ability	Number of failures	Outcome	Prob- ability	Number of failures
$P_1 \cap G_1 \cap A_1$	0.336	0	$P_2 \cap G_2 \cap A_1$	0.042	2
$P_1 \cap G_1 \cap A_2$	0.096	1	$P_2 \cap G_2 \cap A_2$	0.012	3
$P_1 \cap G_1 \cap A_3$	0.048	1	$P_2 \cap G_2 \cap A_3$	0.006	3
$P_1 \cap G_2 \cap A_1$	0.084	1	$P_3 \cap G_1 \cap A_1$	0.056	1
$P_1 \cap G_2 \cap A_2$	0.024	2	$P_3 \cap G_1 \cap A_2$	0.016	2
$P_1 \cap G_2 \cap A_3$	0.012	2	$P_3 \cap G_1 \cap A_3$	0.008	2
$P_2 \cap G_1 \cap A_1$	0.168	1	$P_3 \cap G_2 \cap A_1$	0.014	2
$P_2 \cap G_1 \cap A_2$	0.048	2	$P_3 \cap G_2 \cap A_2$	0.004	3
$P_2 \cap G_1 \cap A_3$	0.024	2	$P_3 \cap G_2 \cap A_3$	0.002	3

Note that one of these outcomes corresponds to no failures, 5 comprise the event that one subsystem fails, 8 comprise the event that two subsystems fail, while 4 comprise the event that three subsystems fail. Using the special law of addition, we thus find that the probability for the failure of exactly one subsystem is

$$P(1) = 0.096 + 0.048 + 0.084 + 0.168 + 0.056$$
$$= 0.452$$

Similarly, we obtain the values shown in the following table:

Failures	0	1	2	3
Probability	0.336	0.452	0.188	0.024

The numbers 0, 1, 2, and 3 in this table are values of the *random variable* describing the number of subsystems that fail. Observe that to each outcome in the sample space there corresponds one and only one value x of this random variable. *Thus, a random variable may be thought of as a function defined over the elements of a sample space.* Note further that to find the probability that a random variable takes on any one value within its range, we have only to make use of the probability function defined on the elements of the sample space and Axiom 3 or 3'. (It is assumed here and throughout this chapter that the sample spaces with which we are dealing are finite or countably infinite.) We thus define another function, which associates with each value of a random variable the probability that this value will be assumed. Such a function, an example of which is exhibited by the above table, is called a *probability distribution function,* or simply a *probability distribution.* To denote the values of a probability distribution we shall use such symbols as $f(x)$, $P(x)$, $\phi(z)$, $g(y)$, and so on.

Whenever possible, we try to define probability distributions by means of appropriate equations; otherwise we must give a table which actually exhibits the correspondence between the values assumed by the random

variable and the associated probabilities. For instance, it is easily verified
that the equation

$$f(x) = 1/2 \qquad \text{for } x = 0, 1$$

gives the probability distribution for the number of heads obtained when
tossing a balanced coin; on the other hand, it would be difficult to give the
probability distribution for the number of subsystems that fail in the missile
example by means of an equation.

Note also that if $f(x)$ is a value of a probability distribution, it must
satisfy the following properties:

(1) $f(x) \geq 0 \qquad$ for all x,

(2) $\sum\limits_{\text{all } x} f(x) = 1.$

This follows from the fact that $f(x)$ is a probability and that the sum of
the probabilities over the entire sample space must equal 1.

It is often helpful to visualize probability distributions by means of
graphs like those of Figures 3.1 and 3.2. The first of these is called a
histogram; the heights of the rectangles are proportional to the corresponding probabilities and their bases touch so that there are no gaps between
the rectangles representing the successive values of the random variable.
The graph of Figure 3.2 is called a *bar chart* and the heights of the rectangles
are again proportional to the corresponding probabilities.

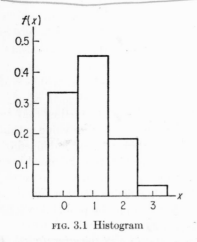

FIG. 3.1 Histogram

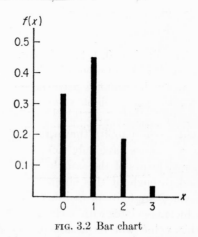

FIG. 3.2 Bar chart

As we shall see later in this chapter, there are many problems in which
we are interested not only in the probability $f(x)$ that the value of a random
variable is x, but also in the probability that the value of a random variable
is *less than or equal to x.* Writing this probability as $F(x)$, we refer to the
function which assigns a value $F(x)$ to each x within the range of the

random variable as the *cumulative distribution function*, or simply as the *distribution function*. Referring again to the missile-firing example, we thus have

x	0	1	2	3
$F(x)$	0.336	0.788	0.976	1.000

3.2 The Binomial Distribution

Many statistical problems deal with situations referred to as "repeated trials." For example, if we want to know the probability that 1 of 5 rivets will shear in a tensile test, that 9 of 10 vacuum tubes will last at least 1000 hours, that at least 60 of a shipment of 75 units are effective, we are in each case concerned with a number of "trials" and we are interested in the probability of getting a certain number of "successes."

Letting n represent the number of trials and x the number of successes, problems like these can be solved using the so-called *binomial distribution*, provided that they satisfy the following assumptions:

1. There are only two possible outcomes for each trial, arbitrarily called "success" and "failure" without inferring that a success is necessarily a desirable outcome. (For example, the occurrence of a defective unit in sampling inspection may be called a "success.")

2. The probability of a success is constant from trial to trial; it will be denoted by the letter p and, hence, the probability of a failure is denoted $1 - p$.

3. There are n trials, where n is a given constant.

4. The n trials are independent.

Of course, if these assumptions cannot be met, the problem will have to be solved with an appropriately different probability distribution.

To begin with, let us find the probability of getting x successes in n trials *in a given order*. Denoting success and failure, respectively, by the letters S and F, consider the sequence

$$\underbrace{S \; S \; \ldots \; S}_{x} \; \underbrace{F \; F \; \ldots \; F}_{n - x}$$

consisting of x successes, followed by $n - x$ failures. By the assumption of independence, the probability of this sequence is the product of the probabilities of the individual outcomes; there are x factors p, $n - x$ factors $1 - p$, and, hence, the probability is $p^x(1 - p)^{n-x}$. Note that the identical result would have been obtained for any other sequence containing x successes and $n - x$ failures *in a given order*. There would also have been

x factors p and $n - x$ factors $1 - p$, and the desired probability would also have been given by their product.

To obtain the probability of x successes and $n - x$ failures *in any order*, we must now add the probabilities of all sequences containing x successes and $n - x$ failures in some order. Since each of these sequences has the probability $p^x(1 - p)^{n-x}$, we have only to find the number of such sequences and multiply this number by $p^x(1 - p)^{n-x}$. Note that $p^x(1 - p)^{n-x}$ is, thus, multiplied by the number of ways in which the x letters S can be distributed among the n trials. To find this number, suppose that we temporarily assume that the S's are *distinguishable*, say, by giving them subscripts and writing them as $S_1, S_2, \ldots, S_x$. Beginning with S_1, we can assign it to any one of the n trials, that is, we can assign it in n different ways. After that we can assign S_2 in $n - 1$ different ways, S_3 in $n - 2$ ways, $\ldots$, and, finally, S_x in $n - x + 1$ different ways. According to Theorem 2.1 on page 8, all of these S's can, thus, be distributed among the n trials in $n(n - 1)(n - 2) \cdot \ldots \cdot (n - x + 1)$ different ways. If we now omit the subscripts, we find that the various arrangements which we have considered are not all distinct. For instance, $S_1FS_2S_3F$, $S_1FS_3S_2F$, $S_2FS_1S_3F$, $S_2FS_3S_1F$, $S_3FS_1S_2F$, and $S_3FS_2S_1F$ all lead to $SFSSF$. In general, the x letters S with subscripts can be arranged among themselves in $x(x - 1) \cdot \ldots \cdot 2 \cdot 1$ different ways according to Theorem 2.1, and, hence, this many arrangements of the S's with subscripts lead to a single arrangement once the subscripts are dropped. The number of ways in which the x letters S can be distributed among the n trials is, thus, given by

$$\frac{n(n - 1)(n - 2) \cdot \ldots \cdot (n - x + 1)}{x(x - 1) \cdot \ldots \cdot 2 \cdot 1}$$

which in the *factorial notation* can be written as $n!/x!(n - x)!$.* It follows that under the assumptions stated on page 39 the probability of x successes in n trials is given by

$$b(x; n, p) = \frac{n!}{x!(n - x)!} p^x(1 - p)^{n-x} \quad \text{for } x = 0, 1, \ldots, n$$

The probability distribution defined by this equation is called the *binomial distribution*. In fact, this equation defines a family of probability distributions, with each member of this family being characterized by given values of the *parameters* n and p.

To give an example where the binomial distribution can be applied,

---

* The expression $\dfrac{n!}{x!(n - x)!}$ is often referred to as a *binomial coefficient* since it is the coefficient of a^x in the binomial expansion of $(a + b)^n$; it is often represented by the symbol $\binom{n}{x}$.

suppose we want to find the probability that exactly 9 out of 10 vacuum tubes will last at least 1000 hours, given that the probability that any one of these tubes will last at least 1000 hours is 0.80. Assuming that the conditions underlying the binomial distribution can be met and substituting $n = 10$ and $p = 0.80$, we get

$$b(9; 10, 0.80) = \frac{10!}{9!1!} (0.80)^9 (0.20)^1 = 0.268$$

To find the probability that *at least* 9 out of 10 such tubes will last at least 1000 hours, we have only to use the special law of addition and write

$$b(9; 10, 0.80) + b(10; 10, 0.80) = 0.268 + 0.107 = 0.375$$

The probability that *at most* 8 of these tubes will last at least 1000 hours is given by the sum

$$\sum_{x=0}^{8} b(x; 10, 0.80)$$

but rather than evaluate each of the 9 probabilities required for this sum, it is easier to find the probability that at least 9 tubes will last at least 1000 hours, and subtract the result from 1. We thus obtain $1 - 0.375 = 0.625$.

If n is large, the calculation of binomial probabilities can become quite tedious; in that case it may be desirable to use numerical approximations or refer to special tables. Values of the binomial distribution and the corresponding cumulative distribution function have been tabulated for $n = 2$ to $n = 49$ by the National Bureau of Standards and for $n = 50$ to $n = 100$ by H. G. Romig (see the Bibliography at the end of the book). Table I at the end of this book gives the values of

$$B(x; n, p) = \sum_{k=0}^{x} b(k; n, p) \qquad \text{for } x = 0, 1, 2, \dots, n$$

for $n = 2$ to $n = 20$ and $p = 0.05, 0.10, 0.15, 0.20, \dots, 0.50$. We tabulated the cumulative probabilities rather than the values of $b(x; n, p)$, because the values of $B(x; n, p)$ are the ones needed more often in statistical applications. Note, however, that the values of $b(x; n, p)$ can be obtained with the use of Table I by making use of the identities in parts (c) and (d) of Theorem 3.1 below. Also note that values of $B(x; n, p)$ cannot be obtained directly from Table I when p is greater than 0.50, but that they can be obtained from this table with the use of the identity given in part (b).

THEOREM 3.1

(a) $b(x; n, p) = b(n - x; n, 1 - p)$

(b) $B(x; n, p) = 1 - B(n - x - 1; n, 1 - p)$

(c) $b(x; n, p) = B(x; n, p) - B(x - 1; n, p)$

(d) $b(x; n, p) = B(n - x; n, 1 - p) - B(n - x - 1; n, 1 - p)$

The first of these identities can be verified by substituting on both sides the corresponding expressions given by the equation defining the binomial distribution; the second identity follows from (a) and the definition of a cumulative distribution; the third identity follows directly from the definition of a cumulative distribution; and the fourth identity follows by substitution from parts (a) and (c). The reader will be asked to verify these identities in detail in Exercises 5 and 6 on page 45.

To illustrate the use of Table I and identities (a) and (c) of Theorem 3.1, let us suppose that in a very large shipment of vacuum tubes, the probability of failure for any one tube is 0.20. Assuming, furthermore, that the assumptions underlying the binomial distribution are approximately met, the probability that *at most 3 tubes fail in a sample of 20* is given by

$$B(3; 20, 0.20) = 0.4114$$

Also, the probability that *5 or more tubes fail in a sample of 16* is given by

$$\sum_{x=5}^{16} b(x; 16, 0.20) = 1 - B(4; 16, 0.20) = 1 - 0.7982 = 0.2018$$

the probability that *exactly 12 tubes do not fail in a sample of 15* is

$$b(12; 15, 0.80) = b(3; 15, 0.20) = 0.2502$$

and the probability that *exactly 5 tubes fail in a sample of 18* is given by

$$b(5; 18, 0.20) = B(5; 18, 0.20) - B(4; 18, 0.20)$$
$$= 0.8671 - 0.7164 = 0.1507$$

To illustrate the use of identities (b) and (d) of Theorem 3.1, let us suppose that the probability is 0.75 that a driver will not have an accident in a given period of time. Then, the probability that *fewer than 16 of 20 drivers will not have an accident* is given by

$$B(15; 20, 0.75) = 1 - B(4; 20, 0.25)$$
$$= 1 - 0.4148 = 0.5852$$

and the probability that *exactly 12 of 15 drivers will not have an accident* is given by

$$b(12; 15, 0.75) = B(3; 15, 0.25) - B(2; 15, 0.25)$$
$$= 0.4613 - 0.2361 = 0.2252$$

To illustrate the use of the binomial distribution in a problem of decision making, suppose a manufacturer claims that his production process does not turn out more than 10 per cent defectives, and that the decision whether to accept or reject his claim has to be made on the basis of a shipment of

20 units among which 5 are defective. To justify the decision one way or the other, let us first find the probability of getting 5 or more defectives in a sample of 20 when the "true" percentage of defectives is 0.10; that is, the probability is 0.10 that a unit inspected is defective. Since we get

$$\sum_{x=5}^{20} b(x; 20, 0.10) = 1 - B(4; 20, 0.10) = 0.0432$$

which is very small, it would seem reasonable to reject the manufacturer's claim. (Note that this probability would have been even smaller if we had used a value of p less than 0.10.) If the sample had contained only 3 defectives, it would have been much more difficult to reach a decision. The probability of getting 3 or more defectives in a sample of 20, when the probability that any one unit is defective is 0.10, is 0.3230. This can hardly be described as a "rare event" and it certainly does not justify rejecting the manufacturer's claim.

An interesting property of binomial distributions is illustrated in Figures 3.3, 3.4, and 3.5. First, if $p = 0.50$ the equation for the binomial distribution becomes

$$b(x; n, 0.50) = \frac{n!}{x!(n-x)!} (0.50)^n$$

and $b(x; n, 0.50) = b(n - x; n, 0.50)$; that is, the histogram of a binomial distribution with $p = 0.50$ is *symmetrical*, as is illustrated in Figure 3.3 in

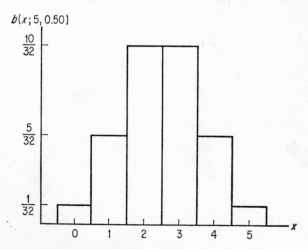

FIG. 3.3 Symmetrical binomial distribution

the special case where $n = 5$. Now, note that *if p is less than 0.50*, it is more likely that x will be small rather than large compared to n; similarly, the reverse holds if p is greater than 0.50. This is illustrated in Figures 3.4

and 3.5, containing the histograms of binomial distributions with $n = 5$ and $p = 0.20$ and $p = 0.80$, respectively. A probability distribution which has a histogram like that of Figure 3.4 or Figure 3.5 is said to be *skewed*;

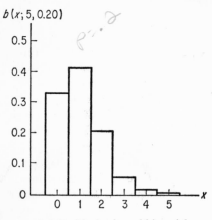

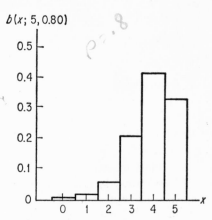

FIG. 3.4 Positively-skewed binomial
distribution

FIG. 3.5 Negatively-skewed binomial
distribution

it is said to be *positively skewed* if the long "tail" is on the right as in Figure 3.4, and it is said to be *negatively skewed* if the long "tail" is on the left as in Figure 3.5.

EXERCISES

1. Suppose that a probability of 1/20 is assigned to each outcome in the sample space of Figure 2.5. Find the probability distribution of the total number of defective components in the whole assembly.

2. An experiment consists of three tosses of a coin. Denoting the outcomes $HHT, THT, \ldots$, and assuming that all 8 outcomes are equally likely, find the probability distribution for the total number of heads.

3. If a random variable can assume the values $x = 0, 1, 2, 3, 4,$ and 5, check whether each of the following defines a probability distribution:
   (a) $f(x) = 1/6$ for all x,
   (b) $f(x) = x/15$ for all x,
   (c) $f(x) = x^2/50$ for all x,
   (d) $f(x) = \dfrac{x - 1}{9}$ for all x.

4. Given that

$$f(x) = k(1/3)^x$$

is a probability distribution for a random variable assuming the values $x = 0, 1, 2, \ldots$, find k and also find an expression for the corresponding cumulative probabilities $F(x)$.

5. Prove parts (a) and (b) of Theorem 3.1 on page 41.

6. Prove parts (c) and (d) of Theorem 3.1 on page 41.

7. Prove that

$$\frac{b(x+1; n, p)}{b(x; n, p)} = \frac{p(n-x)}{(1-p)(x+1)}$$

for $x = 0, 1, 2, \ldots, n - 1$.

8. Use the recursion formula of Exercise 7 to calculate the probabilities of the binomial distribution with $n = 5$ and $p = 0.30$, and draw its histogram. Verify your results by referring to Table I.

9. Using Table I find

  (a) $B(5; 15, 0.40)$,   (d) $b(8; 12, 0.70)$,

  (b) $b(5; 15, 0.40)$,   (e) $\sum_{k=5}^{20} b(k; 20, 0.10)$,

  (c) $B(8; 12, 0.70)$,   (f) $\sum_{k=3}^{9} b(k; 9, 0.80)$.

10. Using Table I find

  (a) $B(8; 18, 0.45)$,   (d) $b(9; 10, 0.90)$,

  (b) $b(8; 18, 0.45)$,   (e) $\sum_{k=3}^{10} b(k; 10, 0.30)$,

  (c) $B(9; 10, 0.90)$,   (f) $\sum_{k=2}^{4} b(k; 8, 0.40)$.

11. The probability that a car driving the entire length of a certain turnpike will have a blowout is 0.05. Find the probability that among 17 cars traveling the length of this turnpike

  (a) exactly one will have a blowout,

  (b) at most 3 will have a blowout,

  (c) 2 or more will have a blowout.

12. The probability that a certain kind of vacuum tube will survive a given thermal shock test is 0.85. Find the probability that among 20 such tubes

  (a) exactly 17 will survive,

  (b) at least 15 will survive,

  (c) at least 3 will not survive.

13. A manufacturer claims that at most 10 per cent of his product is defective. To test this claim, 18 units are inspected and his claim is accepted if among these 18 units at most 2 are defective. Find the probability that the manufacturer's claim will be accepted if the actual probability that a unit is defective is

(a) 0.05,   (c) 0.15,

(b) 0.10,   (d) 0.20.

3.3 The Hypergeometric Distribution

Suppose a sample of n units is to be drawn from a lot containing N units, of which a are defective. The sample is to be drawn in such a way that at each successive drawing whatever units are left in the lot have the same chance of being included in the sample. Thus, for the first drawing the probability of obtaining a defective unit is a/N, but for the second drawing it remains a/N *only if the first unit drawn is replaced.* Otherwise, this probability is $\dfrac{a-1}{N-1}$ or $\dfrac{a}{N-1}$ depending on whether or not a defective unit was obtained in the first drawing. *Assumption 4 underlying the binomial distribution is, therefore, met only if the sample is drawn with replacement.* In practice, this is seldom the case, and we shall, thus, have to derive a new probability distribution, called the *hypergeometric distribution*, which applies to this kind of situation.

To solve this problem of "sampling without replacement," let us refer to the result obtained on page 40, namely, that a subset of x objects can be selected from a set of n objects in

$$\binom{n}{x} = \frac{n!}{x!(n-x)!}$$

ways. We proved this in connection with the problem of the distribution of x successes among n trials, that is, choosing subsets on which the x successes are to occur. We referred to $\binom{n}{x}$ as a binomial coefficient, and it is also called the "number of combinations of n objects taken x at a time."

Returning now to the problem of finding the probability of getting x defectives in a sample of n units taken without replacement, note first that the sample space for this experiment has $\binom{N}{n}$ possible outcomes, namely, the number of ways in which a subset of n objects can be selected from among a set of N objects. Furthermore, the x defectives can be selected from the a defectives in $\binom{a}{x}$ ways, the $n-x$ nondefective units in the sample can be selected from the $N-a$ nondefective units in the lot in

$\begin{pmatrix} N - a \\ n - x \end{pmatrix}$ ways, and according to Theorem 2.1, the whole sample can be

selected in $\begin{pmatrix} a \\ x \end{pmatrix} \begin{pmatrix} N - a \\ n - x \end{pmatrix}$ ways. Assuming that each of the $\begin{pmatrix} N \\ n \end{pmatrix}$ samples
has the same probability of being selected, which is equivalent to the
assumption stated in the first paragraph of this section, the required probability for x "successes" in n trials without replacement is

♦ $$h(x; n, a, N) = \frac{\begin{pmatrix} a \\ x \end{pmatrix} \begin{pmatrix} N - a \\ n - x \end{pmatrix}}{\begin{pmatrix} N \\ n \end{pmatrix}} \qquad \text{for } x = 0, 1, \ldots, n$$ ♦

by virtue of Theorem 2.3. A probability distribution having this equation
is called a *hypergeometric distribution;* the parameters of this family of
distributions are the *sample size n,* the *lot size* (or *population size*) *N*, and
the number of "successes" in the lot *a*, which in our special example was
the total number of defectives in the lot (or population).

To illustrate the use of a hypergeometric distribution, let us calculate
the probability of obtaining 2 defectives in a sample of size 10 taken without
replacement from a lot of 20 units containing 5 defectives. Substituting
$x = 2$, $n = 10$, $a = 5$, and $N = 20$, we obtain

$$h(2; 10, 5, 20) = \frac{\begin{pmatrix} 5 \\ 2 \end{pmatrix} \begin{pmatrix} 15 \\ 8 \end{pmatrix}}{\begin{pmatrix} 20 \\ 10 \end{pmatrix}} = \frac{10 \cdot 6435}{184,756} = 0.348$$

To simplify the calculation of probabilities like this, one can use tables of
binomial coefficients or tables of the logarithms of factorials, which can be
found in almost any handbook of mathematical tables.

Note that if we had made the mistake of using the binomial distribution
with $n = 10$ and $p = \frac{5}{20} = 0.25$ to calculate the probability of getting
2 defectives, the result would have been 0.282, a considerable underestimate
of the actual probability. The sample size $n = 10$ was large compared to
the lot size $N = 20$ in this example, and the effect of not replacing the units
has been rather severe. However, had the sample size been small compared
to the lot size, the composition of the lot would not have been "disturbed"
very much by drawing a sample, and it would be reasonable to expect that
the binomial distribution with $p = \dfrac{a}{N}$ should yield a close approximation.

To illustrate this point, suppose that the lot contains 100 units, rather
than 20, and that 1/4, or 25 of these units, are defective. The exact probability of drawing a sample of size 10 with 2 defectives is now

$$h(2; 10, 25, 100) = \frac{\binom{25}{2}\binom{75}{8}}{\binom{100}{10}} = 0.292$$

The approximation of 0.282 given by the binomial distribution with $n = 10$ and $p = 0.25$ is now reasonably close to the actual probability.

In most practical situations, the sample size is small in comparison with the lot size (the size of the population), and the binomial distribution provides a good approximation to the hypergeometric distribution. In fact, it can be shown that $h(x; n, a, N)$ approaches $b(x; n, p)$ when $N \to \infty$ and $\frac{a}{N} = p$ remains fixed. A good rule of thumb is to use the binomial distribution as an approximation to the hypergeometric distribution only if $N \geq 10n$.

Although we have introduced the hypergeometric distribution in connection with a problem of sampling inspection, it has many other applications. For instance, it can be used to find the probability that 3 out of 12 housewives prefer Brand A detergent to Brand B, if they are selected from among 200 housewives among whom 40 actually prefer Brand A to Brand B. Also, it can be used in connection with a problem of selecting industrial diamonds, some of which have superior qualities and some do not, in connection with a problem of sampling income tax returns, where a among N returns filed contain questionable deductions, and so on.

3.4 The Poisson Distribution

Let us now consider another problem that can be solved by means of the binomial distribution. Suppose we are examining a length L of enameled steel wire for imperfections such as pits, slivers, seams, and so forth. We shall assume that for each small interval of length ΔL the probability of an imperfection is $\alpha \cdot \Delta L$, where α (alpha) is a constant which depends on the quality of the wire, and ΔL is sufficiently small so that the probability of two or more imperfections in an interval of length ΔL is negligible. What we are interested in is the probability of finding x imperfections in a length L of wire.

Suppose that there are n intervals of length ΔL, that is $n \cdot \Delta L = L$, and suppose, furthermore, that the occurrence of an imperfection in any given interval is independent of the occurrence of imperfections in any of the other intervals. We can, thus, think of the n intervals as forming a sequence of n independent trials with the constant probability $\alpha \Delta L$ of an imperfection on any given trial. It follows that the probability of x imperfections in a length $n \cdot \Delta L$ of wire is

$$b(x; n, \alpha \, \Delta L) = \binom{n}{x} (\alpha \, \Delta L)^x (1 - \alpha \, \Delta L)^{n-x} \qquad \text{for } x = 0, 1, \ldots, n$$

Since the assumption that the probability of getting more than one imperfection per interval is negligible is reasonable only if ΔL is very small, let us now find the limit approached by the above probability when $\Delta L \to 0$. This should give us the desired probability for getting x imperfections in a length L of the given kind of wire.

Substituting $\dfrac{L}{n}$ for ΔL and simplifying the resulting expression for $b(x; n, \alpha \, \Delta L)$, we obtain

$$\begin{aligned}
b(x; n, \alpha \, \Delta L) &= \frac{n!}{x!(n-x)!} \left(\frac{\alpha L}{n}\right)^x \left(1 - \frac{\alpha L}{n}\right)^{n-x} \\
&= \frac{n(n-1)(n-2)\cdot \ldots \cdot(n-x+1)}{x!\,n^x} (\alpha L)^x \left(1 - \frac{\alpha L}{n}\right)^{n-x} \\
&= \frac{\left(1 - \frac{1}{n}\right)\left(1 - \frac{2}{n}\right) \cdot \ldots \cdot \left(1 - \frac{x-1}{n}\right)}{x!} (\alpha L)^x \left(1 - \frac{\alpha L}{n}\right)^{n-x}
\end{aligned}$$

If we now let $n \to \infty$, we find that

$$\left(1 - \frac{1}{n}\right)\left(1 - \frac{2}{n}\right) \cdot \ldots \cdot \left(1 - \frac{x-1}{n}\right) \to 1$$

that

$$\left(1 - \frac{\alpha L}{n}\right)^{n-x} = \left[\left(1 - \frac{\alpha L}{n}\right)^{n/\alpha L}\right]^{\alpha L} \left(1 - \frac{\alpha L}{n}\right)^{-x} \to e^{-\alpha L}$$

and, hence, that the binomial probability approaches

$$\frac{e^{-\alpha L}(\alpha L)^x}{x!} \qquad \text{for } x = 0, 1, 2, \ldots$$

This is the desired probability distribution for obtaining x imperfections on a length L of the given kind of wire and it belongs to the family of so-called *Poisson distributions*. Substituting for αL the single parameter λ, *lambda*, the equation for a Poisson distribution in general is

$$\blacklozenge \qquad f(x; \lambda) = e^{-\lambda} \frac{\lambda^x}{x!} \qquad \text{for } x = 0, 1, 2, \ldots \qquad \blacklozenge$$

Although the Poisson distribution is defined over a sample space which is countably infinite, it is apparent from the manner in which it was introduced that with $\lambda = np$ it should provide a good approximation for the binomial distribution when n is large and p is small. To illustrate, let us compare $b(2; 100, 0.05)$ with $f(2; 5)$, where $\lambda = n \cdot p = 100(0.05) = 5$. Substituting into the appropriate expressions, we get

$$b(2; 100, 0.05) = \binom{100}{2} (0.05)^2(0.95)^{98} = 0.081$$

$$f(2; 5) = e^{-5}\frac{5^2}{2!} = 0.084$$

and it is interesting to note that the error is as small as 0.003. An acceptable rule of thumb is to use the Poisson distribution to approximate binomial probabilities if $n \geq 20$ and $p \leq 0.05$. (If $n \geq 100$, the approximation is excellent so long as $np \leq 10$.)

Table II at the end of the book gives the values of the probabilities $F(x; \lambda) = \sum_{k=0}^{x} f(k; \lambda)$ for values of λ in varying increments from 0.02 to 25. To illustrate the use of this table, suppose that $n \cdot p = 3.6$ for the distribution of the weekly number of absentees in the accounting department of a given firm. To find the probability that at most 5 employees are absent during a certain week, we use the Poisson approximation with $\lambda = 3.6$ and we find from Table II that

$$F(5; 3.6) = 0.844$$

Using this approximation, we assumed that the number of employees is very large and that the probability for any employee's absence is very small. Implicit, also, is the assumption that the absence of any given employee is not affected by the presence or absence of any other employee, although this assumption may be somewhat questionable.

Table II can also be used to find values of $f(x; \lambda)$, using an identity analogous to (c) of Theorem 3.1, namely,

$$f(x; \lambda) = F(x; \lambda) - F(x - 1; \lambda)$$

Using this identity and, thus, subtracting successive values of $F(x; \lambda)$, we obtained the values of the Poisson distribution with $\lambda = 2$ shown in Figure 3.6. Note that this distribution is *positively skewed;* in fact, **it**

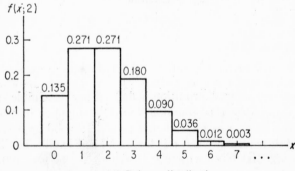

FIG. 3.6 Poisson distribution

should be apparent from the discussion on page 44 that Poisson distributions are positively skewed for any value of $\lambda > 0$.

a   40 9 4

EXERCISES   *A   4 2 0 1*

1. An urn contains 15 marbles of which 10 are red and 5 are white. If 6 marbles are drawn from the urn without replacement, find the probability that

   (a) there are 2 white marbles and 4 red ones,

   (b) there are at most 2 white marbles,   *102/143*

   (c) there are at least 4 red marbles,   *102/143*

   (d) there are at least 2 red marbles.   *999/1001*

2. Certain missile components are shipped in lots of 25. Three components are selected from each lot and the lot is accepted if none of them is defective. What is the probability that a lot will be accepted if it contains

   (a) 5 defectives,   (c) 15 defectives,

   (b) 10 defectives,   (d) 20 defectives.

3. A taxicab company has 12 Chevrolets and 8 Fords. If 5 of these taxicabs are in the shop for repairs and a Chevrolet is as likely to be in for repairs as a Ford, what is the probability that

   (a) 3 of them are Chevrolets and 2 are Fords?

   (b) at least 3 of them are Chevrolets?

   (c) all 5 of them are of the same make?

4. It was pointed out on page 48 that values of the hypergeometric distribution can sometimes be approximated with values of the binomial distribution. Verify this statement by comparing $h(1; 5, 20, 100)$ with $b(1; 5, 0.20)$.

5. Repeat Exercise 2, approximating the required probabilities with binomial probabilities having $n = 3$ and $p = 0.20, 0.40, 0.60$, and 0.80, respectively. Comment on the goodness of these approximations.

6. Prove that for the Poisson distribution

$$\frac{f(x + 1; \lambda)}{f(x; \lambda)} = \frac{\lambda}{x + 1}$$

   for $x = 0, 1, 2, \ldots$.

7. Use the recursion formula of Exercise 6 to calculate the values of the Poisson distribution with $\lambda = 2$ for $x = 0, 1, 2, \ldots$, and 9, and draw the histogram of this distribution. Verify your results by referring to Table II.

8. Using Table II, find

   (a) $F(4; 6)$,   (c) $\sum_{k=6}^{19} f(k; 10)$.

   (b) $f(4; 6)$,

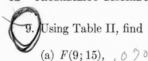

9. Using Table II, find

   (a) $F(9; 15)$, $, 0 \; 9 \; 0$

   (b) $f(9; 15)$, $. \; 0 \; 33$

   (c) $\sum_{k=3}^{12} f(k; 8.5)$. $0. \; 900$

10. It was pointed out on page 49 that values of the binomial distribution can sometimes be approximated with corresponding values of the Poisson distribution. Verify this statement by comparing $b(4; 50, 0.10)$ with $f(4; 5)$.

11. In the inspection of tin plate produced by a continuous electrolytic process, the probability of spotting an imperfection in a very small interval of time Δt is $(0.2) \Delta t$, time being measured in minutes. What are the probabilities of spotting, respectively, 0, 1, and 2 imperfections in 5 minutes?

12. The number of weekly breakdowns of a computer is a random variable having a Poisson distribution with $\lambda = 0.4$. What is the probability that the computer will operate without a breakdown for two consecutive weeks?

13. The number of gamma rays emitted per second by a certain radioactive substance is a random variable having the Poisson distribution with $\lambda = 5.6$. If a recording instrument becomes inoperative when there are more than 12 rays per second, what is the probability that this instrument becomes inoperative during any given second?

14. The number of hurricanes reaching the East Coast of the United States per year is a random variable having the Poisson distribution with $\lambda = 1.9$. Find the probabilities that in a given year the number of hurricanes reaching the East Coast of the United States is (a) zero, (b) exactly 3, (c) 2 or more.

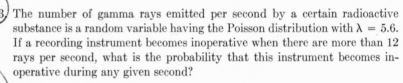

3.5 The Mean and Variance of a Probability Distribution

In Section 3.2 we introduced one important characteristic of a probability distribution (or the corresponding histogram), namely, that of the symmetry or skewness of a distribution. Two other important characteristics are illustrated in Figure 3.7, which show the histograms of two binomial distributions, one with the parameters $n = 4$ and $p = 1/2$ (unshaded) and the other with the parameters $n = 16$ and $p = 1/2$ (shaded). Essentially, these two distributions differ in two respects. The first distribution is "centered" about $x = 2$ while the second is "centered" about $x = 8$, and we thus say that the two distributions differ in their *location*. Another distinction between the two distributions is that the histogram of the second is more "spread out," the probabilities represented by the rectangles are more "dispersed," and we say that the two distributions differ in *variation*. In this section we shall introduce two of the foremost measures describing the location and the variation of a probability distribution; they are called the *mean* and the *variance*.

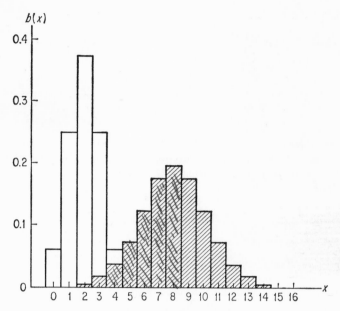

FIG. 3.7 Distributions having different means and variances

Concentrating for the moment on the first distribution of Figure 3.7, it can easily be verified that the probabilities for $x = 0$, 1, 2, 3, or 4 are, respectively, 1/16, 4/16, 6/16, 4/16, and 1/16. Hence, we can say that *in the long run* $x = 0$ about 1/16 of the time, $x = 1$ about 4/16 of the time, ..., $x = 4$ about 1/16 of the time, and that the value assumed by this random variable *on the average* is

$$0(1/16) + 1(4/16) + 2(6/16) + 3(4/16) + 4(1/16) = 2$$

Note that this is the value which we used in the preceding paragraph to describe the "center" of the distribution. Indeed, this average is what we call the *mean* of the probability distribution.

In general, the *mean* of a probability distribution with values $f(x)$ is defined by the equation

$$\blacklozenge \qquad \mu = \sum_{\text{all } x} x \cdot f(x) \qquad \blacklozenge$$

and it is denoted by the Greek letter μ (*mu*). It measures the "center" of a probability distribution in the sense of an average or, better, in the sense of a center of gravity. Note that the above formula for μ is, in fact, the *first moment about the origin* of a discrete system of masses $f(x)$ arranged on a straight line at distances x from the origin. We do not have to divide here by $\sum_{\text{all } x} f(x)$, as we do in the usual formula for the x-coordinate of the center of gravity, since this sum is by definition equal to 1.

Returning now to the second distribution of Figure 3.7, we could find its mean by substituting the appropriate probabilities into the above formula for the mean. However, if we reflect for a moment, we might argue that there is a fifty-fifty chance for a success on each trial, there are 16 trials, and it would seem reasonable to expect *on the average* 8 successes in 16 trials. Similarly, we might argue that if a binomial distribution has the parameters $n = 200$ and $p = 0.20$, we can expect a success about 20 per cent of the time and, hence, on the average $200(0.20) = 40$ successes in 200 trials. Indeed, this argument can be extended to any binomial distribution and we shall now prove that *the mean of the binomial distribution with the parameters n and p* is given by

$$\mu = n \cdot p$$

Substituting the expression which defines $b(x; n, p)$ into the formula for μ, we get

$$\mu = \sum_{x=0}^{n} x \cdot \frac{n!}{x!(n-x)!} p^x (1-p)^{n-x}$$

Making use of the fact that $\dfrac{x}{x!} = \dfrac{1}{(x-1)!}$ and $n! = n(n-1)!$, and factoring out n and p, we obtain

$$\mu = np \sum_{x=1}^{n} \frac{(n-1)!}{(x-1)!(n-x)!} p^{x-1}(1-p)^{n-x}$$

where the summation starts with $x = 1$ since the original summand is zero for $x = 0$. If we now let $y = x - 1$ and $m = n - 1$, we obtain

$$\mu = np \sum_{y=0}^{m} \frac{m!}{y!(m-y)!} p^y (1-p)^{m-y}$$

and this last sum can easily be recognized as that of all the terms of the binomial distribution with the parameters m and p. Hence, this sum equals 1 and it follows that $\mu = np$.

The result which we have obtained applies, of course, only to the binomial distribution, but given any other special distribution, we can, similarly, find an appropriate formula which expresses the mean in terms of the parameters of the distribution. For *the hypergeometric distribution with the parameters n, a, and N* we thus find that

$$\mu = n \cdot \frac{a}{N}$$

and for *the Poisson distribution with the parameter* λ we find that

$$\mu = \lambda$$

Using methods similar to the one we employed in deriving the formula for the mean of the binomial distribution, the reader will be asked to prove these results in Exercises 5 and 6 on page 60. Note that in the case of the Poisson distribution we could also show that $\mu = \lambda$ by referring to the limiting process through which the Poisson distribution was obtained from the binomial distribution.

Considering again the two distributions of Figure 3.7, note that for the first distribution there is a high probability that we will get a value close to the mean; so far as the second distribution is concerned, there is a higher probability for getting values scattered over considerable distances away from the mean. Using this property, it might seem reasonable to measure the variation of a probability distribution with the formula

$$\sum_{\text{all } x} (x - \mu) \cdot f(x)$$

namely, the average amount by which the values of the random variable *deviate* from the mean. Unfortunately,

$$\sum_{\text{all } x} (x - \mu) \cdot f(x) = \sum_{\text{all } x} x \cdot f(x) - \sum_{\text{all } x} \mu \cdot f(x)$$

$$= \mu - \mu \cdot \sum_{\text{all } x} f(x) = \mu - \mu = 0$$

so that this expression is always equal to zero. However, since we are really interested only in the *magnitude* of the deviations $x - \mu$ (not in their signs), it suggests itself that we average the *absolute values* of these deviations from the mean. This would, indeed, provide a measure of variation, but on purely theoretical grounds we prefer to work instead with the *squares* of the deviations from the mean. These quantities cannot be negative either, and their average is indicative of the spread or dispersion of a probability distribution. We thus define the *variance* of a probability distribution with values $f(x)$ as

$$\sigma^2 = \sum_{\text{all } x} (x - \mu)^2 \cdot f(x)$$

where σ (*sigma*) is the lower-case Greek letter for s. This measure is not in the same units (or dimension) as the values of the random variable, but we can adjust for this disadvantage by taking its square root, thus defining the *standard deviation*

$$\sigma = \sqrt{\sum_{\text{all } x} (x - \mu)^2 \cdot f(x)}$$

To illustrate how the standard deviation measures the spread of a probability distribution, let us calculate σ for the two distributions of Figure 3.7. Having already shown that the mean of the first distribution is equal to 2, we find that its variance equals

$$\sigma^2 = (0 - 2)^2(1/16) + (1 - 2)^2(4/16) + (2 - 2)^2(6/16)$$
$$+ (3 - 2)^2(4/16) + (4 - 2)^2(1/16)$$
$$= 1$$

and, hence, that the standard deviation is $\sigma = 1$. Similarly, it can be shown that for the second distribution $\sigma = 2$, and it can be seen that *the distribution with the greater spread also has the greater standard deviation.*

Given any probability distribution, we can always calculate σ^2 by substituting the corresponding probabilities $f(x)$ into the formula which defines the variance. As in the case of the mean, however, this work can be simplified to a considerable extent when we deal with special kinds of distributions. For instance, it can be shown that *the variance of the binomial distribution with the parameters n and p is given by the formula*

$$\sigma^2 = n \cdot p \cdot (1 - p) \qquad \text{bin}$$

We shall not prove this formula here, but applying it to the two distributions of Figure 3.7, which represent binomial distributions with the parameters $n = 4$, $p = 1/2$, and $n = 16$, $p = 1/2$, we find that their respective variances are 1 and 4; this agrees with the values obtained above.

Substituting the appropriate expressions for the probabilities $f(x)$, it can similarly be shown that *the variance of the hypergeometric distribution with the parameters n, N, and a is given by*

$$\sigma^2 = \frac{n \cdot a \cdot (N - a) \cdot (N - n)}{N^2 \cdot (N - 1)} \qquad \text{hypo}$$

and that *the variance of the Poisson distribution with the parameter λ is given by*

$$\sigma^2 = \lambda \qquad \text{Poisson}$$

When we first defined the variance of a probability distribution, it may have occurred to the reader that the formula looked exactly like the one which we use in physics to define second moments, or moments of inertia. Indeed, it is customary in statistics to define the *kth moment about the origin* as

$$\mu_k' = \sum_{\text{all } x} x^k \cdot f(x)$$

and the *kth moment about the mean* as

$$\mu_k = \sum_{\text{all } x} (x - \mu)^k \cdot f(x)$$

Thus, the mean μ is the first moment about the origin, and the variance σ^2 is the second moment about the mean. Higher moments are often used in statistics to give further descriptions of probability distributions. For instance, the third moment about the mean (divided by σ^3 to make this measure independent of the scale of measurement) is used to describe the symmetry or skewness of a distribution; the fourth moment about the mean (divided by σ^4) is, similarly, used to describe its "peakedness," or *kurtosis.* To determine moments about the mean, it is usually easiest to express them in terms of moments about the origin and then to calculate the necessary moment about the origin. For the second moment about the mean we thus have the important formula

◆ $$\sigma^2 = \mu_2' - \mu^2$$ *origin* ◆

which the reader will be asked to prove in part (a) of Exercise 12 on page 60; part (b) of this exercise contains a similar formula for expressing μ_3 in terms of moments about the mean.

3.6 Chebyshev's Theorem

Earlier in this chapter we used examples to show how the standard deviation measures the variation of a probability distribution, that is, how it controls the concentration of probability in the neighborhood of the mean. If σ is small, there is a high probability for getting a value close to the mean; if σ is large there is a correspondingly higher probability for getting values further away from the mean. Formally, this idea is expressed by the following theorem:

THEOREM 3.2 (*Chebyshev's theorem*). *If a probability distribution has the mean μ and the standard deviation σ, the probability of obtaining a value which deviates from the mean by more than k standard deviations is less than $1/k^2$. Symbolically,*

$$P(|x - \mu| > k\sigma) < 1/k^2$$

To prove this theorem, consider any probability distribution having the values $f(x)$, the mean μ, and the variance σ^2. Dividing the sum defining the variance into three parts as indicated in Figure 3.8, we have

$$\sigma^2 = \sum_{\text{all } x} (x - \mu)^2 f(x)$$

$$= \sum_{R_1} (x - \mu)^2 f(x) + \sum_{R_2} (x - \mu)^2 f(x) + \sum_{R_3} (x - \mu)^2 f(x)$$

where R_1 is the region for which $x < \mu - k\sigma$, R_2 is the region for which $\mu - k\sigma \le x \le \mu + k\sigma$, and R_3 is the region for which $x > \mu + k\sigma$. Since $(x - \mu)^2 f(x)$ cannot be negative, the above sum over R_2 is nonnegative, and without it the sum of the summations over R_1 and R_3 is less than or equal to σ^2, that is,

$$\sigma^2 \ge \sum_{R_1} (x - \mu)^2 f(x) + \sum_{R_3} (x - \mu)^2 f(x)$$

But $x - \mu < -k\sigma$ in the region R_1 and $x - \mu > k\sigma$ in the region R_3, so that in either case $|x - \mu| > k\sigma$; hence, in both regions $(x - \mu)^2 > k^2\sigma^2$. If we now replace $(x - \mu)^2$ in each sum by $k^2\sigma^2$, a number less than $(x - \mu)^2$, we obtain the inequality

$$\sigma^2 > \sum_{R_1} k^2\sigma^2 f(x) + \sum_{R_3} k^2\sigma^2 f(x)$$

or

$$1/k^2 > \sum_{R_1} f(x) + \sum_{R_3} f(x)$$

Since $\sum_{R_1} f(x) + \sum_{R_3} f(x)$ represents the probability that x is in the region $R_1 \cup R_3$, namely, that $|x - \mu| > k\sigma$, we finally have

$$P(|x - \mu| > k\sigma) < 1/k^2$$

and this completes the proof of Theorem 3.2.

To obtain an alternate form of *Chebyshev's inequality,* as the inequality of Theorem 3.2 is sometimes called, note that the event $|x - \mu| \leq k\sigma$ is the complement of the event $|x - \mu| > k\sigma$; hence,

♦ $$P(|x - \mu| \leq k\sigma) > 1 - 1/k^2$$ ♦

which states that the probability of getting a value within k standard deviations of the mean is greater than $1 - 1/k^2$.

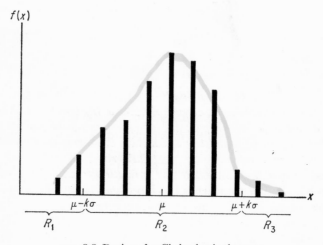

FIG. 3.8 Regions for Chebyshev's theorem

Theoretically speaking, the most important feature of Chebyshev's theorem is that it applies to *any* probability distribution for which μ and σ exist. So far as applications are concerned, however, this generality is also its greatest weakness; it only provides an *upper limit* (often a very poor one) to the probability of getting a value which deviates from the mean by more than k standard deviations. Thus, we can assert *in general* that the probability of getting a value which deviates from the mean by more than two standard deviations is less than 0.25, whereas the corresponding *exact* probability for the binomial distribution with the parameters $n = 16$ and

$p = 1/2$ is 0.021. Similarly, we can assert *in general* that the probability of getting a value which deviates from the mean by more than three standard deviations is less than 0.112, whereas the corresponding *exact* probability for the Poisson distribution with the parameter $\lambda = 9$ is 0.0024.

An important theoretical result is obtained if we apply Chebyshev's theorem to the binomial distribution. Substituting $\mu = np$ and $\sigma = \sqrt{np(1-p)}$, we get

$$P(|x - np| > k\sqrt{np(1-p)}) < 1/k^2$$

or

$$P\left(\left|\frac{x}{n} - p\right| > k\sqrt{\frac{p(1-p)}{n}}\right) < 1/k^2$$

after we divide both terms of the inequality inside the parentheses by n. If we now substitute ϵ for $k\sqrt{\dfrac{p(1-p)}{n}}$ we obtain

$$P\left(\left|\frac{x}{n} - p\right| > \epsilon\right) < \frac{p(1-p)}{n\epsilon^2}$$

and it follows that

$$\blacklozenge \qquad \lim_{n\to\infty} P\left(\left|\frac{x}{n} - p\right| > \epsilon\right) = 0 \qquad \blacklozenge$$

for any $\epsilon > 0$. This equation expresses the *weak law of large numbers*. In words: *as the sample size increases, the probability that the observed proportion of successes differs from p by more than any arbitrary positive constant ϵ approaches 0.* Note that we cannot conclude from this that for large n the actual *number* of successes must necessarily be close to $\mu = np$. In fact, it can be shown that although the probability that the *proportion* of successes is close to p approaches 1 as n becomes large, the probability that the *number* of successes is close to np approaches 0.

EXERCISES

/-7, 9, /2

1. A probability distribution has the values $g(0) = 16/31$, $g(1) = 8/31$, $g(2) = 4/31$, $g(3) = 2/31$, and $g(4) = 1/31$. Find μ and σ^2.

2. Given a binomial distribution with the parameters $n = 5$ and $p = 0.30$, find μ and σ^2 (a) directly from their definitions using the probabilities of Table I, and (b) using the special formulas on pages 54 and 56.

3. Given a hypergeometric distribution with the parameters $n = 3$, $a = 4$, and $N = 5$, find μ and σ^2 (a) directly from their definitions, and (b) using the special formulas on pages 54 and 56.

4. Given a Poisson distribution with the parameter $\lambda = 0.2$, find μ and σ
   (a) directly from their definitions using the probabilities of Table II, and
   (b) using the special formulas on pages 54 and 56.

5. Prove that the mean of the hypergeometric distribution with the parameters n, a, and N is given by $\mu = n \cdot \dfrac{a}{N}$. [*Hint:* Make use of the identity

$$\sum_{r=0}^{k} \binom{m}{r}\binom{s}{k-r} = \binom{m+s}{k}$$

6. Prove that the mean of the Poisson distribution with the parameter λ is given by $\mu = \lambda$.

7. Find the mean and the variance of the probability distribution given by $f(x) = 1/n$ for $x = 1, 2, \ldots, n$. [*Hint:* The sum of the first n positive integers is $\frac{1}{2}n(n+1)$, and the sum of their squares is $\frac{1}{6}n(n+1)(2n+1)$.]

8. Construct a table showing (i) the upper limits provided by Chebyshev's theorem for the probabilities of obtaining values differing from the mean by more than 1, 2, and 3 standard deviations, (ii) the corresponding exact probabilities for a binomial distribution with the parameters $n = 16$ and $p = 1/2$, and (iii) the corresponding exact probabilities for a Poisson distribution with the parameter $\lambda = 9$.

9. Use Chebyshev's theorem to find a lower limit to the probability that the number of heads obtained in 16 tosses of a balanced coin will lie between 2 and 14, inclusive. What is the corresponding exact probability?

10. Use Chebyshev's theorem to find an upper limit to the probability that a random variable having the Poisson distribution with $\lambda = 16$ will assume a value less than 8 or greater than 24. What is the corresponding exact probability?

11. Use Chebyshev's theorem to determine the smallest value of the parameter n of a binomial distribution for which we can assert with a probability greater than or equal to 0.90 that

$$\left| \frac{x}{n} - p \right| < 0.1$$

12. Prove that
    (a) $\sigma^2 = \mu_2' - \mu^2$,
    (b) $\mu_3 = \mu_3' - 3\mu_2' \cdot \mu + 2\mu^3$.

3.7 The Multinomial Distribution

An immediate generalization of the binomial distribution arises when each trial can have more than two possible outcomes. This happens, for example, when a manufactured product is classified as superior, average, or poor, when a student's performance is judged by giving him an A, B, C, D, or F, or when an experiment is judged successful, unsuccessful, or inconclusive. To treat this kind of problem in full generality, let us consider the case where there are n independent trials, with each trial permitting k mutually exclusive outcomes whose respective probabilities are $p_1, p_2, \ldots, p_k$ (with $\sum_{i=1}^{k} p_i = 1$). Referring to the outcomes as being of the first kind, the second kind, $\ldots$, and the kth kind, we shall be interested in the probability $f(x_1, x_2, \ldots, x_k)$ of getting x_1 outcomes of the first kind, x_2 outcomes of the second kind, $\ldots$, and x_k outcomes of the kth kind, with $\sum_{i=1}^{k} x_i = n$. Using arguments similar to those which we employed in deriving the equation for the binomial distribution in Section 3.2, it can be shown that the desired probability is given by

$$\blacklozenge \qquad f(x_1, x_2, \ldots, x_k) = \frac{n!}{x_1! x_2! \cdot \ldots \cdot x_k!} \, p_1^{x_1} \cdot p_2^{x_2} \cdot \ldots \cdot p_k^{x_k} \qquad \blacklozenge$$

for $x_i = 0, 1, \ldots, n$, subject to the restriction that $\sum_{i=1}^{k} x_i = n$. The probability distribution whose values are given by these probabilities is called the *multinomial distribution;* it owes its name to the fact that for various values of the x_i the probabilities are given by corresponding terms of the multinomial expansion of $(p_1 + p_2 + \ldots + p_k)^n$.

To give an illustration, suppose the probability that a certain kind of light bulb will burn out in fewer than 500 hours is 0.50, the probability that it will burn out in fewer than 800 but more than 500 hours is 0.30, and the probability that it will last more than 800 hours is 0.20. To find the probability that among 10 such light bulbs 4 will burn out in fewer than 500 hours, 4 will burn out in fewer than 800 but more than 500 hours, while 2 will last more than 800 hours, we have only to substitute $x_1 = 4$, $x_2 = 4$, $x_3 = 2$, $n = 10$, $p_1 = 0.50$, $p_2 = 0.30$, $p_3 = 0.20$, and we get

$$f(4, 4, 2) = \frac{10!}{4!4!2!} \, (0.50)^4 (0.30)^4 (0.20)^2$$

$$= 0.064$$

EXERCISES

1. A balanced die is rolled 8 times. What is the probability of obtaining 3 twos, 2 fours, 1 five, and 2 sixes?

2. Defective glass bricks are classified according to whether they have cracks, discolorations, or both. If the respective probabilities are 0.50, 0.40, and 0.10, find the probability that among 10 such defective glass bricks 6 have cracks, 3 have discolorations, and 1 has both.

3. If the probabilities that an airplane crash results in minor, severe, or fatal injuries to the pilot are 0.20, 0.50, and 0.10, respectively, find the probability that in 6 accidents the pilot is fatally injured in 3, uninjured in 1, and severely injured in 2.

4 | PROBABILITY DENSITIES

4.1 Continuous Random Variables

When we first introduced the concept of a random variable in Chapter 3, we presented it as a real-valued function defined over the sample space of an experiment, that is, over the set of all possible outcomes of the experiment. On page 37 we illustrated this idea with the random variable giving the number of subsystems that failed in the missile experiment, assigning the numbers 0, 1, 2, or 3 (whichever was appropriate) to the 18 possible outcomes of the experiment. In the continuous case, where random variables can assume values on a continuous scale, the procedure is very much the same. The outcomes of an experiment are represented by the points on a line segment or a line, and the value of a random variable is a number appropriately assigned to each point by means of some rule or equation. When the value of a random variable is given directly by a measurement or observation, we usually do not bother to differentiate between the value of the random variable, the measurement which we obtain, and the outcome of the experiment, the corresponding point on the real axis. Thus, if an experiment consists of determining what force is required to break a given tensile-test specimen, the result itself, say, 138.4 pounds, is the value of the random variable with which we are concerned. There is no real need in that case to add that the sample space of the experiment consists of all (or part of) the points on the positive real axis.

In order to extend the concept of probability to the continuous case, suppose we know that x, the force required to break a given tensile-test specimen, falls between the two positive constants a and b. Suppose, furthermore, that we divide the interval from a to b into n equal sub-intervals of width Δx, containing the points $x_1, x_2, \ldots, x_n$, and that the probability that the force required to break the test specimen will fall into the subinterval containing x_i is given by $f(x_i) \cdot \Delta x$. Then, the probability that the force required to break the test specimen will lie between a and b, namely, the probability that x, the value of the random variable with which we are concerned, will assume a value on the interval from a to b, is given by

$$P(a \leq x \leq b) = \sum_{i=1}^{n} f(x_i) \cdot \Delta x$$

Now, if **f** is an integrable function defined for all values of the random variable with which we are concerned ($x \geq 0$ in this case), we shall *define* the probability that the value of the random variable falls between a and b by letting $\Delta x \to 0$, namely, as

$$\blacklozenge \qquad P(a \leq x \leq b) = \int_a^b f(x)\, dx \qquad \blacklozenge$$

Our definition of probability in the continuous case thus presupposes the existence of some function **f** which, integrated from any constant a to any constant b (with $b \geq a$) gives the probability that the random variable assumes a value on the interval from a to b. Note that the value $f(x)$ of **f** does not give the probability that the random variable assumes the value x; *in the continuous case probabilities are given by integrals and not by the values of* **f**. The probability that the random variable actually assumes the value x may be obtained by first considering the probability that it assumes a value on the interval from $x - \Delta x$ to $x + \Delta x$. If we let $\Delta x \to 0$, it becomes apparent that *the probability is zero that the continuous random variable actually assumes any given value x.* As an immediate consequence, we find that it does not matter whether we include either endpoint of the interval from a to b, namely, that

$$P(a \leq x \leq b) = P(a \leq x < b) = P(a < x \leq b) = P(a < x < b)$$

The fact that the probability is *zero* that a continuous random variable assumes any given value x should not be disturbing. In fact, our definition of probability in the continuous case provides a remarkably good model for dealing with measurements or observations. Owing to the limits of our ability to measure, experimental data never seem to come from a continuous sample space. Thus, while temperatures are fruitfully thought of as points on a continuous scale, any temperature *measurement* actually represents an interval on this scale. If we report a temperature measurement of 74.8 degrees centigrade, we really mean that the temperature lies in the interval from 74.75 to 74.85 degrees centigrade, and not that it is exactly 74.8000 . . . . It is important to add that *when we say that there is a zero probability that a random variable will assume any given value x, this does not mean that it is impossible actually to get the value x.* A zero probability, therefore, does not imply logical impossibility in the continuous case, but the whole matter is largely academic since we are always interested in probabilities connected with intervals and not with isolated points. As was pointed out above, this is due to the limitations of our ability to measure and to observe.

There is a revealing analogy between the function **f** used to define probabilities connected with continuous random variables and the density ρ of a substance. Consider a rod of length L so constructed that its density at a distance x from one end is $\rho(x)$, expressed in pounds per cubic inch, and that it has a uniform cross section area of 1 square inch. Thus, if we cut a thin slice of this rod from x to $x + \Delta x$ and weigh it, it would weigh approximately $\rho(x)\,\Delta x$ pounds. Now, as $\Delta x \to 0$, the approximation $\rho(x)\,\Delta x$ to the actual weight of the thin slice becomes better and better, but in the limit as $\Delta x \to 0$, the actual weight of the slice becomes 0. Because of its close similarity to such a density function ρ, we shall call the function **f**, whose existence we stipulated in extending our definition of probability to the continuous case, a *probability density function*, or simply a *probability density*. We can speak of weight only if we integrate the density function between appropriate limits, and we can speak of probability only if we correspondingly integrate the probability density.

Since a probability density, integrated between any two constants a and b, gives the probability that a random variable assumes a value between these limits, **f** cannot be just any real-valued integrable function. However, if we impose the conditions that

(1) $f(x) \geq 0$ for all x within the domain of **f**,

(2) $\int_{-\infty}^{\infty} f(x)\,dx = 1$,

it can be shown that the axioms of probability (with the modification discussed in Section 2.7) are satisfied. Note the similarity between these properties and those given on page 38 for probability distributions.

As in the discrete case, we shall write as $F(x)$ the probability that a random variable assumes a value less than or equal to x and we shall refer to the corresponding function **F** as the *cumulative distribution function,* or simply the *distribution function* of the random variable. Thus, if a random variable with values x has the probability density **f**, the values of its distribution function are given by

$$\blacklozenge \qquad F(x) = \int_{-\infty}^{x} f(t) \, dt \qquad \blacklozenge$$

It immediately follows from this definition that

$$P(a \leq x \leq b) = F(b) - F(a)$$

and according to the fundamental theorem of integral calculus that

$$\frac{dF(x)}{dx} = f(x)$$

wherever this derivative exists.

To illustrate the concepts we have introduced, let us consider a random variable whose probability density function is given by

$$f(x) = \begin{cases} 2e^{-2x} & \text{for } x > 0 \\ 0 & \text{for } x \leq 0 \end{cases}$$

Note that, although the random variable cannot assume negative values, we artificially extended the domain of **f** to include all the real numbers. This is a practice we shall follow throughout this book. It is also apparent from the graph of this function in Figure 4.1 that it has a discontinuity at

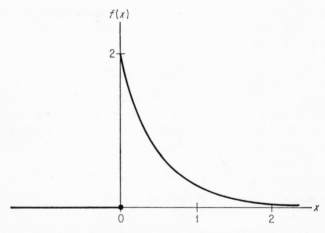

FIG. 4.1 Graph of a density function

$x = 0$; indeed, a probability density function need not be everywhere continuous, so long as it is integrable between any two limits a and b (with $b \geq a$).

Leaving it to the reader to verify that the above function satisfies the two conditions on page 65 and therefore, that it can serve as the probability density function of some random variable, let us now find some probabilities connected with this random variable. The probability that it will assume a value between 1 and 3 is

$$P(1 \leq x \leq 3) = \int_1^3 2e^{-2x}\, dx = e^{-2} - e^{-6} = 0.133$$

and the probability that it assumes a value less than 1 is

$$P(x \leq 1) = \int_0^1 2e^{-2x}\, dx = 1 - e^{-2} = 0.865$$

Note that we did not have to integrate over negative values of x since the probability density is 0 for $x \leq 0$.

The cumulative distribution function which corresponds to this example is given by

$$F(x) = \begin{cases} 0 & \text{for } x \leq 0 \\ \int_0^x 2e^{-2t}\, dt = 1 - e^{-2x} & \text{for } 0 < x \end{cases}$$

and it can be shown, for example, that

$$P(x \leq 1) = F(1) = 1 - e^{-2} = 0.865$$

Of course, this agrees with the value which we obtained before. It should also be noted that this distribution function is *nondecreasing* and that $F(-\infty) = 0$ and $F(\infty) = 1$. Indeed, it can easily be shown that these properties are shared by *all* cumulative distribution functions.

Replacing summations with integrals, we define the *kth moment about the origin* of a probability density as

$$\mu_k' = \int_{-\infty}^{\infty} x^k \cdot f(x)\, dx$$

analogous to the definition we gave on page 56. The first moment about the origin is again referred to as the *mean* and denoted as μ; as before, it is the *average value* the random variable can be expected to assume. We also define the *kth moment about the mean* as

$$\mu_k = \int_{-\infty}^{\infty} (x - \mu)^k \cdot f(x)\, dx$$

In particular, the second moment about the mean is again referred to as the *variance* and written as σ^2; as before, the variance measures the spread of a probability density (or its graph) in the sense that it gives the *average value* for the squared deviations from the mean. Applying these formulas to the above example, we find that the mean is

$$\mu = \int_0^{\infty} x \cdot 2e^{-2x}\, dx = \frac{1}{2}$$

and that the variance is

$$\sigma^2 = \int_0^\infty \left(x - \frac{1}{2}\right)^2 \cdot 2e^{-2x}\, dx = \frac{1}{4}$$

It might have been easier to obtain the variance of this probability density by first calculating the first two moments about the origin and then substituting into the formula

$$\sigma^2 = \mu_2' - \mu^2$$

In Exercise 6 below, the reader will be asked to prove that this formula holds also in the continuous case.

EXERCISES

1. Verify that the function given on page 66 is, in fact, a probability density.

2. Given

$$f(x) = \begin{cases} kx^3 & \text{for } 0 < x < 1 \\ 0 & \text{elsewhere} \end{cases}$$

(a) find k so that this function is a probability density,

(b) find $P(1/4 < x < 3/4)$,

(c) find $P(x < 1/2)$,

(d) find $P(x > 0.8)$,

(e) find $F(x)$. [*Hint:* $F(x)$ must be given separately for $x \le 0$, $0 < x < 1$, and $x \ge 1$.]

3. Given the probability density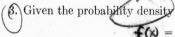

$$f(x) = \begin{cases} ke^{-x/5} & \text{for } x > 0 \\ 0 & \text{elsewhere} \end{cases}$$

(a) find k,

(b) find $F(x)$.

Using $F(x)$ find

(c) $P(3 < x < 5)$,

(d) $P(x < 4)$,

(e) $P(x > 6)$.

4. Given

$$f(x) = \begin{cases} kx(1 - x) & \text{for } 0 < x < 1 \\ 0 & \text{elsewhere} \end{cases}$$

(a) find k so that this function is a probability density,

(b) find $F(x)$. [*Hint:* $F(x)$ must be given separately for $x \le 0$, $0 < x < 1$, and $x \ge 1$.]

Find $P(1/4 < x < 1/2)$

(c) by integrating the probability density,

(d) by using $F(x)$.

5. Given the probability density $f(x) = \dfrac{k}{1 + x^2}$ for $-\infty < x < \infty$, find k.

6. Prove that the identity $\sigma^2 = \mu_2' - \mu^2$ holds for any probability density for which these moments exist.

7. Find μ and σ^2 for the probability density of Exercise 2.

8. Find μ and σ^2 for the probability density of Exercise 3.

9. Find μ and σ^2 for the probability density of Exercise 4.

10. Show that, for the probability density of Exercise 5, μ_2' and therefore σ^2 do not exist.

4.2 The Normal Distribution

In Section 3.4 we introduced the Poisson distribution as a limiting form of the binomial distribution as $n \to \infty$ and $p \to 0$ while np remains fixed at the value λ. Subsequently, we used the Poisson distribution to *approximate* the binomial distribution when n is sufficiently large and p is sufficiently small. Since there are many applications of the binomial distribution where n is large but p is not small enough to use the Poisson approximation, it would seem helpful to investigate the limiting form of the binomial distribution as $n \to \infty$ while p remains fixed. Unfortunately, there is an obstacle to this, because $\mu = np$ and $\sigma^2 = np(1 - p)$ both increase without limit as $n \to \infty$. In order to overcome this difficulty, let us perform a simple transformation, referred to as *"standardizing a random variable."* If a random variable has the values x and a distribution with the mean μ and the variance σ^2, the corresponding *standardized random variable* has the values

$$z = \frac{x - \mu}{\sigma}$$

and its distribution has *zero mean* and *unit variance*. To prove this assertion, suppose that the original random variable is discrete, the probability that it assumes the value x is $f(x)$, and the mean and the variance of the distribution of the standardized random variable are written as μ_z and σ_z^2. We then have

$$\mu_z = \sum_{\text{all } x} \frac{x - \mu}{\sigma} \cdot f(x)$$

$$= \frac{1}{\sigma} \left[\sum_{\text{all } x} x \cdot f(x) - \sum_{\text{all } x} \mu \cdot f(x) \right]$$

$$= \frac{1}{\sigma} [\mu - \mu \cdot 1] = 0$$

and
$$\sigma_z^2 = \sum_{\text{all } x} \left(\frac{x - \mu}{\sigma}\right)^2 \cdot f(x)$$

$$= \frac{1}{\sigma^2} \sum_{\text{all } x} (x - \mu)^2 \cdot f(x)$$

$$= \frac{1}{\sigma^2} \cdot \sigma^2 = 1$$

This result holds also for the continuous case, where, in the proofs, integrals replace sums.

Returning now to the binomial distribution, we find that the values of the corresponding standardized random variable are given by

$$z = \frac{x - np}{\sqrt{np(1 - p)}}$$

and referring to this standardized random variable, let us state the following theorem:

THEOREM 4.1. *If x is a value of a random variable having the binomial distribution with the parameters n and p, and if*

$$z = \frac{x - np}{\sqrt{np(1 - p)}}$$

then the limiting form of the distribution function of this standardized random variable as $n \to \infty$ is given by

$$F(z) = \int_{-\infty}^{z} \frac{1}{\sqrt{2\pi}} e^{-\frac{1}{2}t^2} dt \qquad -\infty < z < \infty$$

Note that although x assumes only the values $0, 1, 2, \ldots, n$, in the limit as $n \to \infty$ the distribution function of the standardized random variable is continuous, and the corresponding density function is given by

$$f(z) = \frac{1}{\sqrt{2\pi}} e^{-\frac{1}{2}z^2} \qquad -\infty < z < \infty \qquad \blacklozenge$$

We call this density the *standard normal density* or the *standard normal distribution.** Its mean is equal to zero, its variance is equal to one, and it is symmetrical about $z = 0$, as can be seen from its graph in Figure 4.2. The probability that a random variable having the standard normal density assumes a value between a and b is given by

$$\frac{1}{\sqrt{2\pi}} \int_{a}^{b} e^{-\frac{1}{2}z^2} dz$$

---

* The words "density" and "distribution" are often used interchangeably in the literature of applied statistics.

Since such integrals cannot be evaluated by exact methods, we usually obtain such probabilities with the use of special tables. Table III on page 398 is a table of areas under the standard normal distribution, that is, its entries are the values of

$$F(z) = \frac{1}{\sqrt{2\pi}} \int_{-\infty}^{z} e^{-\frac{1}{2}t^2} dt$$

for $z = 0.00, 0.01, 0.02, \ldots, 3.49$. To find $P(a \leq z \leq b)$, where z is the value of a random variable having the standard normal distribution, we use the equation

$$P(a \leq x \leq b) = F(b) - F(a)$$

For example, it follows immediately from Table III that

$$P(0.35 \leq z \leq 1.65) = F(1.65) - F(0.35)$$
$$= 0.9505 - 0.6368 = 0.3137$$

If a or b is negative, we can make use of the identity

◆ $$F(-z) = 1 - F(z)$$ ◆

which follows directly from the symmetry of the standard normal distribution (see also Exercise 2 on page 74). For example,

$$P(-1.59 \leq z \leq 2.07) = F(2.07) - F(-1.59)$$
$$= F(2.07) - [1 - F(1.59)] = 0.9249$$

and

$$P(-3.29 < z < -0.98) = [1 - F(0.98)] - [1 - F(3.29)]$$
$$= F(3.29) - F(0.98) = 0.1630$$

Reversing the process of standardization, it can be shown that if z is the value of a random variable having the standard normal distribution, then

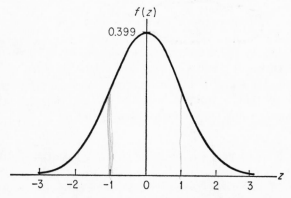

FIG. 4.2 Standard normal curve

$x = \sigma \cdot z + \mu$ (which is equivalent to $z = \dfrac{x - \mu}{\sigma}$) is the value of a random variable whose density is given by

$$\blacklozenge \qquad f(x; \mu, \sigma^2) = \frac{1}{\sqrt{2\pi}\,\sigma}\, e^{-\frac{1}{2}\left(\frac{x-\mu}{\sigma}\right)^2} \qquad -\infty < x < \infty \qquad \blacklozenge$$

which is the *general form of the normal distribution*. In Section 4.4 we shall prove that the parameters μ and σ^2 of this distribution are, in fact, its mean and its variance.

The normal distribution is important in statistics not only because it provides a good approximation to the binomial distribution for large values of n, but also because it often provides a good approximation to distributions of data met in applications. It has been found through experience that most errors of measurement and a large variety of physical observations have approximately normal distributions. In Chapter 7 we shall give some further theoretical foundations for the normal distribution, which to some extent explains its frequent appearance in nature.

If we want to find the probability that a random variable having a normal distribution with the mean μ and the variance σ^2 assumes a value between a and b, we have only to calculate the probability that a random variable having the *standard* normal distribution assumes a value between $\dfrac{a - \mu}{\sigma}$ and $\dfrac{b - \mu}{\sigma}$. Thus,

$$P(a \leq x \leq b) = F\left(\frac{b - \mu}{\sigma}\right) - F\left(\frac{a - \mu}{\sigma}\right)$$

where $F\left(\dfrac{b - \mu}{\sigma}\right)$ and $F\left(\dfrac{a - \mu}{\sigma}\right)$ can be obtained from Table III. To illustrate, suppose that the distribution of the diameters of the ball bearings in a certain shipment is approximately normal with the mean $\mu = 0.500$ cm and the standard deviation $\sigma = 0.010$ cm. Then, if a ball bearing is effective when its diameter lies between 0.490 and 0.515 cm, the probability of obtaining an effective ball bearing from this shipment is

$$P(0.490 \leq x \leq 0.515) = F\left(\frac{0.515 - 0.500}{0.010}\right) - F\left(\frac{0.490 - 0.500}{0.010}\right)$$
$$= F(1.50) - F(-1.00)$$
$$= 0.7745$$

Thus, approximately 77 per cent of the ball bearings in this shipment can be presumed to be effective.

Let us now return to the problem for which we originally introduced the normal distribution, namely, that of approximating the binomial distribution when n is large and p is not sufficiently small to use the Poisson approximation. First, let us find the probability of obtaining at most 15 rejects in a lot of 100 diodes, assuming from past information that the proportion of defective diodes produced is 0.20. Assuming that the assumptions underlying the binomial distribution are met, the exact answer to this problem is given by

$$\sum_{x=0}^{15} b(x; 100, 0.20) = B(15; 100, 0.20)$$

Since Table I does not include values of n as large as 100, let us approximate this probability by using the normal distribution with the mean $\mu = np = 100(0.20) = 20$ and the variance $\sigma^2 = np(1 - p) = 100(0.20)(0.80) = 16$. Observe from Figure 4.3 that we are actually approximating the sum of the

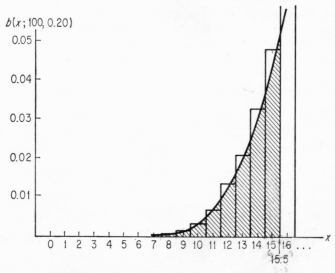

FIG. 4.3 Normal approximation to the binomial distribution

areas of the first 16 rectangles (corresponding to $x = 0, 1, 2, \ldots, 15$) of the histogram of the binomial distribution by means of the shaded area under a continuous curve. Thus, we must find the area under the approximating normal curve not between 0 and 15, but between -0.5 and 15.5 or, what is practically the same, between $-\infty$ and 15.5. Making this *continuity correction*, we obtain

$$B(15; 100, 0.20) \simeq F\left(\frac{15.5 - 20}{4}\right)$$

$$= F(-1.13) = 0.1292$$

which is close to the exact value $B(15; 100, 0.20) = 0.1285$. The same kind of approximation can also be used for the probability that x is exactly 15 in the preceding example. Making the *continuity correction*, wherein the event $x = 15$ is represented in this case by the equivalent event $14.5 \leq x \leq 15.5$, we obtain

$$b(15; 100, 0.20) \simeq F\left(\frac{15.5 - 20}{4}\right) - F\left(\frac{14.5 - 20}{4}\right)$$
$$= F(-1.13) - F(-1.38)$$
$$= 0.0454$$

which is fairly close to the exact value $b(15; 100, 0.20) = 0.0481$. Note that whenever the normal distribution is used to approximate the binomial distribution, each x is replaced by the corresponding interval from $x - \frac{1}{2}$ to $x + \frac{1}{2}$. This is the *continuity correction* referred to in the above examples.

EXERCISES

1. Prove for the continuous case that the mean and the variance of the distribution of a standardized random variable are 0 and 1, respectively.

2. Verify the identity $F(-z) = 1 - F(z)$ given on page 71.

3. If a random variable has the standard normal distribution, find the probability that it assumes a value
   (a) less than 2.00,
   (b) less than -1.96,
   (c) greater than 2.58,
   (d) greater than -2.33,
   (e) between 0 and 1.00,
   (f) between 0.58 and 2.12,
   (g) between -1.65 and -0.84,
   (h) between -2.42 and 1.86.

4. Find z if the probability that a random variable having the standard normal distribution assumes a value
   (a) less than z is 0.9265,
   (b) greater than z is 0.2843,
   (c) greater than z is 0.8531,
   (d) between $-z$ and z is 0.9312.

5. By making the change of variable $z = \dfrac{x - \mu}{\sigma}$ in the integral

$$\int_a^b \frac{1}{\sqrt{2\pi} \cdot \sigma} e^{-\frac{1}{2}\left(\frac{x-\mu}{\sigma}\right)^2} dx$$

verify the identity $P(a \leq x \leq b) = F\left(\dfrac{b - \mu}{\sigma}\right) - F\left(\dfrac{a - \mu}{\sigma}\right)$ given on page 72.

6. Given a random variable having the normal distribution with $\mu = 100$ and $\sigma = 20$, find the probability that it assumes a value

    (a) less than 97.3,

    (b) greater than 110.0,

    (c) between 112.1 and 115.8,

    (d) between 95.6 and 104.4,

    (e) between 81.3 and 92.9,

    (f) less than 87.3 or greater than 108.5.

7. Given a random variable having the normal distribution with the mean 12.8 and the variance 6.25, find the probability that it assumes a value

    (a) greater than 17.0,

    (b) less than 11.3,

    (c) between 10.1 and 14.9,

    (d) less than 9.2 or greater than 15.7.

8. If x is a value of a random variable having the binomial distribution with $n = 20$ and $p = 0.40$, use an appropriate normal distribution to approximate (a) the probability $P(x = 10)$, (b) the probability $P(x \leq 12)$, and compare with the corresponding values in Table I.

9. A balanced coin is tossed 400 times. What is the probability of getting (a) more than 220 heads, and (b) anywhere from 185 to 215 heads, inclusive?

10. If a balanced die is rolled 600 times, find the probability that the observed number of 6's differs from the expected number by more than 15.

11. The probability that a certain kind of component will fail in 1000 hours or less is 0.25. Use the normal approximation to find the probability that among 100 such components fewer than 30 will fail in 1000 hours or less.

12. Specifications for a certain job call for washers with an inside diameter of 0.250 ± 0.005 in. If the inside diameters of the washers made by a given manufacturer are normally distributed with $\mu = 0.251$ and $\sigma = 0.003$, what percentage of these washers will meet specifications?

13. A study showed that the lifetimes of a certain kind of automobile battery are normally distributed with a mean of 1248 days and a standard deviation of 185 days. If the manufacturer wishes to guarantee the battery for 36 months (a month is taken to be 30 days), what percentage of the batteries will have to be replaced under the guarantee?

4.3 Other Probability Densities

       In the application of statistics to problems in engineering and physical science, we shall encounter many probability densities other than the normal distribution. Among these are the t, F, and chi-square distributions, the fundamental *sampling distributions* which we shall introduce in Chapter 7, and the exponential and Weibull distributions, which we shall apply to problems of reliability and life testing in Chapter 16. In this section we shall discuss three continuous distributions, the

(SKIP)

uniform distribution, the *log-normal distribution,* and the *gamma distribution,* for the twofold purpose of giving further examples of probability densities and of laying a foundation for future applications.

The *uniform distribution* with the parameters α and β is defined by the equation

$$f(x) = \begin{cases} \dfrac{1}{\beta - \alpha} & \text{for } \alpha < x < \beta \\ 0 & \text{elsewhere} \end{cases}$$

and its graph is shown in Figure 4.4. Note that all values of x from α to β are "equally likely" in the sense that the probability that x lies in a narrow interval of width Δx entirely contained in the interval from α to β is equal to $\Delta x/(\beta - \alpha)$, regardless of the exact location of the interval.

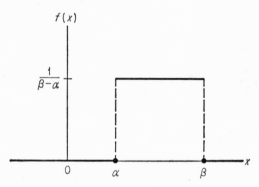

FIG. 4.4 Uniform density function

To give an example of a physical situation that might give rise to a uniform distribution, suppose that a wheel of a locomotive has the radius r and that x is the location of a point on its circumference measured along the circumference from some reference point 0. When the brakes are applied, some point will make sliding contact with the rail, and heavy wear will occur at that point. For repeated application of the brakes, it would seem reasonable to assume that x is a value of a random variable having the uniform distribution with $\alpha = 0$ and $\beta = 2\pi r$. If this assumption were incorrect, that is, if some set of points on the wheel made contact more often than others, the wheel would eventually exhibit "flat spots" or wear out of round.

The *log-normal distribution* occurs in practice whenever we encounter a random variable such that its logarithm has a normal distribution. This probability density function is given by

$$f(x) = \begin{cases} \dfrac{1}{\sqrt{2\pi}\,\beta}\, x^{-1}e^{-(\ln x - \alpha)^2/2\beta^2} & x > 0, \beta > 0 \\ 0 & \text{elsewhere} \end{cases}$$

where "ln x" stands for the natural logarithm of x. A graph of the log-normal distribution with $\alpha = 0$ and $\beta = 1$ is shown in Figure 4.5, and it can be seen from the figure that this distribution is positively skewed.

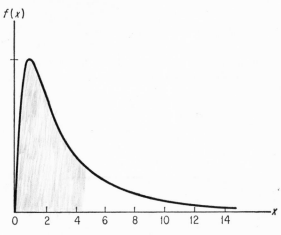

FIG. 4.5 Log-normal density function

To find the probability that a random variable having the log-normal distribution assumes a value between a and b $(0 < a < b)$, we write

$$P(a \le x \le b) = \int_a^b \frac{1}{\sqrt{2\pi}\,\beta}\, x^{-1}e^{-(\ln x - \alpha)^2/2\beta^2}\, dx$$

Changing variables by letting $y = \ln x$ and, hence, $dy = x^{-1}\, dx$, we obtain

$$P(a \le x \le b) = \int_{\ln a}^{\ln b} \frac{1}{\sqrt{2\pi}\,\beta}\, e^{-(y - \alpha)^2/2\beta^2}\, dy$$

and it can be seen that this probability equals the probability that a random variable having the normal distribution with $\mu = \alpha$ and $\sigma = \beta$ assumes a value between $\ln a$ and $\ln b$. Thus,

$$P(a \le x \le b) = F\left(\frac{\ln b - \alpha}{\beta}\right) - F\left(\frac{\ln a - \alpha}{\beta}\right)$$

where $F(z)$ is the probability that a random variable having the standard normal distribution assumes a value less than or equal to z.

As an example of the application of the log-normal distribution, suppose that a series of experiments have shown that the current gains of certain transistors (which are proportional to the logarithm of I_o/I_i, the ratio of the output to the input current) are normally distributed. If current gain is measured in units for which it equals $\ln(I_o/I_i)$, and if it is normally distributed with $\mu = 2$ and $\sigma^2 = 0.01$, then the probability that I_o/I_i, which now has the log-normal distribution, assumes a value between 6.1 and 8.2 is given by

$$P(6.1 \leq I_o/I_i \leq 8.2) = F\left(\frac{\ln 8.2 - 2}{0.1}\right) - F\left(\frac{\ln 6.1 - 2}{0.1}\right)$$

$$= F(1.0) - F(-2.0)$$

$$= 0.8185$$

Several important probability densities which we shall study later on are special cases of the *gamma distribution*, whose equation is given by

$$f(x) = \begin{cases} \dfrac{1}{\beta^\alpha \Gamma(\alpha)}\, x^{\alpha-1} e^{-x/\beta} & x > 0,\, \alpha > 0,\, \beta > 0 \\ 0 & \text{elsewhere} \end{cases}$$

where $\Gamma(\alpha)$ is a value of the *gamma function*, defined by

$$\Gamma(\alpha) = \int_0^\infty x^{\alpha-1} e^{-x}\, dx$$

Integration by parts shows that

$$\Gamma(\alpha) = (\alpha - 1)\Gamma(\alpha - 1)$$

for any $\alpha > 0$ and, hence, that $\Gamma(\alpha) = (\alpha - 1)!$ when α is a positive integer. Graphs of several gamma distributions are shown in Figure 4.6 and they

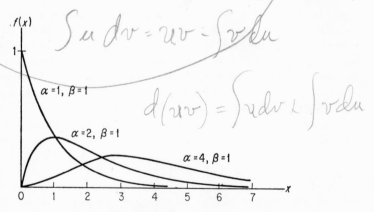

FIG. 4.6 Gamma density functions

exhibit the fact that these distributions are positively skewed. In fact, the skewness decreases as α increases for any fixed value of β.

The special gamma distribution for which $\alpha = 1$ is called the *exponential distribution;* it was used as an illustration on page 66 with $\beta = 1/2$. The exponential distribution is used in connection with problems of *waiting times,* that is, the time intervals between the occurrence of certain kinds of events, and we shall discuss it further in this connection in Chapters 5 and 16.

4.4 The Means and Variances of Special Distributions

In this section we shall derive formulas for the mean and the variance of the distributions introduced in the last two sections. First, let us show that the parameters μ and σ^2 of the normal distribution, as given on page 72, are indeed the mean and the variance of this distribution. According to the definition of the mean, we have for the mean of the normal distribution

$$\frac{1}{\sqrt{2\pi}\,\sigma} \int_{-\infty}^{\infty} x \cdot e^{-(x-\mu)^2/2\sigma^2}\, dx$$

and upon letting $z = (x - \mu)/\sigma$, this becomes

$$\frac{1}{\sqrt{2\pi}} \int_{-\infty}^{\infty} (z\sigma + \mu)e^{-z^2/2}\, dz$$

or

$$\frac{\sigma}{\sqrt{2\pi}} \int_{-\infty}^{\infty} z \cdot e^{-z^2/2}\, dz + \mu \cdot \frac{1}{\sqrt{2\pi}} \int_{-\infty}^{\infty} e^{-z^2/2}\, dz$$

Since the integrand of the first integral is *odd,* the integral from $-\infty$ to ∞ is equal to 0; the second integral is μ times the area under the standard normal distribution and, hence, equals $\mu \cdot 1 = \mu$. We have, thus, shown that the parameter μ in the equation for the normal distribution is, in fact, the mean of this distribution. In Exercise 6 on page 81, the reader will be asked to show by similar means that the parameter σ^2 in the equation for the normal distribution is, in fact, the variance.

Turning now to the *uniform distribution,* we find by direct substitution that its mean is

$$\mu = \int_{\alpha}^{\beta} x \cdot \frac{1}{\beta - \alpha}\, dx = \frac{\alpha + \beta}{2}$$

To find the variance of this distribution, we make use of the formula $\sigma^2 = \mu_2' - \mu^2$, obtaining

$$\sigma^2 = \int_\alpha^\beta x^2 \cdot \frac{1}{\beta - \alpha} \, dx - \left(\frac{\alpha + \beta}{2}\right)^2$$

$$= \frac{\alpha^2 + \alpha\beta + \beta^2}{3} - \frac{(\alpha + \beta)^2}{4} = \frac{(\alpha - \beta)^2}{12}$$

To find the mean of the *log-normal distribution*, we write

$$\mu = \frac{1}{\sqrt{2\pi}\,\beta} \int_0^\infty x \cdot x^{-1} e^{-(\ln x - \alpha)^2/2\beta^2} \, dx$$

and upon letting $y = \ln x$, this becomes

$$\mu = \frac{1}{\sqrt{2\pi}\,\beta} \int_{-\infty}^\infty e^y e^{-(y-\alpha)^2/2\beta^2} \, dy$$

This integral can be evaluated by completing the square on the exponent $y - (y - \alpha)^2/2\beta^2$, thus obtaining an integrand which has the form of a normal density. The final result, which the reader will be asked to verify in Exercise 8 on page 81, is

$$\mu = e^{\alpha + \beta^2/2}$$

Similar, but more lengthy, calculations yield

$$\sigma^2 = e^{2\alpha + \beta^2}(e^{\beta^2} - 1)$$

for the variance of the log-normal distribution. Referring to the example on page 78, we find that the mean of the log-normal distribution with $\alpha = 2$ and $\beta = 0.1$ is

$$\mu = e^{2 + (0.01)/2} = 7.4$$

and that its variance is

$$\sigma^2 = e^{4 + (0.01)}(e^{0.01} - 1) = 0.56$$

The mean and the variance of the *gamma distribution* are obtained by making use of the gamma function and its special properties mentioned on page 78. For the mean we have

$$\mu = \frac{1}{\beta^\alpha \Gamma(\alpha)} \int_0^\infty x \cdot x^{\alpha - 1} e^{-x/\beta} dx$$

and after letting $y = x/\beta$ and, hence, $dy = dx/\beta$, we obtain

$$\mu = \frac{\beta}{\Gamma(\alpha)} \int_0^\infty y^\alpha e^{-y} \, dy = \frac{\beta\Gamma(\alpha + 1)}{\Gamma(\alpha)} = \alpha\beta$$

Using similar methods, it can be shown that the variance of the gamma distribution is given by

$$\sigma^2 = \alpha\beta^2$$

Since the *exponential distribution* was defined as the special gamma distribution for which $\alpha = 1$, we find that for the exponential distribution

$$\mu = \sigma = \beta$$

EXERCISES

1. Find the cumulative distribution function corresponding to the uniform density on page 76.

2. If a random variable has the log-normal distribution with $\alpha = -2$ and $\beta = 2$, find (a) the mean and the standard deviation of this distribution, and (b) the probability that this random variable assumes a value between 4.5 and 9.8.

3. If a random variable has the gamma distribution with $\alpha = 2$ and $\beta = 3$, find the probability that it assumes a value between 1.8 and 11.1.

4. Prove that $\Gamma(\alpha) = (\alpha - 1)\Gamma(\alpha - 1)$.

5. Find the cumulative distribution function corresponding to the exponential density

$$f(x) = \begin{cases} \dfrac{1}{\beta} \cdot e^{-x/\beta} & \text{for } x > 0 \\ 0 & \text{elsewhere} \end{cases}$$

Use the result to find the probability that a random variable having this distribution assumes a value greater than 2β.

6. Verify that the parameter σ^2 in the expression for the normal density on page 72 is, in fact, its variance.

7. Show that the normal density has a relative maximum at $x = \mu$ and inflection points at $x = \mu \pm \sigma$.

8. Verify the expression given for the mean of the log-normal distribution on page 80.

9. Verify that for the gamma distribution on page 78 the variance is given by $\sigma^2 = \alpha \cdot \beta^2$.

10. A random variable has the *beta distribution* if its density is given by

$$f(x) = \begin{cases} k \cdot x^{\alpha-1}(1 - x)^{\beta-1} & \text{for } 0 < x < 1 \\ 0 & \text{elsewhere} \end{cases}$$

where $\alpha > 0$ and $\beta > 0$. Find k for the special case where $\alpha = 12$ and $\beta = 2$. Also find μ and σ^2 for this special beta distribution.

11. A random variable has a *Weibull distribution* if its density is given by

$$f(x) = \begin{cases} k \cdot x^{\beta-1} e^{-\alpha x^\beta} & \text{for } x > 0 \\ 0 & \text{elsewhere} \end{cases}$$

Find k, μ, and σ^2 in terms of α and β.

12. In a certain area, the daily consumption of electric power (in millions of kilowatt-hours) can be treated as a random variable having the log-normal distribution with $\alpha = 3/2$ and $\beta = 1/2$. If the power plant servicing this area has a daily capacity of 10 million kilowatt-hours, what is the probability that this power supply is inadequate on any given day?

13. Suppose that the service lives of certain semiconductor units have the Weibull distribution (Exercise 11) with the parameters $\alpha = 0.005$ and $\beta = 0.50$. If 10 such units are put on life test, find the probability that at least 8 will still be operating satisfactorily at the end of 40,000 hours.

4.5 Joint Probability Densities

There are many experiments in which we describe the outcome by giving the values of several random variables. For example, we may measure the height and the weight of an individual, the volume, pressure, and temperature of a gas, or the thickness, color, and compressive strength of a piece of glass. If $x_1, x_2, \ldots, x_k$ are the values of k random variables, we shall refer to a function $\mathbf{f}$ with values $f(x_1, x_2, \ldots, x_k)$ as the *joint probability density* of these random variables if the probability that $a_1 \leq x_1 \leq b_1$ and $a_2 \leq x_2 \leq b_2, \ldots,$ and $a_k \leq x_k \leq b_k$ is given by the multiple integral

$$\int_{a_1}^{b_1} \int_{a_2}^{b_2} \ldots \int_{a_k}^{b_k} f(x_1, x_2, \ldots, x_k) \, dx_1 \, dx_2 \ldots dx_k$$

Note that if $f(x_1, x_2, \ldots, x_k) \geq 0$ for all values of $x_1, x_2, \ldots, x_k$ for which the probability density is defined and

$$\int_{-\infty}^{\infty} \int_{-\infty}^{\infty} \ldots \int_{-\infty}^{\infty} f(x_1, x_2, \ldots, x_k) \, dx_1 \, dx_2 \ldots dx_k = 1$$

this definition is again consistent with the axioms of probability as modified in Section 2.7.

Writing as $F(x_1, x_2, \ldots, x_k)$ the probability that the first random variable assumes a value less than or equal to x_1, the second random variable assumes a value less than or equal to $x_2, \ldots,$ and the kth random variable assumes a value less than or equal to x_k, we refer to the corresponding function $\mathbf{F}$ as the *joint distribution function* of the k random variables.

To illustrate, let us consider the joint probability density given by

$$f(x_1, x_2) = \begin{cases} 6e^{-2x_1 - 3x_2} & \text{for } x_1 > 0, x_2 > 0 \\ 0 & \text{elsewhere} \end{cases}$$

The probability that the first random variable assumes a value between 1 and 2 while the second assumes a value between 2 and 3 is given by

$$\int_1^2 \int_2^3 6e^{-2x_1 - 3x_2} \, dx_1 \, dx_2 = (e^{-2} - e^{-4})(e^{-6} - e^{-9})$$

$$= 0.0003$$

and the probability that the first random variable assumes a value less than 2 while the second random variable assumes a value greater than 2 is given by

$$\int_0^2 \int_2^\infty 6e^{-2x_1 - 3x_2} \, dx_1 \, dx_2 = (1 - e^{-4})e^{-6}$$

$$= 0.0025$$

Also, the joint distribution function of this pair of random variables is given by

$$F(x_1, x_2) = \begin{cases} \int_0^{x_1} \int_0^{x_2} 6e^{-2u - 3v} \, du \, dv & \text{for } x_1 \geq 0, \, x_2 \geq 0 \\ 0 & \text{elsewhere} \end{cases}$$

or

$$F(x_1, x_2) = \begin{cases} (1 - e^{-2x_1})(1 - e^{-3x_2}) & \text{for } x_1 \geq 0, \, x_2 \geq 0 \\ 0 & \text{elsewhere} \end{cases}$$

Following the definition of independence given in Chapter 2, we shall say that *k random variables are independent if and only if*

$$F(x_1, x_2, \ldots, x_k) = F_1(x_1) \cdot F_2(x_2) \cdot \ldots \cdot F(x_k)$$

for all values of $x_1, x_2, \ldots, x_k$ for which the functions are defined, where $F_i(x_i)$ for $i = 1, 2, \ldots, k$ is the corresponding value of the distribution function of the ith random variable. It immediately follows from this definition that if k random variables are independent, any value of their joint probability density equals the product of the values of the probability densities of the individual random variables. In other words, it follows that

$$f(x_1, \ldots, x_k) = f_1(x_1) \cdot f_2(x_2) \cdot \ldots \cdot f_k(x_k)$$

where $f_i(x_i)$ for $i = 1, 2, \ldots, k$ is the corresponding value of the probability density of the ith random variable. Referring again to our numerical example, note that the two random variables are independent.

In general, the probability density of the ith random variable can be obtained from the joint density by integrating out the other variables, namely,

$$f_i(x_i) = \int_{-\infty}^\infty \ldots \int_{-\infty}^\infty \int_{-\infty}^\infty \ldots \int_{-\infty}^\infty f(x_1, x_2, \ldots, x_k) \, dx_1 \ldots dx_{i-1} \, dx_{i+1} \ldots dx_k$$

In this context, $f_i(x_i)$ is called the *marginal density* of the ith random variable. For instance, in the above example the marginal density of the first random variable is given by

$$f_1(x_1) = \int_0^\infty 6e^{-2x_1 - 3x_2} \, dx_2 = 2e^{-2x_1}$$

for $x_1 > 0$, and $f_1(x_1) = 0$ elsewhere.

The following is another concept which is of importance when dealing with k random variables. If a random variable assumes the value

$g(x_1, x_2, \ldots, x_k)$ whenever k random variables assume the values $x_1, x_2, \ldots, x_k$, then the average, or mean, of the first random variable is defined by the integral

$$\int_{-\infty}^{\infty} \int_{-\infty}^{\infty} \cdots \int_{-\infty}^{\infty} g(x_1, \ldots, x_k) f(x_1, \ldots, x_k) \, dx_1 \, dx_2 \ldots dx_k$$

For example, if we are interested in the average value of the *product* of the two random variables in the above numerical example, we obtain

 $$\int_0^{\infty} \int_0^{\infty} x_1 x_2 \cdot 6 e^{-2x_1 - 3x_2} \, dx_1 \, dx_2 = \frac{1}{6}$$

EXERCISES

1. Two random variables have the joint density given by

$$f(x, y) = \begin{cases} 4xy & \text{for } 0 < x < 1, 0 < y < 1 \\ 0 & \text{elsewhere} \end{cases}$$

(a) Find the probability that $0 \le x \le 1/2$ and $1/8 \le y \le 1/4$.

(b) Find the probability that $y > x$.

2. Two random variables have the joint density given by

$$f(x, y) = \begin{cases} k(x^2 + y^2) & \text{for } 0 < x < 3, 1 < y < 6 \\ 0 & \text{elsewhere} \end{cases}$$

(a) Find k.

(b) Find the probability that $1 < x < 2$ and $2 < y < 4$.

(c) Find the probability that $2 \le x \le 3$.

(d) Find the probability that $x + y > 5$.

3. Three random variables have the joint density given by

$$f(x, y, z) = \begin{cases} k(x + y)e^{-z} & \text{for } 0 < x < 1, 0 < y < 1, z > 0 \\ 0 & \text{elsewhere} \end{cases}$$

(a) Find k.

(b) Find the probability that $x < y$ and $z < 1$.

(c) Find the probability that $z > 2$.

4. Referring to the joint density of Exercise 1,

(a) find an expression for the cumulative distribution of the first random variable,

(b) find an expression for the cumulative distribution of the second random variable,

(c) show that the two random variables are independent.

5. Referring to the joint density of Exercise 2,

  (a) find an expression for the cumulative distribution of the first random variable,

  (b) find an expression for the cumulative distribution of the second random variable,

  (c) check for independence.

6. A pair of random variables has the "circular normal distribution" if their joint density is given by

$$f(x_1, x_2) = \frac{1}{2\pi\sigma^2} e^{-\frac{1}{2\sigma^2}[(x_1 - \mu_1)^2 + (x_2 - \mu_2)^2]}$$

  for $-\infty < x_1 < \infty$ and $-\infty < x_2 < \infty$.

  (a) If $\mu_1 = 1$, $\mu_2 = -3$, and $\sigma = 10$, use Table III to find the probability that $-14 < x_1 < 16$ and $-9 < x_2 < 15$.

  (b) If $\mu_1 = \mu_2 = 0$ and $\sigma = 4$, find the probability that (x_1, x_2) is contained in the region between the circles $x_1^2 + x_2^2 = 4$ and $x_1^2 + x_2^2 = 16$. [*Hint:* Use polar coordinates.]

7. A bomb aimed at a point target has a lethal radius of 400 feet. Using the target as the origin of a rectangular system of coordinates, assume that the coordinates (x, y) of the point of impact are values of a pair of random variables having the circular normal distribution (see Exercise 6) with $\mu_1 = \mu_2 = 0$ and $\sigma = 250$ feet. What is the probability that the target will be destroyed?

8. Referring to the joint density of Exercise 1, find the average value of the random variable whose values are given by $g(x, y) = x + y$.

9. Referring to the joint density of Exercise 2, find the average value of the random variable whose values are given by $g(x + y) = x^2 y$.

10. If measurements of the length and the width of a rectangle have the joint density

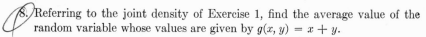

$$f(x, y) = \begin{cases} \dfrac{1}{ab} & \text{for } L - \dfrac{a}{2} < x < L + \dfrac{a}{2}, \ W - \dfrac{b}{2} < y < W + \dfrac{b}{2} \\ 0 & \text{elsewhere} \end{cases}$$

  find the mean and the variance of the corresponding distribution of the area of the rectangle.

5 | APPLICATIONS TO OPERATIONS RESEARCH

Omit

5.1 Introduction

Developments in the last few decades have brought about the growth of a new technology which is partly mathematics, partly statistics, partly engineering, and partly a new approach. It is called *operations research* and it may be defined as *the application of modern scientific techniques to problems involving the operation of a "system" looked upon as a whole*—say, the conduct of a war, the management of a firm, the manufacture of a product, the planning of an economy, and so forth.

Among the topics usually included under the heading of operations research we find such things as "scientific" decision making, the theory of games, linear programming, the theory of random processes, methods of handling problems of inventory, allocation, transportation, and others. In this brief chapter we shall study some of these methods as special applications of the theory introduced in the preceding chapters.

5.2 Mathematical Expectation and Decision Making

Many problems of science, engineering, and business management are such that outcomes (or consequences of actions taken) are subject to chance. Suppose, for example, that in the manufacture of a certain product the unit cost of production is $12, a good item can be sold for $17, the probability of producing a defective item is 0.20, and a defective item constitutes a total loss. Thus, in terms of profit, each unit manufactured represents either a gain of $5 or a loss of $12 (that is, a gain of −$12).

This information in itself may not enable us to decide whether or not to manufacture the product, but it will certainly aid in any such decision. Note, for example, that about 80 per cent of the units represent a gain of $5, and about 20 per cent of the units represent a loss of $12, so that in the long run there is an average gain of $5(0.80) − 12(0.20) = $1.60 per unit. We obtained this value by multiplying each possible outcome (a gain of $5 or a loss of $12) by the corresponding probability, and we refer to it as the *expected value* of the profit or, simply, as the *expected profit*. Comparing the method of computing such an expected value with the equation for μ on page 53, we observe that *the expected value of a random variable is simply the mean of its probability distribution.*

To give another illustration of the calculation of an expected value, suppose that an engineering firm is faced with the task of preparing a proposal for a research contract; the cost of preparing the proposal is $5000, and it is assumed to be known that the probabilities for potential gross profits of $30,000, $20,000, $10,000, or $0 are, respectively, 0.20, 0.50, 0.20, and 0.10, provided the proposal is accepted. Assessing the probability that the proposal will be accepted as 0.30, we find that there is a probability of (0.30)(0.20) = 0.06 of making a net profit of $25,000 ($30,000 minus the cost of the proposal). Similarly, the probabilities of making net profits of $15,000 or $5000 are, respectively, (0.50)(0.30) = 0.15 and (0.20)(0.30) = 0.06, while the probability of a $5000 loss is (0.10)(0.30) + 0.70 = 0.73, allowing for the eventuality that the proposal will not be accepted. We are, thus, faced by the situation described in the following table:

Net profit	$25,000	$15,000	$5000	−$5000
Probability	0.06	0.15	0.06	0.73

and we find that the *expected net profit* is

$$(25,000)(0.06) + (15,000)(0.15) + (5000)(0.06) - (5000)(0.73) = \$400$$

Whether or not it is wise to risk $5000 to make an expected profit of $400 is not a question of statistics. If a company has little capital and can make only few such proposals, the 0.73 chance of losing $5000 may well make the venture unattractive. On the other hand, if a company is well capitalized and prepares many such proposals, the risk may be worth taking, for it promises an *expected return* of 8 per cent on the original investment.

In the example which follows, expected values are used to determine optimum conditions for a typical inventory problem. Suppose it is known from past experience that the daily demand for a certain perishable product has the following probability distribution:

Number of orders	3	4	5	6	7	8	9
Probability	0.05	0.12	0.20	0.24	0.17	0.14	0.08

Each item costs $35 (including the cost of carrying it in stock), it is sold for $50 provided it is in stock, and an item remaining in stock at the end of a day represents a total loss. On the basis of this information we want to determine how many items should be stocked each day so as to *maximize the expected profit.*

For 3 units stocked, the profit in dollars is obviously $150 - 105 = 45$, as there is a probability of 1.00 that there will be a demand for 3 units or more. For 4 units stocked, there is a probability of 0.05 that exactly 3 units can be sold, a probability of 0.95 that there will be a demand for 4 or more, and there is, therefore, an expected dollar profit of

$$150(0.05) + 200(0.95) - 140 = 57.50$$

Similarly, for 5 units stocked there is a probability of 0.05 that exactly 3 units will be sold, a probability of 0.12 that exactly 4 units will be sold, a probability of 0.83 that there will be a demand for 5 or more, and there is, therefore, an expected dollar profit of

$$150(0.05) + 200(0.12) + 250(0.83) - 175 = 64.00$$

Continuing in this manner it can be shown that for 6 units stocked the expected profit is $60.50, for 7 units stocked the expected profit is $45.00, etc., and that the expected profit is a maximum when 5 units are stocked (see also Exercise 6 on page 91).

In recent years, expected values (or *mathematical expectations*, as they are also called) have been playing an increasingly important role in "scientific" decision making. As we have indicated in connection with the example on page 87, they may not serve as the sole criterion for making decisions, but they nevertheless provide important information for making rational decisions. As a further illustration, let us observe how expected values can be used in selecting a most profitable action from a *continuous* set of alternatives. Suppose that an engineer has the choice of setting an automatic stamping machine at the rate of r operations per hour, but that the proportion of defectives p increases with r. There is a profit of \$1.00 for each effective stamping operation, a loss of \$20.00 for each defective operation, and it is known from past records that for a fixed stamping rate r the probability distribution for the proportion of defectives is well approximated by

$$f(p) = \begin{cases} (0.001)rp^{0.001r-1} & \text{for } 0 < p < 1 \\ 0 & \text{elsewhere} \end{cases}$$

In order to find the most profitable stamping rate, let us first determine the expected hourly profit for a given value of r, using the formula for μ on page 67 instead of the one on page 53. For fixed r and p the hourly profit is

$$(1.00)r(1 - p) - (20.00)rp = r(1 - 21p)$$

so that for fixed r the expected hourly profit is

$$\int_0^1 r(1 - 21p)f(p)\, dp = \int_0^1 r(1 - 21p)(0.001)rp^{0.001r-1}\, dp$$

$$= \frac{1000r - 20r^2}{1000 + r}$$

Finally, differentiating with respect to r and equating the resulting expression to zero, we find that the expected hourly profit is a maximum when $r = 25$ and that for this stamping rate the expected profit is \$12.10 per hour.

In applying the methods of decision making illustrated in this section, there are essentially two practical limitations: first, we must be able to assign "cash values" to the various outcomes, and second, we must have adequate information concerning all relevant probabilities. The problem of assigning cash values to the various outcomes can be much more difficult than it was in our examples. For instance, if an Air Force officer were faced with the decision of how many bombers to send over a particular target, it would be extremely difficult for him to assign a cash value to the destruction of the target or to the loss of a bomber and its crew due to enemy action. In assigning a cash value to a bomber and its crew he would have to take into account the costs of procurement and training and also the inestimable cost of human life.

The specification of probabilities concerning the various outcomes can be equally difficult. In the preceding example we postulated a certain distribution for the proportion of defectives corresponding to given stamping rate r. In practice it would require a great deal of experimentation to discover such a distribution and even then it would only be an estimate (or approximation). Although past experience can often be used to estimate relevant probability distributions (as we have implied in most of our examples), there are situations where there is no choice but to fall back on subjective judgment. For instance, in the example on page 87 (the one dealing with the preparation of the research proposal), it would be extremely difficult to estimate the probability that a given proposal will be accepted. This would have to depend not only on the quality of the proposal itself, but on such unknown factors as the number and quality of competing proposals as well as the policy of the sponsoring agency. The estimate of 0.30 in our example was purely subjective, being based on some executive's "feeling" about the situation measured against the background of his personal experience. While such estimates of probabilities are not without value, they do leave open the possibility that different individuals (acting in the same situation and having the same information) would arrive at different "optimum" decisions.

EXERCISES

1. A lot of 50 parts, among which 8 are defective, is put up for sale "as is" at $12.50 per part with no inspection allowed. If a defective part represents a complete loss and a good part can be resold for $14.50, is it worthwhile to buy one of these parts (selecting it at random)?

2. Five prizes are awarded in a lottery, consisting of a first prize of $1000, a second prize of $500, a third prize of $300, and fourth and fifth prizes of $100 each. If 1500 tickets are sold, what is the value of each ticket?

3. The following is a variation of a classical problem of probability theory: two players ante $8 each to bet on a series of flips of a coin, with the winner (who takes all) being the one who wins at least three times out of five. For some reason, the game has to stop after the first toss, which was won by Player A.

   (a) Draw a tree diagram to show that after he has won the first toss, Player A's probability of winning the whole game is 11/16.

   (b) How should the two players divide the $16 anted, if the game has to stop after the first toss, which was won by Player A?

4. If two teams are evenly matched, the probabilities that a World Series will end in 4, 5, 6, or 7 games are, respectively, 1/8, 1/4, 5/16, and 5/16. What is the expected length of a World Series when the two teams are evenly matched?

5. It costs $50 to test a certain component of a machine. If a defective component is installed, it costs $1000 to repair the resulting damage to the machine. Is it more profitable to install the component without testing if it is known that 3 per cent of all components produced are defective? If 6 per cent are defective?

6. Referring to the example on page 88, verify that for 6 and 7 units stocked, the expected profits are \$60.50 and \$45.00, respectively.

7. A merchant can buy an item for \$2.10 and sell it for \$4.50. The probabilities for a demand of 0, 1, 2, 3, 4, or "5 or more" items are, respectively, 0.05, 0.15, 0.30, 0.25, 0.15, and 0.10. Calculate the expected profits resulting from stocking 0, 1, 2, 3, 4, or 5 items and determine how many the merchant should stock so as to maximize his expected profit.

8. If n salesmen are employed in a door-to-door selling campaign, the gross sales volume in thousands of dollars can be regarded as a random variable having the gamma distribution with the parameters $\alpha = 100\sqrt{n}$ and $\beta = 1/2$. If the sales costs are \$5000 per salesman, how many salesmen should be employed to maximize the profit?

9. From experience Mr. Harris has found that the low bid on a construction job can be regarded as a random variable having the uniform density

$$(x) = \begin{cases} \dfrac{3}{4C} & \text{for } \dfrac{2C}{3} < x < 2C \\ 0 & \text{elsewhere} \end{cases}$$

where C is his own estimate of the cost of the job. What percentage should Mr. Harris add to his cost estimate when submitting bids to maximize his expected profit?

10. A company rents out time on a computer for periods of t hours, for which it receives \$400 an hour. The number of times the computer breaks down during t hours is a random variable having the Poisson distribution with $\lambda = (0.8)t$, and if the computer breaks down x times during t hours it costs $50x^2$ dollars to fix it. How should the company select t in order to maximize its expected profit? [*Hint:* Use results obtained in Section 3.5.]

5.3 Random Processes

Generally speaking, the term "random process" is used in connection with physical processes which are wholly or in part controlled by some sort of random mechanism. It is applied to sequences of repeated flips of a coin, to repeated measurements of the quality of a manufactured product coming off an assembly line, to the vibrations of airplane wings, to the "noise" in radio signals, and to numerous other phenomena. What characterizes such processes is their "time-dependence," namely, the fact that certain events do or do not take place (depending on chance) at regular intervals of time or throughout a continuous interval of time.

In this section we shall be concerned with processes taking place over continuous intervals of time, such as the occurrence of imperfections on a continuously produced bolt of cloth, the recording of radiation by means of a Geiger counter, the arrival of telephone calls at a switchboard, or the passing by cars of an electronic checking device. An appropriate mathematical theory which applies to many such phenomena is provided by the Poisson distribution, introduced in Section 3.4. Let us generalize the assumptions made in Section 3.4; specifically, we shall suppose that we are concerned with the occurrence of a certain kind of event and that the probability that it occurs during a very small interval of time Δt is given by $\alpha \cdot \Delta t$. We shall assume further that the probability of its occurrence more than once during an interval of length Δt equals zero, and that the occurrence or nonoccurrence of the event during the interval from t to $t + \Delta t$ does not depend on what happened prior to time t. Duplicating the argument on page 49, we conclude from these assumptions that the probability distribution of the number of occurrences of the event during a time interval of length T is given by

$$f(x) = \frac{e^{-\alpha T}(\alpha T)^x}{x!} \qquad \text{for } x = 0, 1, 2, 3, \ldots$$

This is the Poisson distribution with the mean αT, and it follows that we can interpret α as the mean number of occurrences of the event per unit time. A random process satisfying the assumptions described is called a *Poisson process* with parameter α.

Although we introduced the Poisson distribution originally for the purpose of providing an approximation to the binomial distribution, we have already used it in some of the exercises on page 52 in connection with continuous random processes. At the time we applied it to problems dealing with imperfections in a continuous electrolytic process, breakdowns in a computer, gamma radiation emitted by a radioactive substance, and the incidence of hurricanes on the East Coast of the United States.

In problems dealing with random processes it is often important to consider the time t between successive occurrences of the event in question. By virtue of the random nature of the process, t is a value of a random variable, and it must have some kind of a probability density in a continuous random process. To find this density for a Poisson process, first we observe that the statement: "The waiting time between two successive occurrences of the event is greater than t" is equivalent to the statement: "The number of occurrences of the event from time 0 to time t is equal to zero." Thus, if for a Poisson process $F(t)$ stands for the probability that *the waiting time is less than or equal to t*, we have

$$1 - F(t) = \frac{e^{-\alpha t}(\alpha t)^0}{0!}$$

or

$$F(t) = 1 - e^{-\alpha t}$$

Differentiating with respect to t (see page 66) we find that the density of the waiting time between successive occurrences of the event is that of the *exponential distribution*

$$f(t) = \begin{cases} \alpha \cdot e^{-\alpha t} & t > 0 \\ 0 & t \le 0 \end{cases}$$

which was first introduced on page 79. Recall that the mean of this distribution is $\mu = 1/\alpha$; thus, the mean waiting time between successive occurrences of the event is $1/\alpha$, which is consistent with the fact that α is the mean number of occurrences per unit time.

An interesting application of a Poisson process and an exponential waiting-time distribution arises in *queueing problems*, where arrivals for service often constitute a Poisson process while the actual time required to perform the service has an exponential distribution. The resulting theory may apply to customers arriving for service at a cafeteria, ships or trucks waiting to be unloaded at a receiving dock, aircraft to be landed at an airport, and so on; it even may apply to court cases waiting to be heard. In most of these problems we are interested in such things as the average length of the queue (or waiting line), the probability that exactly x customers are waiting for service or being served, the average time a customer spends waiting and being served, and the like.

To illustrate such a queueing problem, suppose that the arrival of cars at a gas station with one pump is a Poisson process with a mean arrival rate of α cars per hour, and that cars can be served at a mean rate of β per hour with the time required for service having an exponential distribution. Furthermore, we shall assume that there is a zero probability for *both* an arrival and a completion of service during any small interval of time Δt. (In what follows it will also be assumed that $\alpha < \beta$, that is, the mean number of arrivals per unit time is less than the mean number of services that can be completed per unit time.)

We shall be interested in $P(k)$, the probability that there are k cars in the gas station at any given time. If $k = 0$ there are no cars in the gas station; therefore, none are waiting to be served; but if $k > 0$ there are $k - 1$ cars in the "waiting line." To find $P(k)$ we shall first obtain a set of "recursion relations" expressing $P(k)$ in terms of $P(k - 1)$ and $P(k - 2)$. To illustrate how these relations are obtained, let us find the probability that there are no cars in the station ($k = 0$) at time $t + \Delta t$. If $k = 0$ at time $t + \Delta t$, by the assumption of Poisson arrivals the only values that k could have had at time t are 0 and 1. If $k = 0$ at time t, then no new cars arrived in the interval from t to $t + \Delta t$ (with probability $1 - \alpha \cdot \Delta t$), but if $k = 1$ at time t, then a service was completed in this interval (with probability $\beta \cdot \Delta t$). Using the rule of elimination (page 29) we conclude that

or
$$P(0) = P(0)(1 - \alpha \cdot \Delta t) + P(1)\beta \cdot \Delta t$$

$$P(1) = \frac{\alpha}{\beta} P(0)$$

In general, the situation is typified by the tree shown in Figure 5.1, and the rule of elimination leads to the following recursion relation:

$$P(k) = P(k - 1)\alpha \cdot \Delta t + P(k)[1 - (\alpha + \beta) \Delta t] + P(k + 1)\beta \cdot \Delta t$$

$$(k \geq 1)$$

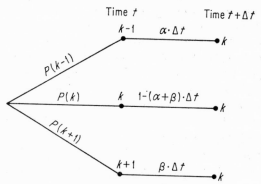

FIG. 5.1 Tree diagram for queueing problem

The reader will be asked in Exercise 3 on page 98 to verify that a solution of this set of equations is given by

$$P(k) = \left(1 - \frac{\alpha}{\beta}\right)\left(\frac{\alpha}{\beta}\right)^k \qquad \text{for } k = 0, 1, 2, \ldots$$

The resulting probability distribution is called the *geometric distribution*, and several important properties of the queue are revealed by working with it. Note first that, by the assumption $\alpha < \beta$, or $\alpha/\beta < 1$, we have

$$\lim_{k \to \infty} P(k) = 0$$

so that the probability is 1 that the waiting line remains finite. (In fact, it can be shown that if $\alpha \geq \beta$ there is a nonzero probability that the waiting line will eventually grow beyond all bounds.) The mean number of cars in the station (being served and waiting to be served) is given by the mean of the geometric distribution, $\sum_{k=0}^{\infty} kP(k)$, which equals $\frac{\alpha}{\beta - \alpha}$. The distribution of the number of cars in the queue waiting for service is given by $P(k + 1)$ for $k \geq 1$ and $P(0) + P(1)$ for $k = 0$. Thus, the mean number of cars in the queue is given by

$$\left(1 - \frac{\alpha}{\beta}\right) \sum_{k=1}^{\infty} k \left(\frac{\alpha}{\beta}\right)^{k+1} = \frac{\alpha^2}{\beta(\beta - \alpha)}$$

To find the mean time a customer spends waiting in the queue, it is necessary first to find the distribution of waiting times, and then to find its mean. We shall omit this work, stating only that the resulting mean waiting time is $\dfrac{\alpha}{\beta(\beta - \alpha)}$.

5.4 Random Walk

Several important applications of probability theory are based on the following interpretation of the binomial distribution. Suppose a point starts from the origin and it moves along the x-axis by means of successive jumps to the left or to the right. For any given jump there is a probability of p that it will be to the right, a probability of $1 - p$ that it will be to the left, and we shall assume that successive jumps are independent. What we are interested in is the probability that the point is x units to the right of the starting point after n jumps. Clearly, to be x units to the right of the origin after n "trials," there must have been x more "successes" than "failures"; that is, there must have been $\dfrac{n + x}{2}$ jumps to the right and $\dfrac{n - x}{2}$ to the left. Using the formula for the binomial distribution, we thus obtain the following distribution for the position of the point after n steps

$$f(x; n, p) = \binom{n}{\dfrac{n + x}{2}} p^{\frac{n+x}{2}} (1 - p)^{\frac{n-x}{2}}$$

which holds for $x = -n, -(n - 2), \ldots, -2, 0, 2, \ldots, (n - 2)$, and n when n is *even*, and for $x = -n, -(n - 2), \ldots, -1, 1, \ldots, (n - 2)$ and n when n is *odd*. As the reader will be asked to verify in Exercise 12 on page 99, the mean of this distribution is $\mu = n(2p - 1)$ and its variance is $\sigma^2 = 4np(1 - p)$.

The situation we have described in the preceding paragraph is a very simple kind of *random walk;* the process takes place along a line, the steps are all of equal size, and there are no restrictions or barriers which might upset or hinder the motion of the point along the line. Immediate generalizations of this kind of process may be obtained by letting the motion take place in two or more dimensions, by letting the steps be of unequal size (they might, themselves, be values of a random variable), or by imposing barriers so that the point cannot move beyond certain limits. All of these generalizations have important applications in the physical sciences and, as we shall see, also in the development of some statistical theory. The first two of these generalizations lead to the theory of Brownian motion and of diffusion, provided we let the individual jumps be very small and n be very large.

In order to derive the fundamental differential equation of diffusion from the model of a random walk, suppose that each jump is of size Δx (to the left or to the right), the time between successive jumps is Δt, and that $f(x, t)$ gives the probability that a particle is at a distance x from the origin along the x-axis after $n = t/\Delta t$ jumps. Considerations like those on page 93 will show that

$$f(x, t + \Delta t) = p \cdot f(x - \Delta x, t) + (1 - p) \cdot f(x + \Delta x, t)$$

Expanding both sides of this equation in Taylor's series (up to second-order terms), we obtain

$$\Delta t \frac{\partial f}{\partial t} + \frac{\Delta t^2}{2} \frac{\partial^2 f}{\partial t^2} + \cdots = (1 - 2p) \Delta x \frac{\partial f}{\partial x} + \frac{(\Delta x)^2}{2} \frac{\partial^2 f}{\partial x^2} + \cdots$$

Before we let $\Delta x \to 0$, let us point out that for n jumps of size Δx (to the left or to the right) the mean and the variance of the total displacement are $n(2p - 1) \Delta x$ and $4np(1 - p)(\Delta x)^2$, as can easily be verified using the results on page 95. Hence if $t = n \cdot \Delta t$, the mean and the variance of the total displacement are $(2p - 1)t \dfrac{\Delta x}{\Delta t}$ and $4p(1 - p)t \dfrac{(\Delta x)^2}{\Delta t}$. Since we want these two quantities to remain bounded for any t (otherwise the process would degenerate or "take off"), we shall let

$$(2p - 1) \frac{\Delta x}{\Delta t} = a \qquad \text{and} \qquad \frac{(\Delta x)^2}{\Delta t} = b.$$

Now, letting $\Delta x \to 0$ and $\Delta t \to 0$ with the restrictions that a and b remain finite, we obtain the differential equation

$$\frac{\partial f}{\partial t} = -a \frac{\partial f}{\partial x} + \frac{b}{2} \frac{\partial^2 f}{\partial x^2}$$

which is the well-known *Fokker-Planck* equation for diffusion with drift. If $p = 1/2$ the mean of $f(x, t)$ is zero for any time t and the *drift coefficient* a is equal to zero. The *diffusion coefficient* b is a measure of the variability of the process, namely, of the extent to which the particles are apt to diffuse.

The examples we have considered so far have all been unrestricted random walks, that is, in each step the point (or particle) could move in either direction. An interesting example of a restricted random walk arises in the problem of *gambler's ruin*, where the process continues only so long as each gambler has any money left to bet. Suppose that two players repeatedly bet on the outcome of a certain kind of event (the flip of a coin, the roll of a die, etc.), the first player has m dollars, the second player has n dollars, on each trial the loser pays the winner \$1.00, and the respective probabilities for the two players' winning on any one trial are p and $1 - p$. We can look upon this situation as a random-walk problem where on each trial a point moves one unit to the right if the first player wins or one unit to the left if the second player wins. The only difference is that now the random walk terminates if the point has moved n units to the right (the second player has lost all of his capital) or m units to the left (the first player has lost all of his capital).

One problem that immediately arises in this kind of situation is that of determining the probability of the first (or second) player's ruin. This problem is equivalent to finding the probability that the point performing the "random walk" reaches n before it reaches $-m$ (or vice versa). A general solution to this problem can be found in Exercise 10 on page 99. Here we shall merely indicate the solution in the special case $p = 1/2$. If $p = 1/2$, the game is "equitable" (or "fair") and each player's *expected gain* must equal zero. Thus, the expected gain of the first player is n dollars *times* the probability P that the second player is ruined, plus $-m$ dollars *times* the probability $1 - p$ that he is ruined, or

$$nP + (-m)(1 - P) = 0$$

Thus, $P = \dfrac{m}{m + n}$; for example, if the first player has \$4 while the second has \$3 and they bet in \$1 increments, then the probability is 4/7 that the second player will be ruined.

An important application of restricted random walks arises in so-called *sequential sampling*, where observations are taken one at a time, and after each observation it is decided whether to accept a certain hypothesis, to reject it, or to continue sampling. For instance, in the inspection of a manufactured product, each defective item might be identified with a jump to the left, each good item with a jump to the right, and the process is continued until a boundary is reached and it can be decided whether or not to accept the lot. The random-walk problem of sequential sampling is complicated by the fact that there are actually "variable boundaries" since the ultimate decision will have to involve the size of the sample, that is, the total number of jumps taken. The theory of sequential sampling can be found in *Sequential Analysis* by A. Wald (see Bibliography), and its application to acceptance sampling will be discussed in this book in Chapter 15.

EXERCISES

1. The arrival of cars at a turnpike tollgate is a Poisson process with $\lambda = 75$ cars per hour (during peak hours). What is the probability that at least two minutes will elapse between the arrival of any two successive cars?

2. The time between successive phone calls arriving at a switchboard is a random variable having an exponential distribution with a mean of 30 seconds. What is the probability that at most 8 calls will arrive at the switchboard during any 5-minute interval?

3. Verify (by substitution) that the geometric distribution is a solution of the recursion relation given on page 94.

4. Differentiating with respect to θ both sides of the equation

$$\sum_{x=1}^{\infty} \theta(1 - \theta)^{x-1} = 1$$

show that the geometric distribution

$$f(x) = \theta(1 - \theta)^{x-1} \qquad \text{for } x = 1, 2, 3, \ldots$$

has the mean $1/\theta$. Use this result to verify that $\dfrac{\alpha}{\beta - \alpha}$ is the mean of the special geometric distribution given on page 94.

5. The arrival of trucks at a receiving dock is a Poisson process with a mean arrival rate of 2 per hour. The trucks can be unloaded at a mean rate of 3 per hour, and the time required for unloading has an exponential distribution.

   (a) What is the average number of trucks being unloaded and waiting to be unloaded?

   (b) What is the mean number of trucks in the queue?

   (c) What is the mean time a truck spends waiting in the queue?

   (d) What is the probability that there are no trucks waiting to be unloaded?

6. Referring to Exercise 5, suppose that the cost of keeping a truck in the system is $15 per hour. If it were possible to increase the mean unloading rate to 3.5 trucks per hour at a cost of $100 per day, would this be worthwhile?

7. In an unrestricted random walk with $p = 1/2$, what is the probability that the moving point will return to the origin at least once during the first 7 steps?

8. The following is an alternate way of introducing the Poisson distribution. Suppose that $f(x, t)$ is the probability of getting x successes during a time interval of length t when (1) the probability of a success during a very small time interval from t to $t + \Delta t$ is $\alpha \cdot \Delta t$, (2) the probability of more than one success occurring during such a time interval is negligible, and (3) the probability of a success during such a time interval does not depend on what happened prior to time t.

(a) Show that

$$f(x, t + \Delta t) = f(x, t)[1 - \alpha \Delta t] + f(x - 1, t)\alpha \Delta t$$

(b) Using the result of part (a), show that

$$\frac{d[f(x, t)]}{dt} = \alpha[f(x - 1, t) - f(x, t)]$$

(c) Verify by substitution that the differential equation obtained in (b) is satisfied by the formula for the Poisson distribution with $\lambda = \alpha t$.

9. Two players having, respectively, \$8 and \$4 bet on x successive flips of a coin.

(a) What is the probability that the player having \$8 will be ruined if they bet \$1 on each flip of the coin?

(b) What is the probability that the player having \$8 will be ruined if they bet \$2 on each flip of the coin?

10. The problem of a gambler's ruin when $p \neq 1/2$ can be solved by methods similar to those on page 94. Let us denote by q_x the probability that the first player will be ruined when his capital is x dollars, so that this player is ruined when $x = 0$ and his opponent is ruined when $x = m + n$. (As before, the players start the game with m dollars and n dollars, respectively.)

(a) Using the rule of elimination show that

$$q_x = p \cdot q_{x+1} + (1 - p)q_{x-1}$$

for $0 < x < m + n$, where it is understood that $q_0 = 1$ and $q_{m+n} = 0$.

(b) Verify by substitution that the solution is given by

$$q_x = \frac{\left(\dfrac{1-p}{p}\right)^{m+n} - \left(\dfrac{1-p}{p}\right)^{x}}{\left(\dfrac{1-p}{p}\right)^{m+n} - 1}$$

for $x = 0, 1, \ldots, m + n$.

(c) Substituting $x = m$ in the expression obtained in (b), find the probability that the first player will be ruined.

11. Using the result obtained in Exercise 10, rework the two parts of Exercise 9 for the case where $p = 1/3$. Also compute the probability that the player having \$8 will be ruined when $p = 1/3$ and they bet \$4 on each flip of the coin. Can you draw any conclusions from these results?

12. Verify that for the random-walk distribution on page 95 we have $\mu = n(2p - 1)$ and $\sigma^2 = 4np(1 - p)$.

5.5 Monte Carlo Methods

In recent years, simulation techniques have been applied to many problems of the physical, biological, and social sciences.

If the processes which are being simulated involve an element of chance, these techniques are referred to as *Monte Carlo methods*. Very often, the use of Monte Carlo simulation eliminates the cost of building and operating expensive equipment; it is used, for instance, in the study of collisions of photons with electrons, the scattering of neutrons, and similar complicated phenomena. Monte Carlo methods are also useful in situations where direct experimentation is impossible—say, in studies of the spread of cholera epidemics, which, of course, cannot be induced experimentally on human populations. In addition, Monte Carlo techniques are sometimes applied to the solution of mathematical problems which actually cannot be solved by direct means, or where a direct solution is too costly or requires too much time.

A classical example of the use of Monte Carlo methods in the solution of a problem of pure mathematics is the determination of π (the ratio of the circumference of a circle to its diameter) by probabilistic means. Early in the eighteenth century George de Buffon, a French naturalist, proved that if a very fine needle of length a is thrown at random on a board ruled with equidistant parallel lines, the probability that the needle will intersect one of the lines is $2a/\pi b$, where b is the distance between the parallel lines. What is remarkable about this fact is that it involves the constant $\pi = 3.1415926\ldots$, which in elementary geometry is approximated by the circumferences of regular polygons enclosed in a circle of radius $1/2$. Buffon's result implies that if such a needle is actually tossed a great many times, the proportion of the time it crosses one of the lines gives an estimate of $2a/\pi b$ and, hence, an estimate of π since a and b are known. Early experiments of this kind yielded an estimate of 3.1519 (based on 5000 trials) and an estimate of 3.155 (based on 3204) trials in the middle of the nineteenth century.

Although Monte Carlo methods are sometimes based on actual gambling devices (for example, the needle tossing in the estimation of π), it is usually expedient to use so-called tables of random digits or random numbers. Tables of random numbers consist of many pages on which the digits 0, 1, 2, $\ldots$, and 9 are set down in a "random" fashion, much as they would appear if they were generated one at a time by a gambling device giving each digit an equal probability of being selected. Actually, we could construct such tables ourselves—say, by repeatedly drawing numbered slips out of a hat or by using a perfectly constructed spinner—but in practice such tables are usually generated by means of electronic computers. For instance, in one such method the computer begins with a 4-digit number, say, 3571, and squares it, getting 12752041. The middle four digits, in this case 7520, are looked upon as a set of 4 random digits. (If necessary, a 0 is added on the left to make the square have eight digits.) Then 7520 is squared, yielding 56550400, and 5504 is looked upon as the next set of 4 random digits. Continuing in this way, we obtain a table of *pseudo-random digits* which are quite satisfactory for most practical purposes.

Although tables of random numbers are constructed so that the digits can be looked upon as values of a random variable having the discrete uniform distribution $f(x) = 1/10$ for $x = 0, 1, 2, \ldots$, or 9, they can be used to simulate values of any discrete random variable, and even continuous random variables. For instance, if we are interested in simulating an experiment in which we repeatedly flip three balanced coins, we can let 0, 2, 4, 6, 8 represent heads, 1, 3, 5, 7, 9 represent tails, and we can look upon any set of 3 random digits as the result obtained in flipping three coins. Thus, if we use the second page of Table VII and the digits in the 9th, 10th, and 11th columns starting from the top, we get

$$480 \quad 280 \quad 085 \quad 265 \quad 303 \quad 288 \quad 295 \quad 388 \quad 127 \quad 222$$

and we interpret this as getting, respectively, 3, 3, 2, 2, 1, 3, 1, 2, 1, and 3 heads in 10 flips of 3 coins. Since the probabilities of getting 0, 1, 2, or 3 heads with 3 balanced coins are, respectively, 1/8, 3/8, 3/8, and 1/8, an alternate way of simulating this experiment is to represent zero heads with the digit 0, one head with the digits 1, 2, and 3, two heads with the digits 4, 5, and 6, and three heads with the digit 7. Omitting the digits 8 and 9 wherever they may occur, we interpret the random digits

$$4 \quad 8 \quad 1 \quad 1 \quad 1 \quad 9 \quad 3 \quad 3 \quad 3 \quad 7 \quad 6 \quad 3 \quad 6 \quad 2 \quad 6 \quad 5 \quad 8 \quad 9 \quad 3 \quad 1 \quad 0 \quad 6$$

in the fifth row of the third page of Table VII as getting, respectively, 2, 1, 1, 1, 1, 1, 1, 3, 2, 1, 2, 1, 2, 2, 1, 1, 0, and 2 heads in 18 tosses of three coins.

The following is a general method for simulating experiments in which we want to obtain values of random variables having given continuous or discrete distributions. It is based on the cumulative distribution of the random variable, using either an appropriate table of cumulative probabilities or a graph of the cumulative distribution. (The theory on which this method is based in the continuous case involves the so-called *probability integral transformation*, which is treated in all of the mathematical statistics texts referred to in the Bibliography at the end of this book.)

Getting a step-function like the one of Figure 5.2 in the discrete case or a curve like the one of Figure 5.3 in the continuous case, we obtain a value of the random variable by first choosing a *random decimal* between 0 and 1 to as many places as desired. For instance, if we want to use three decimals we take samples of three random digits and look upon 134, 056, 836, for example, as the random decimals 0.134, 0.056, and 0.836. We then mark these random decimals on an ordinary vertical scale, as indicated in Figures 5.2 and 5.3, and read the corresponding values of the random variable off the horizontal scale.

To illustrate how this method works in the discrete case, suppose we

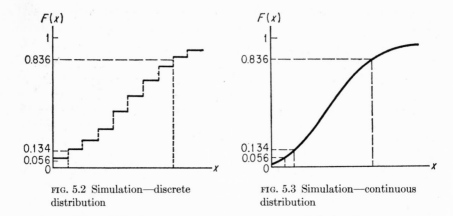

FIG. 5.2 Simulation—discrete   FIG. 5.3 Simulation—continuous
distribution   distribution

want to simulate a traffic study where the daily number of traffic accidents
on a certain stretch of road may be looked upon as values of a random
variable having a Poisson distribution with $\lambda = 0.8$. Getting the necessary
probabilities from Table II, we obtain the cumulative distribution shown
in Figure 5.4. To simulate the number of accidents on 5 consecutive days,
suppose we use three-digit random numbers, and that using the 29th,
30th, and 31st columns of the third page of Table VII starting with the
6th row we obtain 149, 993, 793, 310, and 465. Plotting first the random
decimal 0.149, we find that it corresponds to 0 accidents, and plotting in
succession the random decimals 0.993, 0.793, 0.310, and 0.465, we find
that they correspond, respectively, to 4, 1, 0, and 1 accidents.

To illustrate this method in the continuous case, suppose that we want

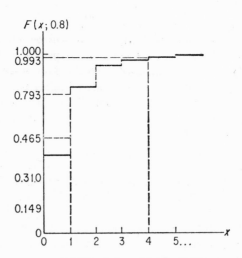

FIG. 5.4 Simulation of traffic study

to simulate an experiment in which hourly readings are taken of the temperature of a kiln and that these readings may be looked upon as values of a random variable having a normal distribution with the mean $\mu = 500$ (degrees Fahrenheit) and the standard deviation $\sigma = 20$. To simulate, say, 10 consecutive readings of the temperature of this kiln, we could proceed as indicated in Figure 5.2, plotting the necessary graph of a cumulative normal distribution with $\mu = 500$ and $\sigma = 20$. Instead of solving this problem graphically, we can also work directly with a table of cumulative normal probabilities (Table III); since tables of normal curve areas are usually readily available, it is actually easier to proceed as follows: given a random decimal between 0 and 1, we merely have to determine the value of the random variable for which the area under the normal curve to its left is equal to the random decimal. Referring to the simulation of the temperatures in the kiln, let us illustrate first how this is done when the random decimal exceeds 0.5000, say, when it equals 0.7091. Checking 0.7091 inside Table III, we find that the closest entry corresponds to $z = 0.55$ and, hence, that the desired value of the random variable having a normal distribution with $\mu = 500$ and $\sigma = 20$ is obtained by solving

$$0.55 = \frac{x - 500}{20}$$

namely, that it is $x = 511$ (degrees Fahrenheit).

If the random decimal is less than 0.5000, say, 0.1662, we check $1 - 0.1662 = 0.8338$ inside Table III, and we find that the closest entry corresponds to 0.97. Then the desired temperature reading is obtained by solving

$$-0.97 = \frac{x - 500}{20}$$

and we find that it equals 480.6 degrees. It will be left to the reader to perform the actual simulation of the given experiment, namely, to simulate 10 readings of the temperature in the kiln. Incidentally, if it is desired to carry more digits in the simulated readings, it may be necessary to interpolate when obtaining the z's from Table III.

EXERCISES

1. To estimate π by means of a simple Monte Carlo technique, repeatedly take a sequence of four random digits, a, b, c, and d, and interpret them as representing the point $(0.ab, 0.cd)$. Then check for each of these points whether or not it lies inside the circle $x^2 + y^2 = 1$.

   (a) Explain why the proportion of points falling inside the circle should give an estimate of $\pi/4$.

(b) Actually perform this experiment 100 times and obtain an estimate of π.

2. In the problem of "gambler's ruin" (see page 97) suppose one gambler has an initial capital of \$1 and the other gambler has \$3. Using a table of random digits, simulate 100 "games" (each game terminates when the capital of one of the gamblers is exhausted) in each of the following cases:

   (a) Assume the probability is 1/2 that either gambler wins \$1 on any given trial. (Compare your result with that obtained by means of the formula on page 97.)

   (b) Assume the probability is 1/4 that the gambler having the initial capital of \$3 wins \$1 on any given trial. (Compare your result with that obtained by means of the formula on page 99.)

3. Depending upon the availability of parts, a company can manufacture 3, 4, 5, or 6 units of a certain item per week with corresponding probabilities of 0.10, 0.40, 0.30, and 0.20. The probabilities that there will be a weekly demand for 0, 1, 2, 3, ..., or 8 units are, respectively, 0.05, 0.10, 0.30, 0.30, 0.10, 0.05, 0.05, 0.04, and 0.01. If a unit is sold during the week that it is made it will yield a profit of \$100; this profit is reduced by \$20 for each week that a unit has to be stored. Use random numbers to simulate the operations of this company for 50 consecutive weeks and estimate their expected weekly profit.

4. Suppose that the occurrence of breakdowns of a radar tracking system is a Poisson process with $\lambda = 0.01$ per hour, and the time required to repair any breakdown is fixed at 10 hours. Simulate 1000 hours of operation of this system and estimate the proportion of "down time." [*Hint:* Simulate the waiting times between successive breakdowns using an appropriate exponential distribution.]

5. Since many simulation experiments entail sampling from normal populations, statisticians have constructed special tables of so-called *random normal deviates* (see Bibliography at the end of the book), which are looked upon as values of a random variable having the standard normal distribution. Using the method indicated on page 103, construct a table of 100 such random normal deviates. Then use this table to simulate an experiment in which a random sample of size 25 is taken from a normal population having $\mu = 24.6$ and $\sigma = 1.8$.

6. A system has two components, A and B, which operate independently in sequential order, $ABABAB\ldots$, and the probability is 0.90 that either component will actuate properly when its turn comes. If component B fails, however, its function can be assumed by component A, but the probability of success of component A becomes 0.70 from that point on. Estimate the probability that the system operates throughout three cycles (such as $ABABAB, ABABAA$, etc.) by simulating 50 sequences.

6 | TREATMENT OF DATA

6.1 Frequency Distributions

Statistical data, obtained from surveys, experiments, or any series of measurements, are often so numerous that they are virtually useless unless they are condensed, or reduced, into a more suitable form. Thus, the first step of a statistical analysis often consists of the construction of a *frequency table*, that is, a table which divides the data into a relatively small number of classes (categories), listing the number of observations belonging to each class. A frequency table, or a *frequency distribution* as it is also called, sacrifices some of the information contained in a set of data; instead of knowing the exact value of each item, we only know that it belongs in a certain class. On the other hand, this kind of grouping often brings out important features of the data, and the gain in "legibility" of the data usually more than compensates for the loss of information. In what follows, we shall consider mainly *numerical* frequency distributions, that is, frequency distributions where the data are grouped according to their numerical size. If the data are grouped according to some quality, or attribute, we shall refer to such a distribution as a *categorical* frequency distribution.

To illustrate the construction of a frequency table, let us consider the following 100 measurements of the iron-solution index of tin-plate samples, designed to measure the corrosion resistance of tin-plated steel:

0.78	0.38	0.72	0.65	0.72	0.92	0.78	0.65	0.92	0.78
1.36	1.43	0.65	0.48	0.83	0.48	0.72	0.48	0.65	0.78
0.65	1.00	0.78	0.78	1.03	1.26	0.48	0.48	1.06	0.96
0.65	0.92	0.72	0.78	0.78	0.48	0.28	0.36	0.83	0.48
0.78	0.49	0.36	0.78	0.78	0.83	0.88	0.96	1.03	1.21
0.88	0.57	0.72	1.03	0.92	0.96	0.78	1.09	0.92	1.12
0.65	0.65	0.83	0.72	0.72	0.78	0.72	1.09	0.83	0.83
0.83	1.06	0.57	0.78	1.23	1.09	1.03	0.18	0.65	1.34
0.96	0.65	0.48	1.18	1.12	0.18	0.48	0.72	0.57	0.55
0.96	0.65	0.96	0.51	0.65	1.21	1.48	0.96	0.96	1.40

The first step in constructing a frequency table consists of deciding how many classes to use and choosing the limits for each class. Generally speaking, the number of classes we use depends on the number of observations, but it is seldom profitable to use fewer than five or more than fifteen classes. Among other things, we base this decision on the *range* of the data, that is, the difference between the largest observation and the smallest. In our example, the largest observation is 1.48, the smallest is 0.18, and the range is 1.30. Choosing limits into which the data can easily be tallied (perhaps by machine), we might choose the fourteen classes having the limits 0.10–0.19, 0.20–0.29, . . . , 1.40–1.49, or we might choose the seven classes having the limits 0.10–0.29, 0.30–0.49, . . . , 1.30–1.49. Note that in either case *the limits of the classes do not overlap* and that *the classes are all of the same size.*

Deciding upon the second of these classifications, we now tally the 100 observations (much like the tally of votes in an election or, for that matter, any kind of count) as shown in the following table:

Class limits	Tally	Frequency
0.10–0.29	///	3
0.30–0.49	ℳ ℳ ///	13
0.50–0.69	ℳ ℳ ℳ //	17
0.70–0.89	ℳ ℳ ℳ ℳ ℳ ℳ //	32
0.90–1.09	ℳ ℳ ℳ ℳ ///	23
1.10–1.29	ℳ //	7
1.30–1.49	ℳ	5

We used the above limits in preference to overlapping limits such as 0.10–0.30, 0.30–0.50, . . . , because we would not have been able to determine where to put 0.30, 0.50, . . . , if these values had occurred among our data. Note that the class limits we used contained as many decimals as the original data. In fact, if the data had been given to three decimals we would have used the class limits 0.100–0.299, 0.300–0.499, . . . , 1.300–1.499; and if they had been rounded to one decimal we would have used the class limits 0.1–0.2, 0.3–0.4, . . . , 1.3–1.4, 1.5–1.6.

The iron-solution indices of our example can be thought of as values of a continuous random variable, although they are, of course, rounded to the nearest one-hundredth. Accordingly, it would seem desirable to have the classes into which we group the data fill a continuous scale. This is not the case if we look upon the chosen classes as in Figure 6.1, but we

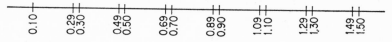

FIG. 6.1 Class limits

can correct this by letting the first class go from 0.095 to 0.295, the second from 0.295 to 0.495, . . . , and the last from 1.295 to 1.495. We refer to these new limits as the *class boundaries*, and it should be noted that there will be no ambiguities even though the boundaries overlap. These class boundaries are, so to speak, "impossible" values, since the data were given to only two decimals. In practice, we use the class boundaries rather than the original class limits chiefly when it is essential to stress the fact that the data are values assumed by a continuous random variable (or that they are otherwise continuous kinds of measurements).

As we have pointed out earlier, each observation in a given class has lost its identity in the sense that its exact value is no longer known. This leads to some difficulties when we want to give further descriptions of the data, but we get around this by representing each observation in a class by its midpoint, called the *class mark*. In general, the class marks of a frequency distribution are obtained by averaging successive class limits or successive class boundaries, and for our distribution we obtain the class marks 0.195, 0.395, 0.595, 0.795, 0.995, 1.195, and 1.395. The common interval between any two successive class marks is called the *class interval* and in our example it is 0.20. This value could also have been obtained from the difference of successive class boundaries, but *not* from the difference of successive class limits. It is, of course, assumed here that the classes are all of equal length; otherwise we cannot speak of the class interval of a distribution, although we can refer to the difference between its boundaries as the *length* of a given class.

When a frequency distribution is presented in its final form, the tally is practically always omitted, and we show only the class limits, the class boundaries, or the class marks, and, of course, the corresponding class frequencies.

There are several alternate forms of distributions into which data are sometimes grouped. Foremost among these are the "less than" or "more than" *cumulative frequency distributions*. A cumulative "less than" distribution shows the total number of observations that are less than given values, and it is easily constructed from the corresponding (ordinary) frequency table. We do not know how many observations are less than the individual class marks, but we do know how many are less than each lower class boundary (or each lower class limit). Hence, we use these class boundaries and for our illustration we obtain

Iron-solution index	Number of observations
less than 0.095	0
less than 0.295	3
less than 0.495	16
less than 0.695	33
less than 0.895	65
less than 1.095	88
less than 1.295	95
less than 1.495	100

Note that instead of "less than 0.095" we could also have written "less than 0.10" or "0.09 or less." The cumulative frequencies of this table were obtained by adding the frequencies, starting from the top of the frequency table. A cumulative "more than" distribution is constructed, similarly, by adding the frequencies, starting at the bottom of the frequency table. In practice, "less than" cumulative distributions are used more widely, and it is not uncommon to refer to a cumulative "less than" distribution simply as a cumulative distribution.

If it is desired to compare two or more frequency distributions whose total frequencies are not equal, it may be necessary (or at least advantageous) to convert them into so-called *percentage distributions*. We simply divide each class frequency by the total number of observations in the distribution and multiply by 100; in this way we indicate what percentage of the data falls into each class of a distribution. The same principle can also be applied to cumulative distributions, by replacing each cumulative frequency by the corresponding cumulative percentage.

As a further illustration, let us construct a frequency table for the following figures representing the number of missing rivets observed per assembly in 50 aircraft assemblies:

7	5	8	28	11	10	7	20	4	4
4	10	13	11	9	8	10	5	6	4
14	10	18	13	15	7	1	2	7	16
12	30	7	11	8	27	2	3	0	3
7	8	8	14	34	6	13	8	15	10

Since these data consist of integers, there will be no ambiguity if we use the class limits 0–3, 4–7, 8–11, . . . , and we thus obtain the following frequency table:

Number of missing rivets	Frequency
0– 3	6
4– 7	14
8–11	15
12–15	8
16–19	2
20 or more	5

Note that we replaced the six classes 16–19, 20–23, 24–27, 28–31, and 32–35, which would ordinarily have been needed, by a single class having no upper limit. This device of using an *open class* is sometimes used (especially in connection with skewed distributions) to eliminate the trouble of listing a large number of classes having very small frequencies. However, this exception to the general rule of using equal classes is to be employed only for the sake of clarity, and never in connection with any class except the first or the last.

6.2 Graphs of Frequency Distributions

Many important properties of frequency distributions, such as their symmetry or skewness, the number of their modes (maxima), and so on, are best exhibited by means of graphs. In this section we shall introduce some of the most widely used forms of graphical presentation of frequency distributions, percentage distributions, and cumulative distributions.

Referring to the frequency table of the iron-solution indices on page 106, we might present the information it contains graphically by first plotting the points (x_i, f_i), where x_i is the class mark of the ith class and f_i is the corresponding frequency, and then drawing straight-line segments to connect successive points. The resulting *frequency polygon* is shown in Figure 6.2; it should be noted that we added classes with zero frequencies at both ends of the distribution in order to "tie down" the graph to the horizontal axis. It is apparent from Figure 6.2 that the distribution of the iron-solution indices is nearly symmetrical and bell-shaped, somewhat resembling the graph of the normal distribution shown in Figure 4.2.

An alternate way of presenting a frequency distribution in graphical form is the *histogram*, first mentioned on page 38 in connection with probability distributions. The histogram of a frequency distribution is constructed like that of a probability distribution; the heights of the rec-

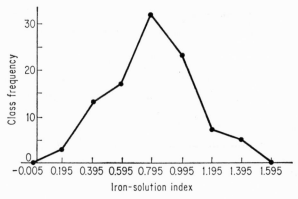

FIG. 6.2 Frequency polygon

tangles represent the class frequencies and the bases of the rectangles extend between successive class boundaries. A histogram of the iron-solution-index data is shown in Figure 6.3.

It is sometimes preferable to look upon the areas of the rectangles, rather than their heights, as representing the class frequencies of a histogram. This applies in particular to situations where we wish to approximate histograms with smooth curves or where there are classes of unequal length (see Exercise 17 on page 116).

Inspection of the graph of a frequency distribution often brings out features that are not immediately apparent from the data themselves. Aside from the fact that such a graph presents a good over-all picture of the data, it can also emphasize irregularities and unusual features. For instance, outlying observations which somehow do not fit the over-all picture, that is, the over-all pattern of the data, may be due to errors of measurement, equipment failure, and similar causes. Also, the fact that

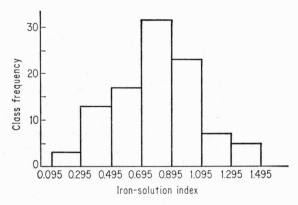

FIG. 6.3 Histogram

a histogram or a frequency polygon exhibits two or more *modes* (maxima) can provide pertinent information. The appearance of two modes may imply, for example, a shift in the process that is being measured, or it may imply that the data come from several sources. With some experience one learns to spot such irregularities or anomalies, and an experienced engineer would find it just as surprising if the histogram of a distribution of vacuum-tube failures were symmetrical as if a distribution of American men's hat sizes were bimodal.

Cumulative distributions are usually represented graphically by means of *ogives*. An ogive is similar to a frequency polygon, except that we plot the cumulative frequencies at the class boundaries instead of the ordinary frequencies at the class marks. The resulting points are again connected by means of straight-line segments, as shown in Figure 6.4, which repre-

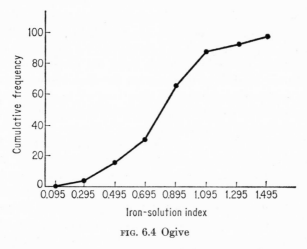

FIG. 6.4 Ogive

sents the cumulative "less than" distribution of the iron-solution index data.

Ogives are nearly always S-shaped, with the relative size of the two tails of the S determined by the symmetry or lack of symmetry of the distribution. If a distribution follows closely the pattern of a normal curve, it is possible to "straighten out" the S by using a special vertical scale, called a *probability scale*. This scale is so designed that any cumulative normal distribution will graph as a straight line. Special graph paper, called *arithmetic probability graph paper*, is commercially available; it has one arithmetic (ordinary) scale and one probability scale (see Figure 6.5). A graph of the cumulative "less than" percentage distribution of the iron-solution indices plotted on probability graph paper is shown in Figure 6.5. Note that the cumulative percentages are plotted at the corresponding class boundaries.

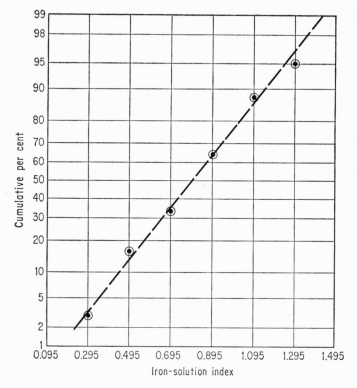

FIG. 6.5 Normal probability graph—grouped data

To check for "normality," probability graph paper can also be used directly with ungrouped data. In that case we first arrange the observations according to size, and if there are n observations we plot $\dfrac{(i - 1/2)}{n} \cdot 100$ or $\dfrac{(100i - 50)}{n}$ per cent on the vertical scale corresponding to the ith largest observation (see Exercise 16 on page 116). If n is large, it is not necessary to plot every point; every fifth or tenth point will generally suffice to check whether the data will fall close to a straight line, that is, whether their distribution follows closely the pattern of a normal distribution. A probability graph of the ungrouped iron-solution index data, plotted for every tenth observation starting with the first, and also the largest observation, is shown in Figure 6.6. It is evident from this graph that the data are approximately normally distributed.

In view of the symmetry of the normal distribution, the mean of the normal distribution which approximates the distribution of the iron-solution indices can be obtained by reading off the horizontal scale of Figure

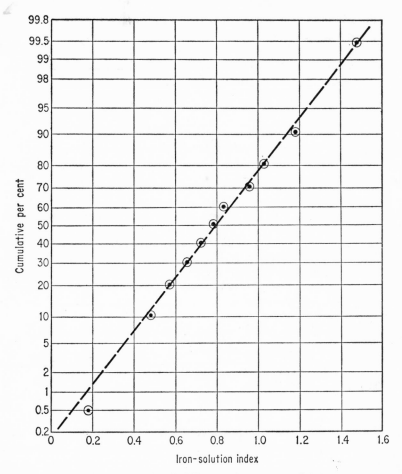

FIG. 6.6 Normal probability graph—ungrouped data

6.5 or Figure 6.6 the iron-solution index which corresponds to 50% on the vertical scale using Figure 6.6, we obtain 0.80. We can also approximate the standard deviation of this distribution by taking the difference between the iron-solution indices which on the probability scale correspond to 84% and 50%. Using the graph of Figure 6.6, we obtain 0.24.

It must be understood that the use of probability graph paper, which should really be called *normal* probability graph paper, is only an approximate (and highly subjective) device for checking whether a distribution follows the pattern of a normal curve. Only large and obvious departures from linearity in such a graph are real evidence that the data do not follow the pattern of a normal curve.

Sometimes other special scales are used to graph cumulative distributions. For example, if it is suspected that a set of data follows the pattern of a log-normal distribution, probability graph paper with a logarithmic scale can be used. Such paper is also commercially available. Various other scales have been devised for checking whether data follow the patterns of corresponding theoretical distributions.

EXERCISES

1. The weights of certain casings are given to the nearest tenth of a pound, the smallest and the largest being 15.1 and 30.9, respectively. Construct a table with 8 equal classes into which these weights might be grouped. Give the class interval, the class limits, the class boundaries, and the class marks.

2. The burning times of a solid-fuel rocket are given to the nearest millisecond, the smallest and the largest values being 4850 and 5072, respectively. Construct a table with 6 equal classes into which these figures might be grouped. Give the class interval, the class limits, the class boundaries, and the class marks.

3. The following are 100 measurements (in pounds per base box) of the tin-coating weights of electrolytic tin plate:

0.23	0.35	0.20	0.29	0.32	0.31	0.14	0.36	0.25	0.29
0.26	0.16	0.28	0.25	0.27	0.33	0.30	0.29	0.33	0.21
0.38	0.30	0.32	0.30	0.30	0.34	0.25	0.23	0.32	0.34
0.33	0.31	0.17	0.40	0.21	0.28	0.22	0.38	0.30	0.28
0.29	0.26	0.23	0.32	0.31	0.23	0.37	0.26	0.27	0.30
0.12	0.32	0.27	0.41	0.29	0.19	0.31	0.18	0.33	0.22
0.28	0.22	0.42	0.24	0.36	0.25	0.34	0.30	0.38	0.25
0.30	0.25	0.32	0.18	0.27	0.32	0.28	0.34	0.27	0.35
0.37	0.20	0.25	0.35	0.44	0.36	0.21	0.33	0.30	0.48
0.26	0.40	0.24	0.29	0.31	0.28	0.33	0.39	0.35	0.33

Group these measurements into a distribution having a class interval of 0.05 and construct a histogram.

4. Convert the distribution of Exercise 3 into a cumulative "less than" distribution and graph its ogive.

5. Convert the cumulative distribution of Exercise 4 into a cumulative percentage distribution and, plotting its graph on arithmetic probability paper, check whether it is reasonable to approximate this distribution by a normal distribution.

6. The following are the 1963 incomes (in dollars) of 80 families living in a rural community:

1920	11750	1420	7350	12800	2800	9450	6850
6250	1200	4710	9200	7860	1760	2650	5210
8750	2500	2460	4500	3620	5110	4720	9700
7400	5620	8800	6770	5840	3490	6750	4900
2320	1790	2110	3240	1470	6400	6900	1700
6430	2460	3100	4560	3750	5920	5500	3780
5150	3810	5120	10600	4540	7950	3870	7410
1380	8640	1520	5330	6200	3900	4790	11250
4190	5400	2200	6370	4320	4110	1580	5090
6430	9650	4040	5920	2510	8790	2580	7600

Group these figures into a suitable number of equal classes and construct a frequency polygon.

7. Convert the distribution of Exercise 6 into a cumulative "less than" percentage distribution and plot its ogive.

8. Plot the cumulative percentage distribution of Exercise 7 on arithmetic as well as logarithmic probability graph paper. What do these graphs suggest about the form of the distribution? (If logarithmic probability paper is not available, plot the logarithms of the class boundaries on arithmetic probability paper.)

9. The following are 15 measurements of the compressive strength of steel specimens (in pounds per square inch):

40,150	65,100	49,500	22,400	38,200
60,400	43,400	26,350	31,200	55,600
47,250	73,200	35,900	45,250	52,400

Plot the data directly on arithmetic probability paper and indicate whether they follow the pattern of a normal distribution.

10. The following are the speeds (in miles per hour) of 120 cars passing a radar check point on an interstate highway:

64	82	60	86	63	56	69	43	60	42	53	107
50	35	77	47	62	81	72	79	75	64	57	86
59	55	65	76	51	75	67	52	87	49	65	46
75	64	62	85	93	54	81	76	57	64	91	73
98	85	78	96	84	60	90	84	60	73	67	50
72	52	95	70	48	59	62	37	65	76	45	70
63	60	41	88	66	67	78	73	54	75	66	50
49	99	76	68	80	48	82	69	70	72	79	57
74	74	70	73	65	72	54	75	74	58	69	73
55	80	53	71	103	65	74	57	63	69	65	58

Group these data into a suitable frequency table and plot its histogram.

11. Convert the distribution obtained in Exercise 10 into a cumulative "less than" percentage distribution and plot its ogive.

12. Plot the cumulative distribution of Exercise 11 on arithmetic probability graph paper and interpret the result.

13. The following are the numbers of imperfections observed in 50 standard samples taken from bolts of cloth:

2	0	4	4	1	4	0	3	2	0
0	1	1	1	0	1	2	4	1	1
1	5	2	2	5	3	4	0	4	0
0	0	3	0	1	4	2	1	2	0
3	1	3	4	2	0	5	6	3	2

(a) Group these data into a frequency table showing how often each of the numbers occurred.

(b) Construct a cumulative "or more" distribution and draw its ogive.

14. Categorical frequency distributions are often represented graphically by means of *pie charts* in which a circle is divided into sectors proportional in size to the frequencies with which the data are distributed among the categories. Construct a pie chart to represent the following distribution:

Physical science major	Number of B.A. degrees conferred in the U.S. in 1960
Engineering	37,808
Mathematics	11,437
Chemistry	7,603
Physics	4,308
Geology	2,428
Geography	973

What might be a suitable caption for this chart?

15. The *pictogram* of Figure 6.7 is intended to illustrate the fact that, in a certain area, average family income has doubled from $3000 in 1950 to $6000 in 1960. Does this pictogram convey a "fair" impression of the actual increase in family income? If not, state how it should be modified.

16. Given a set of observations $x_1, x_2, \ldots,$ and x_n, we define their *empirical cumulative distribution* as the function whose values $F(x)$ equal the proportion of the observations less than or equal to x.

(a) Graph the empirical cumulative distribution for the 15 sample values of Exercise 9.

(b) Verify that the method of curve fitting used on page 112 (the check for "normality" for ungrouped data) amounts to plotting points corresponding to the *midpoints* of the steps of the empirical cumulative distribution.

17. Convert the distribution of iron-solution indices on page 106 into a distribution having the classes 0.10–0.29, 0.30–0.89, 0.90–1.29, and 1.30–1.49. Draw two histograms of this distribution, one in which the class frequencies

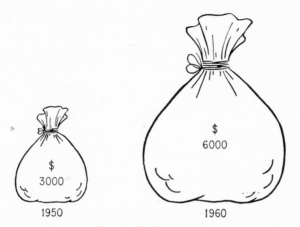

Average family income

FIG. 6.7 Average family income

are given by the *heights* of the rectangles and one in which the class frequencies are given by the *areas* of the rectangles. Why does the first of these histograms give a very misleading picture?

6.3 Descriptive Measures

In Section 3.5 we introduced the mean and the variance of a probability distribution as parameters which measure its center and its spread. In this section we shall define corresponding measures to describe a set of data or its distribution.

Given a set of n measurements or observations, $x_1, x_2, \ldots, x_n$, there are several ways in which we can describe their center (middle, or central location). Foremost among these are the *arithmetic mean* and the *median*, although other kinds of "averages" are sometimes used for special purposes. The arithmetic mean or, more succinctly, the *mean* is defined by the formula

$$\bar{x} = \frac{\sum\limits_{i=1}^{n} x_i}{n}$$

Note that we have written the mean of the x's as $\bar{x}$ and not as μ, the symbol we used for the mean of a probability distribution (or probability density). In this connection, we shall follow the general practice of using Latin letters to denote descriptions of actual data and Greek letters to denote descriptions of theoretical distributions. It is also of interest to note that the above formula would yield the mean of the distribution of a random variable which assumes the values x_i with equal probabilities of $1/n$.

Sometimes it is preferable to use the *median* as a descriptive measure of the center, or location, of a set of data. This is true, particularly, if it is desired to reduce all calculations to a minimum or if it is desired to eliminate the effect of extreme (very large or very small) values. The median of n observations $x_1, x_2, \ldots, x_n$ can be defined loosely as the "middlemost" value once the data are arranged according to size. More precisely, if the observations are arranged according to size and n is an odd number, the median is the value of the observation numbered $\frac{n+1}{2}$; if n is an even number, the median is defined as the mean (average) of the observations numbered $\frac{n}{2}$ and $\frac{n+2}{2}$. Thus, the median of the five observations 5, 4, 2, 7, 3 is 4 (the value of the third-largest observation) and the median of the six observations 7, 2, 5, 9, 4, 6 is 5.5 (the mean of the third- and fourth-largest observations).

Although the mean and the median each provides a single number to represent an entire set of data, the mean is usually preferred in problems of estimation and other problems of statistical inference. An intuitive reason for preferring the mean is that the median does not utilize all the information contained in the observations. A related reason is that the median is generally subject to greater chance fluctuations, that is, it is apt to vary more from sample to sample. This important concept of "sampling variability" will be explored in detail in Chapter 7.

To give one example where the median actually gives a better *description* than the mean, suppose an employer claims that the mean annual salary paid to engineers in his firm is \$15,000. This gives the impression that this firm is a good place to work. However, on further examination it turns out that it is a small company which employs four young engineers at \$5000 each, plus the owner whose income is \$55,000. Thus, the income distribution is highly skewed, its mean of \$15,000 really represents nothing useful, while the median income of \$5000 is at least representative of what a young engineer can expect to earn with this firm.

The *variance* of n observations $x_1, x_2, \ldots, x_n$ measures essentially the average of their squared deviations from their mean, $\bar{x}$, and it is defined by the formula

$$s^2 = \frac{\sum\limits_{i=1}^{n}(x_i - \bar{x})^2}{n-1}$$

There are several reasons for using the divisor $n-1$ instead of n. First, only $n-1$ of the deviations from the mean, $x_i - \bar{x}$, are *independent*, since their sum is always equal to zero (see Exercise 1 on page 123). In other words, $n-1$ of the deviations from the mean automatically determine the nth. Another reason is that if we look upon the x's as values assumed by some random variable, division by $n-1$ in the formula for s^2 makes this variance a *better* estimate of σ^2, the variance of the distribution of this random variable. We shall say more about this in Chapters 8 and 9.

Consistent with the terminology of Chapters 3 and 4, we define the *standard deviation* of n observations $x_1, x_2, \ldots, x_n$ as the square root of their variance, namely, as

$$s = \sqrt{\frac{\sum_{i=1}^{n} (x_i - \bar{x})^2}{n-1}}$$

standard deviation

Note that if we had divided by n instead of by $n-1$, the resulting formula could have been used for the standard deviation of the distribution of a random variable which assumes the values x_i with equal probabilities of $1/n$.

The standard deviation and the variance are measures of *absolute variation*, that is, they measure the actual amount of variation present in a set of data, and they are dependent on the scale of measurement. To compare the variation in several sets of data, it is generally desirable to use measures of *relative variation;* for this purpose we use the so-called *coefficient of variation*

$$CV = \frac{s}{\bar{x}} \cdot 100$$

Note that this measure, which gives the standard deviation as a percentage of the mean, is independent of the scale of measurement. Thus, if a set of data has $\bar{x} = 12.0$ and $s = 1.5$, the coefficient of variation is $CV = 12.5$ per cent; in other words, the standard deviation is 12.5 per cent of the mean.

In this section, we have limited the discussion to the mean, the median, the variance, and the standard deviation. There are, of course, many other ways of describing sets of data. For instance, if we want to determine a value below which we find the lowest 25 per cent of data, we calculate the *first quartile* Q_1; if we want to determine a value above which we find the highest 5 per cent of the data, we calculate the *ninety-fifth percentile* P_{95}; and so on. The calculation of such measures will be discussed in detail in Section 11.2. We may also have occasion to use other measures of variability, perhaps a *sample range* (the largest value minus the smallest), an *average deviation*, or an *interquartile range*. As need arises, new ways and new methods of describing statistical data are constantly being developed.

6.4 The Calculation of $\bar{x}$ and s

In this section we shall discuss methods for calculating $\bar{x}$ and s for raw (ungrouped) as well as grouped data. The methods we shall employ are particularly well-suited for desk calculators, and they are both rapid and accurate.

The calculation of $\bar{x}$ for *ungrouped data* does not pose any problems; we have only to add the values of the observations and divide by n. On the other hand, the calculation of s^2 is usually too cumbersome if we directly use the formula on page 118. Instead, we shall use the algebraically equivalent form

$$s^2 = \frac{n \cdot \sum\limits_{i=1}^{n} x_i^2 - \left(\sum\limits_{i=1}^{n} x_i\right)^2}{n(n-1)}$$

which has the dual advantage of requiring less labor and giving better accuracy. (In Exercise 3 on page 123 the reader will be asked to show that this formula is equivalent to the one on page 118.) The decrease in labor results from the fact that we do not actually have to calculate the deviations from the mean; the increase in accuracy is due to the reduction of the number of divisions and subtractions, and their postponement until the last two steps in the calculation. Another advantage of the above formula is that, using almost any desk calculator, one need scan the observations only once, setting each x-value in the keyboard, squaring, and accumulating the necessary sums of the x's and of their squares in one operation.

To illustrate the calculation of $\bar{x}$ and s let us find the mean and the standard deviation of the following 20 weight losses (in grams) of certain grinding balls:

0.094	0.108	0.114	0.132	0.128
0.117	0.099	0.093	0.105	0.119
0.126	0.122	0.125	0.115	0.097
0.113	0.109	0.111	0.130	0.120

Using a desk calculator, we find that the sum of these figures is 2.277 and that the sum of their squares is 0.261919. Consequently,

$$\bar{x} = \frac{2.277}{20} = 0.1138$$

and

$$s^2 = \frac{20(0.261919) - (2.277)^2}{20 \cdot 19} = 0.0001412$$

and it follows that $s = 0.0119$. Note that in computing the necessary sums we retained all decimal places, rounding off only at the end of the calculations to one more decimal than we had in the original data.

The calculations we have illustrated can be made even simpler by first *coding* the observations. Performing essentially a linear transformation, we can eliminate the decimal points by multiplying each weight loss by 1000; we can then make the resulting numbers smaller and easier to work with by (arbitrarily) subtracting 93 from each value. Instead of the original data we now have the coded values

1	15	21	39	35	24	6	0	12	26
33	29	32	22	4	20	16	18	37	27

which we shall refer to as u's. Calculating the mean and the standard deviation of the u's by the same method that we used before, we obtain 417 for the sum of the u's, 11,377 for the sum of their squares, and, hence,

$$\bar{u} = 20.85, \qquad s_u^2 = 141.2, \qquad s_u = 11.9$$

In order to *undo* the coding, let us observe that the x's and the u's are related by the equation

$$u_i = 1000x_i - 93 \qquad \text{or} \qquad x_i = 0.001u_i + 0.093$$

Continuing from here, simple algebra will show that $\bar{x} = 0.001\bar{u} + 0.093$ and $s_x^2 = (0.001)^2 s_u^2$, where s_x^2 and s_u^2 are, respectively, the variances of the x's and the u's. It will be left to the reader to verify that substituting $\bar{u} = 20.85$ and $s_u = 11.9$ into these formulas yields the previously obtained values $\bar{x} = 0.1138$ and $s_x = 0.0119$. In Exercise 5 on page 123, the reader will be asked to verify that, in general, when data are coded so that

$$x_i = c \cdot u_i + a$$

the corresponding formulas for the mean and the ~~variance~~ standard deviation are

$$\blacklozenge \qquad \bar{x} = c \cdot \bar{u} + a \qquad \text{and} \qquad s_x = c \cdot s_u \qquad \blacklozenge$$

To calculate $\bar{x}$ and s from *grouped data*, we shall have to make some assumption about the distribution of the values within each class. If we represent all values within a class by the corresponding class mark, the sum of the x's and the sum of their squares can now be written

$$\sum_{i=1}^{k} x_i f_i \qquad \text{and} \qquad \sum_{i=1}^{k} x_i^2 f_i$$

where x_i is the class mark of the ith class, f_i is the corresponding class frequency, and k is the number of classes in the distribution. Substituting these sums into the computing formulas for $\bar{x}$ and s^2, we obtain

$$\blacklozenge \qquad \bar{x} = \frac{\sum_{i=1}^{k} x_i f_i}{n} \qquad \blacklozenge$$

$$\blacklozenge \qquad s^2 = \frac{n \cdot \sum_{i=1}^{k} x_i^2 f_i - \left(\sum_{i=1}^{k} x_i f_i \right)^2}{n(n-1)} \qquad \blacklozenge$$

To illustrate, let us return to the frequency table of the iron-solution indices on page 106. Recording the class marks x_i in the first column, the frequencies f_i in the second column, and the products $x_i f_i$ and $x_i^2 f_i$ in the third and fourth columns, we obtain

x_i	f_i	$x_i f_i$	$x_i^2 f_i$
0.195	3	0.585	0.114075
0.395	13	5.135	2.028325
0.595	17	10.115	6.018425
0.795	32	25.440	20.224800
0.995	23	22.885	22.770575
1.195	7	8.365	9.996175
1.395	5	6.975	9.730125
	100	79.500	70.882500

Substituting $n = 100$ and the necessary sums into the formulas for $\bar{x}$ and s, we obtain

$$\bar{x} = \frac{79.500}{100} = 0.795$$

and

$$s^2 = \frac{100(70.8825) - (79.5)^2}{100 \cdot 99} = 0.078$$

These calculations were very tedious, and we went through them mainly to impress the reader with the simplifications that can be attained by *coding*, in this case coding the class marks. The coding we use in connection with distributions is to represent the class marks with successive integers, preferably with 0 near the center of the distribution or near the class which has the highest frequency. Coding the class marks of our distribution as $-3, -2, -1, 0, 1, 2, 3$, and referring to these coded class marks as u's, the above computing table reduces to

u_i	f_i	$u_i f_i$	$u_i^2 f_i$
-3	3	-9	27
-2	13	-26	52
-1	17	-17	17
0	32	0	0
1	23	23	23
2	7	14	28
3	5	15	45
	100	0	192

and the mean and the variance of the u's are

$$\bar{u} = 0$$

$$s_u^2 = \frac{100(192) - (0)^2}{100 \cdot 99} = 1.939$$

Since the coding we used is such that $x_i = (0.20)u_i + 0.795$, the two formulas on page 121 yield $\bar{x} = 0.795$ and $s_x^2 = 0.078$, which agree with the previously found results. In general, if c is the class interval of a distribution and x_0 is the class mark to which we assign 0 in the new scale, the coding is given by $x_i = c \cdot u_i + x_0$ and, hence, the formulas for the mean and the standard deviation are

$$\bar{x} = c \cdot \bar{u} + x_0 \qquad \text{and} \qquad s_x = c \cdot s_u$$

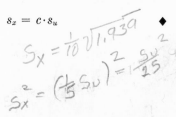

EXERCISES

1. Show that $\displaystyle\sum_{i=1}^{n} (x_i - \bar{x}) = 0$.

2. The following are the numbers of workers absent from a certain plant on 10 consecutive working days: 12, 17, 24, 15, 16, 8, 13, 21, 30, and 14.

    (a) Find the mean.

    (b) Find the median.

    (c) Find s using the formula on page 118.

    (d) Find s using the computing formula on page 120.

3. Show that the formula for s^2 given on page 120 is equivalent to the one given on page 118.

4. The following are 20 temperature readings taken at various locations in a large kiln (in degrees Fahrenheit):

    415, 510, 460, 475, 480, 410, 425, 490, 500, 470
    450, 445, 485, 470, 450, 455, 460, 480, 475, 465

    (a) Find $\bar{x}$.

    (b) Find the variance.

    (c) Find the coefficient of variation.

5. If data are coded so that $x_i = cu_i + a$ (see page 121), show that

$$\bar{x} = c \cdot \bar{u} + a \qquad \text{and} \qquad s_x = c \cdot s_u$$

6. Rework Exercise 4 by using the coding $u = \dfrac{x}{5} - 80$ and compare the results.

7. Calculate $\bar{x}$ and s for the data of Exercise 9 on page 115.

8. Without grouping, calculate $\bar{x}$ and s for the data of Exercise 13 on page 116.

9. Using the grouping obtained in Exercise 13 on page 116, calculate $\bar{x}$ and s, and compare with the results of Exercise 8.

10. Referring to the data of Exercise 3 on page 114, calculate $\bar{x}$ for the ungrouped as well as the grouped data and compare the results.

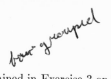

11. Using the grouping obtained in Exercise 3 on page 114, calculate s.

12. Using the grouping obtained in Exercise 10 on page 115, calculate the mean and the standard deviation of the 120 speeds.

13. If k sets of data consist, respectively, of $n_1, n_2, \ldots, n_k$ observations and have the means $\bar{x}_1, \bar{x}_2, \ldots, \bar{x}_k$, then the over-all mean of all the data is given by the formula

$$\bar{x} = \frac{\sum\limits_{i=1}^{k} n_i \bar{x}_i}{\sum\limits_{i=1}^{k} n_i}$$

(a) The average annual salaries paid to top-level management in three companies are \$24,000, \$32,000, and \$29,000. If the respective numbers of executives in these companies are 6, 15, and 9, find the average salary paid to these 30 executives.

(b) Prove the above formula for the over-all mean of the combined data.

14. The formula of Exercise 13 is a special case of the following formula for computing *weighted means:*

$$\bar{x}_w = \frac{\sum\limits_{i=1}^{k} w_i x_i}{\sum\limits_{i=1}^{k} w_i}$$

where w_i is a weight indicating the relative importance of the ith observation. Use this formula to determine a caterer's average cost per lunch box, if he prepares 1500 lunch boxes for a company picnic, packaging 800 at a cost of \$1.20 each, 500 at a cost of \$0.95 each, and 200 at a cost of \$1.10 each.

7 SAMPLING DISTRIBUTIONS

7.1 Populations and Samples

Usage of the term "population" in statistics is a carry-over from the days when statistics was applied mainly to sociological and economic phenomena. Nowadays, it is applied to any set or collection of objects, actual or conceptual, and mainly to sets of numbers, measurements, or observations. For example, if we are interested in determining the average number of television sets per household in the United States, the totality of these figures, one for each household, constitutes the population for this study. Similarly, the population from which inspectors draw a sample to determine some quality characteristic of a manufactured product may be the corresponding measurements for all units in a given lot; depending on the objectives of the inspection, it may also consist of the corresponding measurements for *all* units that may conceivably be manufactured.

In some cases, such as the above example concerning the number of television sets per household, the population is *finite;* in other cases, such as the determination of some characteristic of all units, past, present, and future, that might conceivably be manufactured by a given process, it is convenient to think of the population as *infinite.* Similarly, we look upon the results obtained in a series of flips of a coin as a sample from the hypothetically *infinite* population consisting of all conceivably possible flips of the coin.

Populations are often described by the distributions of their values, and it is common practice to refer to a population in terms of this distribution. (For finite populations, we are referring here to the actual distribution of its values; for infinite populations, we are referring to the corresponding probability distribution or probability density.) For example, we may refer to a number of flips of a coin as a sample from a "binomial population" or to certain measurements as a sample from a "normal population." Hereafter, when referring to a "population $f(x)$" we shall mean a population such that its elements have a frequency distribution, a probability distribution, or a density with values given by $f(x)$.

If a population is infinite it is impossible to observe all its values, and even if it is finite it may be impractical or uneconomical to observe it in its entirety. Thus, it is usually necessary to use a sample, a part of a population, and infer from it results pertaining to the entire population. Clearly, such results can be useful only if the sample is in some way "representative" of the population. It would be unreasonable, for instance, to expect useful generalizations about the population of 1964 family incomes in the United States on the basis of data pertaining to home owners only. Similarly, we can hardly expect reasonable generalizations about the performance of a tire if it is tested only on smooth roads. To assure that a sample is representative of the population from which it is obtained, and to provide a framework for the application of probability theory to problems of sampling, we shall confine the use of the term "sample" to so-called *random samples.* For sampling from finite populations, random samples are defined as follows:

A set of observations $x_1, x_2, \ldots, x_n$ constitutes a random sample of size n from a finite population of size N, if it is chosen so that each subset of n of the N elements of the population has the same probability of being selected.

Note that this definition of randomness pertains essentially to the manner in which the sample values are selected. This holds also for the following definition of a random sample from an infinite population:

A set of observations $x_1, x_2, \ldots, x_n$ constitutes a random sample of size n from the infinite population $f(x)$ if

(1) *each x_i is a value of a random variable whose distribution is given by $f(x)$,*

(2) *these n random variables are independent.*

There are several ways of assuring the selection of a sample that is at least approximately random. When dealing with a finite population, we can serially number the elements of the population and then select a sample with the aid of a table of random digits (see discussion on page 100). For example, if a population has $N = 500$ elements and we wish to select a random sample of size $n = 10$, we can use three arbitrarily selected columns of Table VII to obtain 10 different three-digit numbers less than or equal to 500, which will then serve as the serial numbers of those elements to be included in the sample. If the population size is large, the use of random numbers can become very laborious and at times practically impossible. For instance, if we want to test a sample of 5 shells from among the many thousands stored underground by the army, we can hardly be expected to number all the shells, make a selection with the use of random numbers, and then pull out the ones that were chosen. In a situation like this, we really have very little choice but to make the selection relatively haphazard, hoping that this will not seriously violate the assumption of randomness which is basic to most statistical theory.

When dealing with infinite populations, the situation is somewhat different since we cannot physically number the elements of the population; but efforts should be made to approach conditions of randomness by the use of artificial devices. For example, in selecting a sample from a production line we may be able to approximate conditions of randomness by choosing one unit each half hour; when tossing a coin we can try to flip it in such a way that neither side is intentionally favored, and so forth. The proper use of artificial or mechanical devices for selecting random samples is always preferable to human judgment, as it is extremely difficult to avoid unconscious biases when making almost any kind of selection.

Even with the careful choice of artificial devices, it is all too easy to commit gross errors in the selection of a random sample. To illustrate some of these pitfalls, suppose we have the task of selecting logs being fed into a sawmill by a constant-speed conveyer belt, for the purpose of obtaining a random sample of their lengths. One sampling device, which at first sight would seem to assure randomness, consists of measuring the logs which pass a given point at the end of a certain number of ten-minute intervals. However, further thought reveals that this method of selection favors the longer logs, since they require more time to pass the given point. Thus, the sample is not random since the longer logs have a better chance of being included. Another common mistake in selecting a sample is that of sampling from the wrong population or from a poorly specified population. As we have pointed out earlier, we would hardly get a sample from which we could generalize about family incomes in the United States if we limited our sample to home owners. Similarly, if we wanted to determine the effect of vibrations on a structural member, we should be careful to delineate the frequency band of vibrations that is of relevance, and to vibrate test specimens only at frequencies selected randomly from this band.

The purpose of most statistical investigations is to generalize from information contained in random samples about the population from which the samples were obtained. In particular, we are usually concerned with the problem of making inferences about the *parameters* of populations, such as the mean μ and the standard deviation σ. In making such inferences, we usually use *statistics* such as $\bar{x}$ and s, namely, quantities calculated on the basis of sample observations. Since the selection of a random sample is controlled largely by chance, so are the values we obtain for these statistics. The remainder of this chapter will be devoted to a discussion of *sampling distributions*—distributions which describe the chance fluctuations of statistics calculated on the basis of random samples.

7.2 The Sampling Distribution of the Mean (σ Known)

Suppose a random sample of n observations has been taken from some population and that $\bar{x}$ has been computed, say, to estimate the mean of the population. It should be clear that if we took a second random sample of size n from this population, it would be quite unreasonable to expect the identical value for $\bar{x}$, and if we took several more samples, probably no two of the $\bar{x}$'s would be alike. The differences among such $\bar{x}$'s are generally attributed to chance, and this raises important questions concerning their distribution, specifically concerning the extent of their chance fluctuations.

To approach this question experimentally, let us actually perform a simple experiment in which 50 random samples of size $n = 10$ are taken from a population having the *discrete uniform distribution*

$$f(x) = \begin{cases} \dfrac{1}{10} & \text{for } x = 0, 1, 2, \ldots, 9 \\ 0 & \text{elsewhere} \end{cases}$$

A convenient way of obtaining these samples is to use a table of random digits, like Table VII, letting each sample be a set of 10 consecutive digits in arbitrarily chosen columns. The means we actually obtained in these 50 samples are

4.4	3.2	5.0	3.5	4.1	4.4	3.6	6.5	5.3	4.4
3.1	5.3	3.8	4.3	3.3	5.0	4.9	4.8	3.1	5.3
3.0	3.0	4.6	5.8	4.6	4.0	3.7	5.2	3.7	3.8
5.3	5.5	4.8	6.4	4.9	6.5	3.5	4.5	4.9	5.3
3.6	2.7	4.0	5.0	2.6	4.2	4.4	5.6	4.7	4.3

and the following is a frequency table showing the distribution of these means:

$\bar{x}$	Frequency
2.0–2.9	2
3.0–3.9	14
4.0–4.9	19
5.0–5.9	12
6.0–6.9	3
	50

It is apparent from the histogram representing this distribution in Figure 7.1, that the distribution of the $\bar{x}$'s is fairly bell-shaped, even though the

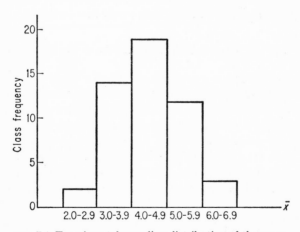

FIG. 7.1 Experimental sampling distribution of the mean

population itself has a uniform distribution. This raises the question whether this kind of result is typical of what we might expect in the long run; in other words, would we get a similar distribution if we took 100 samples, 1000 samples, or perhaps even more? To answer this kind of question, we shall have to investigate the *theoretical sampling distribution of $\bar{x}$* which, for the given example, provides us with the probabilities of getting $\bar{x}$'s between 2.0 and 2.9, between 3.0 and 3.9, . . . , between 6.0 and 6.9, and perhaps values less than 2.0 or greater than 6.9. Although we could actually evaluate these probabilities for this example, it is usually sufficient to refer to some general theorems concerning sampling distributions. The first of these, stated as follows, gives expressions for the mean and the variance of sampling distributions of $\bar{x}$:

THEOREM 7.1.   *If a random sample of size n is taken from a population having the mean μ and the variance σ^2, then $\bar{x}$ is a value of a random variable whose distribution has the mean μ. For samples from infinite populations the variance of this distribution is σ^2/n; for samples from finite populations of size N the variance is $\dfrac{\sigma^2}{n} \cdot \dfrac{N-n}{N-1}$.*

Writing $\mu_{\bar{x}}$ for the mean of the sampling distribution of $\bar{x}$, we shall first prove for the continuous case that $\mu_{\bar{x}} = \mu$. (The proof for the discrete case follows the identical steps, with integral signs replaced by Σ's.) Using the definition on page 84, we have

$$\mu_{\bar{x}} = \int_{-\infty}^{\infty} \int_{-\infty}^{\infty} \cdots \int_{-\infty}^{\infty} \sum_{i=1}^{n} \frac{x_i}{n} f(x_1, x_2, \ldots, x_n)\, dx_1\, dx_2 \ldots dx_n$$

$$= \frac{1}{n} \sum_{i=1}^{n} \int_{-\infty}^{\infty} \int_{-\infty}^{\infty} \cdots \int_{-\infty}^{\infty} x_i f(x_1, x_2, \ldots, x_n)\, dx_1\, dx_2 \ldots dx_n$$

where $f(x_1, x_2, \ldots, x_n)$ is a value of the joint density of the random variables whose values constitute the random sample. Using the assumption of randomness, we can write

$$f(x_1, x_2, \ldots, x_n) = f(x_1)f(x_2) \cdot \ldots \cdot f(x_n)$$

and we now have

$$\mu_{\bar{x}} = \frac{1}{n} \sum_{i=1}^{n} \int_{-\infty}^{\infty} f(x_1)\, dx_1 \cdot \ldots \cdot \int_{-\infty}^{\infty} x_i f(x_i)\, dx_i \cdot \ldots \cdot \int_{-\infty}^{\infty} f(x_n)\, dx_n$$

Since each integral except the one with the integrand $x_i f(x_i)$ equals 1, and the one with the integrand $x_i f(x_i)$ equals μ, we finally obtain

$$\mu_{\bar{x}} = \frac{1}{n} \sum_{i=1}^{n} \mu = \mu$$

and this completes the proof of the first part of the theorem.

To prove that for random samples from infinite populations $\sigma_{\bar{x}}^2$, the variance of the sampling distribution of $\bar{x}$, equals σ^2/n, we shall make the simplifying assumption that $\mu = 0$. As the reader will be asked to show in Exercise 9 on page 135, this does *not* involve any loss of generality; as a matter of fact, we stated a similar result on page 121, which showed that addition of a constant to each value does not affect the standard deviation (or the variance) of a set of data. Using the definition on page 84, we thus have

$$\sigma_{\bar{x}}^2 = \int_{-\infty}^{\infty} \int_{-\infty}^{\infty} \cdots \int_{-\infty}^{\infty} \bar{x}^2 f(x_1, x_2, \ldots, x_n)\, dx_1\, dx_2 \ldots dx_n$$

and making use of the fact that

$$\bar{x}^2 = \frac{1}{n^2} \left(\sum_{i=1}^{n} x_i \right)^2 = \frac{1}{n^2} \left(\sum_{i=1}^{n} x_i^2 + \sum\sum_{i \neq j} x_i x_j \right)$$

we obtain

$$\sigma_{\bar{x}}^2 = \frac{1}{n^2} \sum_{i=1}^{n} \int_{-\infty}^{\infty} \int_{-\infty}^{\infty} \cdots \int_{-\infty}^{\infty} x_i^2 f(x_1, x_2, \ldots, x_n)\, dx_1\, dx_2 \ldots dx_n$$

$$+ \frac{1}{n^2} \sum\sum_{i \neq j} \int_{-\infty}^{\infty} \int_{-\infty}^{\infty} \cdots \int_{-\infty}^{\infty} x_i x_j f(x_1, x_2, \ldots, x_n)\, dx_1\, dx_2 \ldots dx_n$$

where $\sum\sum_{i \neq j}$ extends over all i and j from 1 to n, not including the terms where $i = j$. Again using the fact that $f(x_1, x_2, \ldots, x_n) = f(x_1)f(x_2)\cdot \ldots \cdot f(x_n)$, we can write each of the above multiple integrals as a product of simple integrals, with each simple integral that has an integrand of the form $f(x)$ equalling 1. We thus obtain

$$\sigma_{\bar{x}}^2 = \frac{1}{n^2} \sum_{i=1}^{n} \int_{-\infty}^{\infty} x_i^2 f(x_i)\, dx_i + \frac{1}{n^2} \sum\sum_{i \neq j} \int_{-\infty}^{\infty} x_i f(x_i)\, dx_i \cdot \int_{-\infty}^{\infty} x_j f(x_j)\, dx_j$$

and since each integral in the first sum equals σ^2 while each integral in the second sum equals 0, we finally have

$$\sigma_{\bar{x}}^2 = \frac{1}{n^2} \sum_{i=1}^{n} \sigma^2 = \frac{\sigma^2}{n}$$

This completes the proof of the second part of the theorem. We shall not prove the corresponding result for random samples from finite populations, but it should be noted that in the resulting formula for $\sigma_{\bar{x}}^2$ the factor $\frac{N - n}{N - 1}$ is close to 1 (and can be omitted for most practical purposes) unless the sample constitutes a substantial portion of the population. For instance, if a random sample of size 10 is drawn from a population of size 1000, the factor $\frac{N - n}{N - 1}$, often called the *correction factor for finite populations*, equals approximately 0.991.

Although it is not very surprising that the mean of the theoretical sampling distribution of $\bar{x}$ equals the mean of the population, the fact that its variance equals σ^2/n, for random samples from infinite populations, is interesting and important. To point out its implications, let us apply Chebyshev's theorem to the sampling distribution of $\bar{x}$, substituting $\bar{x}$ for x and $\sigma/\sqrt{n}$ for σ in the inequality given on page 58. We thus obtain

$$P\left(|\bar{x} - \mu| \le \frac{k\sigma}{\sqrt{n}}\right) > 1 - 1/k^2$$

and letting $k\sigma/\sqrt{n} = \epsilon$, we get

$$P(|\bar{x} - \mu| \le \epsilon) > 1 - \frac{\sigma^2}{n\epsilon^2}$$

Thus, for any given $\epsilon > 0$, the probability that $\bar{x}$ differs from μ by at most ϵ can be made arbitrarily close to 1 by choosing n sufficiently large. In less rigorous language, the larger the sample size, the closer we can expect $\bar{x}$ to be to the mean of the population. In this sense we can say that $\bar{x}$ becomes more and more *reliable* as an estimate of μ as the sample size is increased. The reliability of $\bar{x}$ as an estimate of μ is often measured by the expression $\sigma/\sqrt{n}$, also called the *standard error of the mean*. Note that this measure of the reliability of $\bar{x}$ decreases in proportion to the *square root* of n; for example, it is necessary to *quadruple* the size of the sample in order to *halve* the standard deviation of the sampling distribution of the mean. This also indicates what might be called a "law of diminishing returns" so far as increasing the sample size is concerned. Usually it does not pay to take excessively large samples since the extra labor and expense is not accompanied by a proportional gain in reliability. For instance, if we increase the size of a sample from 25 to 2500, the errors to which we are exposed are reduced only by a factor of 10.

Let us now return to the experimental sampling distribution on page 129, and let us check how closely its mean and its variance correspond to the values we should expect in accordance with Theorem 7.1. Since the population from which the 50 samples of size 10 were obtained has the mean

$$\mu = \sum_{x=0}^{9} x \cdot \frac{1}{10} = 4.5$$

and the variance

$$\sigma^2 = \sum_{x=0}^{9} (x - 4.5)^2 \frac{1}{10} = 8.25$$

Theorem 7.1 leads us to expect a mean of $\mu_{\bar{x}} = 4.5$ and a variance of $\sigma_{\bar{x}}^2 = 8.25/10 = 0.825$. Calculating the mean and the variance from the frequency table on page 129, we obtain $\bar{x}_{\bar{x}} = 4.45$ and $s_{\bar{x}}^2 = 0.939$, which are reasonably close to the theoretical values.

Theorem 7.1 provides only partial information about the theoretical sampling distribution of the mean. In general, it is impossible to determine such a distribution exactly without knowledge of the actual form of the population, but it is possible to find the limiting distribution as $n \to \infty$ of a statistic closely related to $\bar{x}$ assuming only that the population has a finite variance σ^2. The statistic we are referring to here is the *standardized mean*

$$z = \frac{\bar{x} - \mu}{\sigma/\sqrt{n}}$$

namely, the difference between $\bar{x}$ and μ divided by the standard deviation of the sampling distribution of $\bar{x}$. With reference to this statistic we have the following theorem, called the *central limit theorem:*

THEOREM 7.2. *If $\bar{x}$ is the mean of a random sample of size n taken from a population having the mean μ and the finite variance σ^2, then*

 Central Limit
$$z = \frac{\bar{x} - \mu}{\sigma/\sqrt{n}}$$
Both Known

is the value of a random variable whose distribution function approaches that of the standard normal distribution as $n \to \infty$.

We shall not be able to prove this theorem in this text, but at least partial (experimental) verification may be obtained by plotting the cumu-

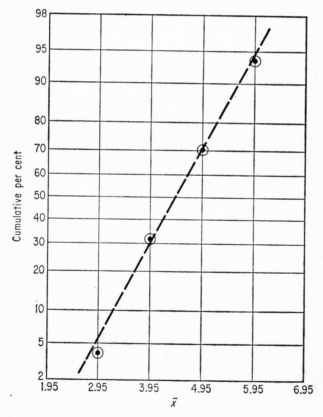

FIG. 7.2 Experimental verification of central limit theorem

lative percentage distribution corresponding to the distribution of Figure 7.1 on arithmetic probability paper. As can be seen from Figure 7.2, the points fall close to a straight line, and it seems that even for $n = 10$ the sampling distribution of $\bar{x}$ for this example follows the over-all pattern of a normal distribution. In practice, the normal distribution provides an excellent approximation to the sampling distribution of $\bar{x}$ for n as small as 25 or 30, with hardly any restrictions on the shape of the population. As we saw in our example, the sampling distribution of $\bar{x}$ had the general shape of a normal distribution even for samples of size 10 from a discrete uniform distribution, and this is true in general provided the shape of the population distribution is not too skewed. In fact, it can be shown that the sampling distribution of $\bar{x}$ is exactly normal (regardless of the size of the sample), when the sample is obtained from a normal population.

To illustrate the actual use of Theorem 7.2, suppose a random sample of size 100 is taken of the inner diameters of certain lengths of seamless pipe. If the mean and the standard deviation of such measurements are, respectively, $\mu = 34.1$ and $\sigma = 1.5$ inches, we may wish to know the probability that the mean of the sample will lie between 34.0 and 34.3 inches. By Theorem 7.2 we shall have to find the normal curve area between

$$z = \frac{34.0 - 34.1}{1.5/10} = -0.67 \quad \text{and} \quad z = \frac{34.3 - 34.1}{1.5/10} = 1.33$$

and checking these values in Table III we obtain a probability of 0.6568. Note also that if $\bar{x}$ had turned out to be much greater than 34.1, say, 34.5, there would have been serious doubt whether the sample actually came from a population having $\mu = 34.1$ and $\sigma = 1.5$; the probability of obtaining such a large mean (a z-value greater than 2.67) is only 0.0038.

EXERCISES

1. An inspector examines every tenth piece coming off an assembly line. List some of the conditions under which this method might not yield a random sample.

2. In 1932 the *Literary Digest* predicted the presidential election by random sampling from telephone directories and from its list of subscribers. The prediction was grossly incorrect; explain why.

3. A market research organization wants to try a new product in 5 of the 50 states. Use random numbers (Table VII) to make this selection.

4. Take 30 slips of paper and label five each −5 and 5, four each −4 and 4, three each −3 and 3, two each −2 and 2, and one each −1 and 1.

(a) If each slip of paper has the same probability of being drawn, find the probabilities of getting $-5, -4, -3, \ldots, 4, 5$, and find the mean and the variance of this distribution.

(b) Draw 50 samples of size 10 from this population, each sample being drawn without replacement, and calculate their means.

(c) Calculate the mean and the variance of the 50 means obtained in part (b).

(d) Compare the results obtained in part (c) with the corresponding values expected according to Theorem 7.1. (Note that μ and σ^2 were obtained in part (a).)

5. Repeat Exercise 4, but select each sample with replacement, that is, replace each slip of paper and reshuffle before the next one is drawn.

6. Use random numbers to take 100 random samples of size 5 from the infinite population having the distribution

x	$f(x)$
1	0.08
2	0.17
3	0.50
4	0.17
5	0.08

(a) Calculate the 100 means, group them, and determine the mean and the standard deviation of their distribution.

(b) Compare the results obtained in part (a) with the corresponding values expected according to Theorem 7.1.

7. Given the infinite population whose distribution is given by

x	$f(x)$
1	0.25
2	0.25
3	0.25
4	0.25

list the 16 possible samples of size 2 and use this list to construct the distribution of $\bar{x}$ for random samples of size 2 from the given population. Verify that the mean and the variance of this sampling distribution are identical with the corresponding values expected according to Theorem 7.1.

8. Prove that $\mu_{\bar{x}} = \mu$ for random samples from discrete populations.

9. If x is a value of a continuous random variable and $y = ax + b$, show that

(a) $\mu_y = a\mu_x + b$,

(b) $\sigma_y^2 = a^2\sigma_x^2$.

10. A random sample of size 64 is taken from an infinite population having the mean $\mu = 112$ and the variance $\sigma^2 = 144$. Use the central limit theorem to find the probability of getting an $\bar{x}$ greater than 114.5.

11. A random sample of size 100 is taken from an infinite population having the mean $\mu = 53$ and the variance $\sigma^2 = 400$. What is the probability of getting an $\bar{x}$ between 50 and 56?

12. A wire-bonding process is said to be in control if the mean pull strength is 10 lb. It is known that the pull-strength measurements are normally distributed with a standard deviation of 1.5 lb. Periodic random samples of size 4 are taken from this process and the process is said to be "out of control" if a sample mean is less than 7.75 lb. Comment.

13. If measurements of the specific gravity of a metal can be looked upon as a sample from a normal population having a standard deviation of 0.05, what is the probability that the mean of a random sample of size 16 will be "off" by at most 0.02?

14. The mean of the weights of 400 male adults residing in a certain community is used to estimate the "true" average weight of all adult males living in this community. If the standard deviation of measurements of this kind is known to be 18 pounds, what is the probability that this estimate is "off" by more than 2.5 pounds?

7.3 The Sampling Distribution of the Mean (σ Unknown)

Use of the theory of the preceding section requires knowledge of the population standard deviation σ. If n is large, it is reasonable to use this theory also when σ is unknown, substituting for it the sample standard deviation s. So far as the statistic $\dfrac{\bar{x} - \mu}{s/\sqrt{n}}$ is concerned, little is known about its exact distribution for small values of n unless we make the assumption that the sample comes from a *normal population*. Under this assumption, it is possible to prove the following theorem:

THEOREM 7.3. *If $\bar{x}$ is the mean of a random sample of size n taken from a normal population having the mean μ and the variance σ^2, then*

$$t = \frac{\bar{x} - \mu}{s/\sqrt{n}}$$

is the value of a random variable having the Student-t distribution with the parameter $\nu = n - 1$.*

---

* The Student-*t* distribution was first investigated in 1908 by W. S. Gosset, who published his findings under the pen name of "Student" because his employers did not permit the publication of research done by their staff.

This theorem is *more general* than Theorem 7.2 in the sense that it does not require knowledge of σ; on the other hand, it is *less general* than Theorem 7.2 in the sense that it requires the assumption of a normal population.

As can be seen from Figure 7.3, the over-all shape of a t distribution is

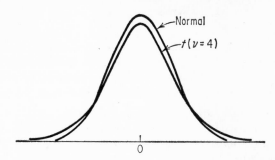

FIG. 7.3 Student-t and standard normal distributions

similar to that of a normal distribution—both are bell-shaped and symmetrical about the mean. Like the standard normal distribution, the t distribution has the mean 0, but its variance depends on the parameter ν (*nu*), called the *number of degrees of freedom*. The variance of the t distribution exceeds 1, but it approaches 1 as $n \to \infty$. In fact, it can be shown that the t distribution with ν degrees of freedom approaches the standard normal distribution as $\nu \to \infty$.

Table IV on page 399 contains selected values of t_α for various values of ν, where t_α is such that the area under the t distribution to its right is equal to α. In this table the left-hand column contains values of ν, the column headings are areas α in the right-hand tail of the t distribution, and the entries are values of t_α (see also Figure 7.4). It is not necessary to

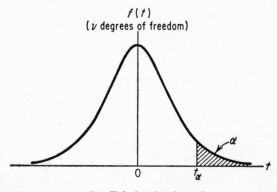

FIG. 7.4 Tabulated values of t

tabulate values of t_α for $\alpha > 0.50$, as it follows from the symmetry of the t distribution that $t_{1-\alpha} = -t_\alpha$; thus, the value of t that corresponds to a left-hand tail area of α is $-t_\alpha$.

Note that in the bottom row of Table IV the entries correspond to the values of z which cut off right-hand tails of area α under the standard normal curve. Using the notation z_α for such a value of z, it can be seen, for example, that $z_{.025} = 1.96 = t_{.025}$ for $\nu = \infty$. This result should really have been expected since the t distribution approaches the standard normal distribution as $\nu \to \infty$. In fact, observing that the values of t_α for 29 or more degrees of freedom are close to the corresponding values of z_α, we conclude that *the standard normal distribution provides a good approximation to the t distribution for samples of size 30 or more.*

To illustrate the use of the t distribution, suppose that a manufacturer of steel wire claims that the average force required to break a given kind of wire is 500 pounds. To test this claim, a sample of 25 lengths of this steel wire are stressed, and the mean and the standard deviation of the forces required to break these specimens are $\bar{x} = 465$ pounds and $s = 55$ pounds. On the assumption that the breaking strengths may be looked upon as a random sample from a normal population with $\mu = 500$, the statistic

$$t = \frac{465 - 500}{55/\sqrt{25}} = -3.18$$

is a value of a random variable having the t distribution with $\nu = 25 - 1 = 24$ degrees of freedom. Now, from Table IV we find that for $\nu = 24$ the probability that t will exceed 2.797 is 0.005 if $\mu = 500$, and hence we conclude that the probability that t will be less than -2.797 is also 0.005. Since the value we obtained for our sample is $t = -3.18$, we are faced with the following two alternatives: either it is true that $\mu = 500$ and we have observed a relatively rare event, or μ does not equal 500 (in fact, it is less than 500). Having to make a choice, we may well be inclined to accept the alternative that the true average force required to break this kind of wire is less than 500 pounds.

The assumption that the sample must come from a normal population is not so severe a restriction as it may first seem. Studies have shown that the distribution of the statistic $t = \dfrac{\bar{x} - \mu}{s/\sqrt{n}}$ is fairly close to a t distribution even for samples from certain nonnormal populations. In practice, it is necessary to make sure primarily that the population from which we are sampling is approximately bell-shaped and not too skewed. A practical way of checking this assumption is to plot the observations on arithmetic probability paper as described on page 112. [If such a plot shows a distinct curve rather than a straight line, it may be possible to "straighten it out" by transforming the data—say, by taking their logarithms or their square roots.]

7.4 The Sampling Distribution of the Variance

So far we have discussed only sampling distributions of the mean, but if we had taken the medians, the ranges, or the standard deviations of the 50 samples mentioned on page 129, we would similarly have obtained experimental sampling of these statistics. In this section we shall be concerned with the theoretical sampling distribution of s^2 for random samples from normal populations. Since s^2 cannot be negative, we should expect that this sampling distribution is *not* a normal curve; in fact, it is related to a *gamma distribution* with the parameters $\alpha = \nu/2$ and $\beta = 2$ (see page 78), called the *chi-square distribution*. Specifically, we have

THEOREM 7.4. *If s^2 is the variance of a random sample of size n taken from a normal population having the variance σ^2, then*

$$\chi^2 = \frac{(n-1)s^2}{\sigma^2}$$

is a value of a random variable having the chi-square distribution with the parameter $\nu = n - 1$.

Table V on page 400 contains selected values of χ_α^2 for various values of ν, again called the *number of degrees of freedom*, where χ_α^2 is such that the area under the chi-square distribution to its right is equal to α. In this table the left-hand column contains values of ν, the column headings are areas α in the right-hand tail of the chi-square distribution, and the entries are values of χ_α^2 (see also Figure 7.5.) Unlike the t distribution, it is neces-

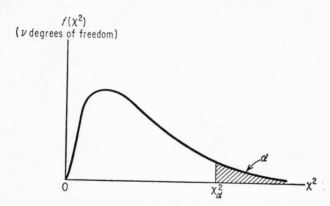

FIG. 7.5 Tabulated values of chi-square

sary to tabulate values of χ_α^2 for $\alpha > 0.50$, because the chi-square distribution is not symmetrical.

To illustrate the use of Theorem 7.4, suppose an optical firm purchases glass to be ground into lenses, and that past experience has shown that the variance of the refractive index of this kind of glass is $1.26 \cdot 10^{-4}$. To grind the glass into lenses having a given focal length, it is important that the various pieces of glass have nearly the same index of refraction; hence, let us suppose that such a shipment of glass is to be rejected if the sample variance of 20 pieces selected at random exceeds $2.00 \cdot 10^{-4}$. Assuming that the sample values may be looked upon as coming from a normal population with $\sigma^2 = 1.26 \cdot 10^{-4}$, the probability that a shipment will be *erroneously* rejected may be computed as follows. First we obtain

$$\chi^2 = \frac{19(2.00 \cdot 10^{-4})}{1.26 \cdot 10^{-4}} = 30.2$$

and then we find from Table V that for 19 degrees of freedom $\chi_{.05}^2 = 30.1$. Thus, the probability that a good shipment will erroneously be rejected by this criterion is less than 0.05.

A problem closely related to that of finding the distribution of the sample variance is that of finding the distribution of the *ratio* of the variances of two independent random samples. This problem is important because it arises in tests in which we want to determine whether two samples come from populations having equal variances. If they do, the two sample variances should be nearly the same; that is, their ratio should be close to 1. To determine whether the ratio of two sample variances is too small or too large, we use the theory given in the following theorem:

THEOREM 7.5. *If s_1^2 and s_2^2 are the variances of independent random samples of size n_1 and n_2, respectively, taken from two normal populations having the same variance, then*

$$F = \frac{s_1^2}{s_2^2}$$

is a value of a random variable having the F distribution with the parameters $\nu_1 = n_1 - 1$ and $\nu_2 = n_2 - 1$.

The F distribution has the two parameters ν_1, the *degrees of freedom for the sample variance in the numerator*, and ν_2, the *degrees of freedom for the sample variance in the denominator;* when referring to a particular F distribution, we always give first the degrees of freedom for the numerator. As it would require too large a table to give values of F_α corresponding to many different right-hand tail areas α, and since $\alpha = 0.05$ and $\alpha = 0.01$ are most commonly used, Table VI contains only values of $F_{.05}$ and $F_{.01}$ for various combinations of values of ν_1 and ν_2 (see also Figure 7.6).

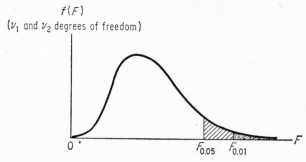

FIG. 7.6 Tabulated values of F

It is possible to use Table VI also to find values of F corresponding to left-hand tails of area 0.05 and 0.01. Writing $F_\alpha(\nu_1, \nu_2)$ for F_α with ν_1 and ν_2 degrees of freedom, we simply use the identity

$$F_{1-\alpha}(\nu_1, \nu_2) = \frac{1}{F_\alpha(\nu_2, \nu_1)}$$

Thus, to find F_α for 10 and 20 degrees of freedom and $\alpha = 0.95$, we have only to write

$$F_{.95}(10, 20) = \frac{1}{F_{.05}(20, 10)} = \frac{1}{2.77} = 0.36$$

Note that Theorem 7.4 as well as Theorem 7.5 requires the assumption that we are sampling from normal populations. As in the case of the t distribution, this assumption can be loosened somewhat in actual practice without materially altering the respective sampling distributions. Again, the use of arithmetic probability paper is suggested to investigate whether it is reasonable to treat the samples as coming from normal populations.

EXERCISES

1. A random sample of size 16 from a normal population has the mean 48 and the standard deviation 5.2. Basing your decision on the t statistic, is it reasonable to say that this information supports the claim that the mean of the population is at least 52?

2. The following are the down times of a computer (in hours) during each of 5 consecutive months: 28, 15, 19, 30, 23. Use the t statistic to check the reasonableness of the claim that *on the average* the computer can be expected to be out of commission at most 20 hours per month.

3. A process for making compression springs is under control if the free lengths of the springs have a mean of 2.5 cm. What can we say about this process if

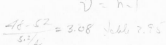

a sample of 10 of these springs has a mean of 2.53 cm and a standard deviation of 0.02 cm?

4. The claim that the variance of a normal population is $\sigma^2 = 64$ is rejected if the variance of a random sample of size 17 exceeds 115.38. What is the probability that the claim is rejected even though $\sigma^2 = 64$?

5. A random sample of 27 observations is taken from a normal population having the variance $\sigma^2 = 16.8$. Find the approximate probability of obtaining a sample standard deviation between 3.0 and 5.2.

6. If two independent random samples of size $n_1 = 21$ and $n_2 = 20$ are taken from a normal population, approximate the probability that the variance of the first sample will be at least 3 times as large as the variance of the second sample.

7. Referring to Exercise 6, find the probability that *either* sample variance will be 3 times as large as the other.

8. The t distribution with 1 degree of freedom is given by

$$f(t) = \frac{1}{\pi} (1 + t^2)^{-1} \qquad -\infty < t < \infty$$

Verify the corresponding value of $t_{.05}$ in Table IV.

9. The chi-square distribution with 4 degrees of freedom is given by

$$f(x) = \begin{cases} \frac{1}{4} \cdot x \cdot e^{-x/2} & x > 0 \\ 0 & x \le 0 \end{cases}$$

Find the probability that the variance of a random sample of size 5 from a normal population with $\sigma = 10$ exceeds 120.

10. The F distribution with 4 and 4 degrees of freedom is given by

$$f(F) = \begin{cases} 6F(1 + F)^{-4} & F > 0 \\ 0 & F \le 0 \end{cases}$$

If random samples of size 5 are taken from two normal populations having the same variance, find the probability that the ratio of the larger to the smaller sample variance exceeds 2.

8 | INFERENCES CONCERNING MEANS

8.1 Point Estimation

On page 128 we stated that statistical inference concerns methods by which information obtained from random samples is used to make generalizations about the populations from which the samples were obtained. In the classical approach to statistical inference, these methods are divided into the major areas of *estimation* and *tests of hypotheses*, with estimation subdivided further into *point estimation* and *interval estimation*. More recently, the methods of statistical inference have been unified under the general concepts of *decision theory*, that is, under the general concepts of decision making in the face of uncertainty. In this section we shall discuss the general problem of point estimation, applying it to the estimation of a population mean, μ, with the mean of a random sample. Basically, point estimation concerns the choosing of a *statistic*, a single number calculated from sample data (and perhaps other information), for which we have some expectation, or assurance, that it is "reasonably close" to the parameter it is supposed to estimate. To explain what we mean here by "reasonably close" is not an easy task; first, the value of the parameter is unknown, and second, the value of the statistic is unknown until after the sample has been obtained. Thus, we can only ask whether, upon repeated sampling, the distribution of the statistic has certain desirable properties akin to "closeness." For instance, we know from Theorem 7.1 that the sampling distribution of $\bar{x}$ has the same mean as the population from which the sample is obtained; hence, we can expect that the means of repeated random samples from a given population will center on the mean of this population and not about some other value. To formulate this property more generally, let us now make the following definition:

A statistic $\hat{\theta}$ is said to be an unbiased estimate of the parameter θ if and only if the mean of its sampling distribution is equal to θ.

Thus, we call a statistic unbiased if "on the average" its values can be expected to equal the parameter it is supposed to estimate.

Generally speaking, the property of unbiasedness is one of the more desirable properties in point estimation, although it is by no means essential and it is sometimes outweighed by other factors. One shortcoming of the criterion of unbiasedness is that it will generally not provide a *unique* statistic for a given problem of estimation. For example, it can be shown that for random samples of size 2 the mean $\dfrac{x_1 + x_2}{2}$ as well as the weighted mean $\dfrac{ax_1 + bx_2}{a + b}$, where a and b are positive constants, are unbiased estimates of the mean of the population, and so are the sample median and the midrange (the mean of the largest value and the smallest) if we assume, furthermore, that the population is symmetric. This suggests that we must seek a further criterion for deciding which of several unbiased estimates is "best" for estimating a given parameter.

Such a criterion becomes evident when we compare the sampling distributions of the mean and the median for random samples of size n taken from the same *normal* population. Although these two distributions have the same mean, namely, the population mean μ, and although they are both symmetrical and bell-shaped, *their variances differ.* In Theorem 7.1 we proved that for infinite populations the variance of the sampling distribution of the mean is σ^2/n, and it can be shown for the corresponding sampling distribution of the median that its variance is approximately $1.57 \cdot \sigma^2/n$. Thus, it is more likely for any given sample that the mean will be closer to μ than the median. Note that this does not imply that the sample mean is necessarily always closer than the median; in fact, in any given problem we have no way of knowing which is actually closer.

This important property, in which we compare the variances of the sampling distributions of statistics, is formalized by means of the following definition:

A statistic $\hat{\theta}_1$ is said to be a more efficient unbiased estimate of the parameter θ than the statistic $\hat{\theta}_2$, if

(1) *$\hat{\theta}_1$ and $\hat{\theta}_2$ are both unbiased estimates of θ,*

(2) *the variance of the sampling distribution of $\hat{\theta}_1$ is less than the variance of the sampling distribution of $\hat{\theta}_2$.*

We have, thus, seen that for random samples from normal populations the mean is more efficient than the median as an estimate of μ; in fact, it can be shown that in most situations met in actual practice the variance of the sampling distribution of no other statistic is less than that of the sampling distribution of the mean. In other words, in most practical situations the sample mean is an acceptable statistic for estimating a population mean μ. (There exist several other criteria for assessing the "goodness" of methods of point estimation, but we shall not discuss them in this book.)

The special properties discussed in this section are important, but they are sometimes outweighed by other considerations. For instance, if it is essential to consider collateral as well as direct information, it may be necessary to use the following kind of inference, called a *Bayesian inference*. A manufacturer receives electronic components from two different vendors. The first vendor supplies 80 per cent of the components and on the basis of long experience it is known that 1 per cent of his components are defective. The remaining 20 per cent are supplied by a second vendor whose percentage of defectives is known to be 2 per cent. Five components are taken from a lot stored in the manufacturer's warehouse and one of them is found to be defective. The sample proportion of defectives is 0.20, and if no other information were available, we would have to accept this figure as an estimate of the true proportion of defectives in the lot, even though the estimate is based on a very small sample. To improve the estimate, let us now make use of the collateral information concerning the two vendors and the rule of Bayes. Letting B_1 represent the event that the lot came from the first vendor, B_2 the event that the lot came from the second vendor, and A the event that a sample of size 5 includes exactly 1 defective, we have $P(B_1) = 0.80$, $P(B_2) = 0.20$,

$$P(A \mid B_1) = \binom{5}{1} (0.01)^1 (0.99)^4 = 0.048$$

and

$$P(A \mid B_2) = \binom{5}{1} (0.02)^1 (0.98)^4 = 0.092$$

Substituting these values into the formula for the rule of Bayes (see page 31), we obtain

$$P(B_1 \mid A) = \frac{(0.80)(0.048)}{(0.80)(0.048) + (0.20)(0.092)} = 0.68$$

and it follows that $P(B_2 \mid A) = 0.32$. We thus have the following probability distribution for p, the proportion of defectives in the lot:

p	Probability
0.01	0.68
0.02	0.32

The mean of this distribution is $(0.01)(0.68) + (0.02)(0.32) = 0.013$, and this figure furnishes us with a *Bayesian estimate* of the proportion of defectives in the lot. Note that this estimate combines collateral information about the past performance of the two vendors with the direct evidence.

8.2 Interval Estimation

When we use a sample mean to estimate the mean of a population, we know that although we are using a method of estimation which has certain desirable properties, the chances are slim that the estimate is *exactly* equal to μ. Hence, it would seem desirable to accompany such a point estimate of μ with some statement as to how close we might reasonably expect the estimate to be. The error, $\bar{x} - \mu$, is the difference between the estimate and the quantity it is supposed to estimate. To examine this error, let us make use of the fact that for large n

$$\frac{\bar{x} - \mu}{\sigma/\sqrt{n}}$$

is a value of a random variable having approximately the standard normal distribution. Consequently, we can assert with a probability of $1 - \alpha$ that

$$-z_{\alpha/2} < \frac{\bar{x} - \mu}{\sigma/\sqrt{n}} < z_{\alpha/2}$$

or that

$$\frac{|\bar{x} - \mu|}{\sigma/\sqrt{n}} < z_{\alpha/2}$$

where $z_{\alpha/2}$ is such that the normal curve area to its right equals $\alpha/2$. If we now let E stand for $|\bar{x} - \mu|$, the magnitude of the error of estimate, we have

$$E < z_{\alpha/2} \cdot \frac{\sigma}{\sqrt{n}}$$

with a probability of $1 - \alpha$. In other words, if we estimate μ by means of a random sample of size n, we can assert with a probability of $1 - \alpha$ that the error, $|\bar{x} - \mu|$, is less than $z_{\alpha/2} \cdot \sigma/\sqrt{n}$, at least for sufficiently large values of n.

If we solve the last inequality for n, we obtain

$$n < \frac{z_{\alpha/2}^2 \cdot \sigma^2}{E^2}$$

and it follows that if we select the sample size n so that

$$n = \frac{z_{\alpha/2}^2 \cdot \sigma^2}{E^2}$$

we can assert with a probability of $1 - \alpha$ that the error of estimating μ by means of $\bar{x}$ will be less than E. To be able to use this formula for calculating the sample size needed to estimate μ in a given situation, it is necessary that we specify α, σ, and E. Thus, we must give not only the maximum tolerable error E and the population standard deviation σ, but also the probability $1 - \alpha$ with which we want to assert that the maximum error will be less than E. The population standard deviation is usually estimated with prior data of a similar kind, and sometimes a good guess will have to do.

To illustrate, suppose we want to determine how large a sample of grinding balls must be used to estimate the mean weight loss in mill slurry to within a maximum error of 0.10 gram with a probability of 0.90. For σ we shall use 0.68 gram, a value which supposedly was obtained in a "pilot" sample of relatively few observations. Substituting $z_{.05} = 1.645$, $\sigma = 0.68$, and $E = 0.10$ into the formula for n, we obtain

$$n = \frac{(1.645)^2 (0.68)^2}{(0.10)^2} = 125.1$$

and, rounding upward, we find that the required minimum sample size is 126.

Since point estimates cannot really be expected to coincide with the quantities they are intended to estimate, it is sometimes preferable to replace them with *interval estimates*, that is, intervals for which we can assert with a reasonable degree of certainty that they contain the parameter under consideration. To illustrate the construction of such an interval, suppose that we have a random sample of size n, where n is large, from a population having the unknown mean μ and the *known* variance σ^2. Referring to the double inequality on page 146, namely,

$$-z_{\alpha/2} < \frac{\bar{x} - \mu}{\sigma/\sqrt{n}} < z_{\alpha/2}$$

which we asserted with a probability of $1 - \alpha$, we can now apply simple algebra and rewrite it as

$$\bar{x} - z_{\alpha/2} \cdot \frac{\sigma}{\sqrt{n}} < \mu < \bar{x} + z_{\alpha/2} \cdot \frac{\sigma}{\sqrt{n}}$$

Thus, we can claim with a probability of $1 - \alpha$ that the interval from $\bar{x} - z_{\alpha/2} \cdot \frac{\sigma}{\sqrt{n}}$ to $\bar{x} + z_{\alpha/2} \cdot \frac{\sigma}{\sqrt{n}}$ contains μ. It is customary to refer to an interval of this kind as a *confidence interval for μ* having the *degree of confidence* $1 - \alpha$.

At this point it is well to reconsider just what is meant by the statement: "We can claim with a probability of $1 - \alpha$ that such an interval contains μ." If a random sample of size $n = 100$ is taken from a population having $\sigma = 5.1$ and we obtain a sample mean of 21.6, then a 0.95 confidence interval for μ is given by $21.6 \pm 1.96 \cdot \frac{5.1}{\sqrt{100}}$, namely, the interval from 20.6 to 22.6. Since the mean of the given population either is contained or is not contained in this interval, it would hardly seem reasonable to speak of the probability of such an event. Indeed, what we really mean when we claim that the interval from 20.6 to 22.6 is a 0.95 confidence interval for the mean of the population is that *in repeated sampling* 95 per cent of the confidence intervals obtained with the above formula contain the means of the respective populations. Thus, although we shall never know whether the population mean is really contained in the interval from 20.6 to 22.6 in the given example, *we do have the assurance that the method used to obtain the interval is 95 per cent reliable, that is, it can be expected to work 95 per cent of the time.*

The formula obtained for a $1 - \alpha$ confidence interval for μ has the unfortunate feature that it requires knowledge of the population standard deviation. It is "unfortunate" because in most practical problems σ is unknown; therefore, we generally have little recourse but to replace σ with an estimate in the hope that, at least for large samples, the resulting confidence interval will be a close approximation. Substituting for σ the sample standard deviation s, which has desirable properties as a point estimate of σ (see Chapter 9), we use the interval

$$\bar{x} - z_{\alpha/2} \cdot \frac{s}{\sqrt{n}} < \mu < \bar{x} + z_{\alpha/2} \cdot \frac{s}{\sqrt{n}}$$

as an approximate *large sample confidence interval for μ* having the degree of confidence $1 - \alpha$.

If it is reasonable to assume that we are sampling from a normal population, it is possible to construct exact confidence intervals for μ even when σ is unknown. By Theorem 7.3, the statistic

$$t = \frac{\bar{x} - \mu}{s/\sqrt{n}}$$

is a value of a random variable having the Student-t distribution with
$n - 1$ degrees of freedom, where μ is the mean of the normal population
from which the sample is obtained. Thus, with $t_{\alpha/2}$ as defined on page 137,
we have

$$-t_{\alpha/2} < \frac{\bar{x} - \mu}{s/\sqrt{n}} < t_{\alpha/2}$$

or

$$\bar{x} - t_{\alpha/2} \cdot \frac{s}{\sqrt{n}} < \mu < \bar{x} + t_{\alpha/2} \cdot \frac{s}{\sqrt{n}}$$

with a probability of $1 - \alpha$, and this last inequality provides an *exact* $1 - \alpha$
confidence interval for μ for random samples of any size n from a normal
population. In accordance with the discussion on page 138, this formula
can be used in practice so long as the sample does not exhibit any pro-
nounced departures from normality.

To illustrate the use of this last formula, suppose that in a random sample
of size $n = 16$ the mean weight loss of grinding balls after a certain period
of time in mill slurry was 3.42 grams while the standard deviation of the
weight losses was 0.68 grams. Assuming normality, a 0.99 confidence inter-
val for μ is given by $3.42 \pm 2.947 \cdot \dfrac{0.68}{\sqrt{16}}$, namely, the interval from 2.92
to 3.92.

EXERCISES

1. In a laboratory experiment, 50 engineering students separately measured the
   specific heat of aluminum, obtaining a mean of 0.2210 calories (per centigrade
   degree per gram) and a standard deviation of 0.0240. What can one assert
   with a probability of 0.95 about the possible size of the error, if this sample
   mean is used to estimate the true specific heat of aluminum?

2. Use the data of Exercise 1 to construct a 0.95 confidence interval for the true
   specific heat of aluminum.

3. In a study designed to determine the mean time required for the assembly
   of a certain piece of machinery, 40 workers averaged 42.5 minutes with a
   standard deviation of 3.8 minutes.

   (a) What can we say with a probability of 0.99 about the possible size of
       the error if $\bar{x} = 42.5$ minutes is used as an estimate of the actual average
       time required to do the job?

   (b) Use the data to construct a 0.98 confidence interval for the true average
       time required to assemble the given machinery.

TABLE II

$B/2 = .9522$

$E = |\bar{x} - \mu| = 1$ $Z_{\alpha/2} = \frac{E\sqrt{n}}{\sigma} = \frac{1(\sqrt{40})}{3.8} = 1.667$

$1 - \alpha = .95$

$\alpha = .0956$

$\beta = 1 - \alpha = .9044$

$\alpha/2 = 1 - .9522$

4. Referring to Exercise 3, with what probability can we assert that the sample mean is within 1 minute of the true mean?

5. If we wanted to determine the average mechanical aptitude of a large group of workers, how large a random sample would we need to be able to assert with a probability of 0.95 that the sample mean will be within 2 points of the true mean? Assume that it is known from past experience with similar data that $\sigma = 16$.

$E = \frac{s}{\sqrt{n}} t_{\alpha}$ $E = \frac{s}{\sqrt{n}} t$ Student

$.323$

6. A chemist took 12 measurements of the percentage of manganese in ferromanganese (an alloy of manganese and iron) and obtained a mean of 80.93 per cent and a standard deviation of 0.36 per cent. What can he say with a probability of 0.99 about the possible size of his error, if he uses 80.93 per cent as an estimate of the mean of the population from which the sample was obtained? $1 - \alpha = .99$ $\alpha = .01$ $\frac{\alpha}{2} = .005$

$.0165$

$E = t_{\alpha/2}\frac{s}{\sqrt{n}}$

$\alpha/2 = 1 - .005 = .995$

$\alpha/2 = 2.5$ ns

$E = \frac{}{} = .0098$ $.332 - .344$

7. If 25 measurements of the coefficient of thermal expansion of nickel have a mean of 12.81 and a standard deviation of 0.04, construct a 0.95 confidence interval for the actual coefficient of expansion. (Assume that the 25 measurements may be looked upon as a random sample from a normal population.)

8. To check the diameter of an incoming shipment of "O guage" wire, the diameters of a random sample of 16 pieces of wire were measured, the mean and the standard deviation being 0.338 and 0.012 in., respectively. Assuming that the sample was taken from a normal population, find the maximum error committed with a 99 per cent degree of confidence in estimating the true mean diameter to be 0.338 in. Also, construct a 0.95 confidence interval for the true mean diameter. $\mu - E \leq \bar{x} \leq \mu + E$

9. Find the largest error one could expect to make with a 0.90 degree of confidence when using the mean of a random sample of 100 observations to estimate the mean of a population having a variance of 1.21. If the mean of such a sample is 5.68, construct a 0.90 confidence interval for the population mean.

$Z_{\alpha/2} = \frac{E}{\frac{\sigma}{\sqrt{n}}}$

10. Construct a 99 per cent confidence interval for the mean monthly air mileage of sales engineers for a certain manufacturing firm, if a random sample of 20 monthly vouchers shows a mean mileage of 6510 miles and a standard deviation of 1150 miles. What can one say with a probability of 0.99 about the possible size of the error with which this mean was estimated?

$B/2 = .96$

$B/2 = 1 - B/2 = .04$

$\alpha/2 = 1 - B/2 = $

$\alpha = .08$

11. Suppose a utilities company estimates the mean amount of its past-due accounts by taking a random sample of 81 delinquent bills. If the mean is $9.87 and the standard deviation is $5.14, what is the probability that an error of no more than $1.00 is made when estimating the mean delinquent account to be $9.87?

$\beta = 1 - \alpha = .92$

12. Referring to the information of Exercise 11, find the sample size needed to be able to assert with a degree of confidence of 0.90 that the sample mean will be within $0.25 of the true mean.

$\frac{(1.6)^2 (5.14)^2}{(.25)^2}$ $n = \frac{Z_{\alpha/2}^2 \sigma^2}{E^2}$ $\alpha = (1 - \beta = .)$

$\alpha/2 = .05$

$Z_{\alpha/2} = 1.645$ $B/2 = .95$

If drop interval same, as confidence # > then go farther out to ends of interval as 1-δ gets smaller (1-δ = Prob)

13. Referring to the information given in Exercise 8, find the sample size necessary to be 95 per cent confident of estimating the mean diameter of the shipment of wire with an error no greater than 0.006 in. [*Hint:* First, estimate n_1 by using $z = 1.96$, then use $t_{.025}$ with $n_1 - 1$ degrees of freedom to obtain a second estimate n_2; repeat this procedure until the last two values of n thus obtained are equal.]

14. A small finite population consists of the numbers 3, 6, 9, 12, and 15.

    (a) List all possible samples of size 3 that can be taken without replacement from this population.

    (b) Calculate the mean of each of the samples listed in (a) and, assigning each sample a probability of 1/10, verify that the mean of these $\bar{x}$'s equals 9, namely, the mean of the population.

15. Repeat both parts of Exercise 14 for random samples of size 2 taken with replacement from the given finite population. [*Hint:* All 15 samples do not have the same probability.]

16. Referring to Exercise 14, find the medians of the 10 samples and compare the variance of the probability distribution of the median, obtained by assigning each sample a probability of 1/10, with that of the corresponding probability distribution for the mean.

17. Having had some experience with similar situations, three statisticians estimate subjectively that the average daily demand for a newly designed measuring instrument will be $\mu = 46$, $\mu = 50$, and $\mu = 55$ units, respectively. It is assumed to be known that the daily demand for the new instrument has a standard deviation of $\sigma = 24$ and that one of the above figures for μ must be correct. A priori, the three statisticians are assumed to be about equally reliable, that is, without direct information we assign each of their respective estimates a probability of 1/3. If data obtained later for the demand for the instrument on 100 days have a mean greater than 51.2, what probability can we now assign to the event that $\mu = 50$ by using a *Bayesian inference?* Also find the corresponding probabilities for $\mu = 46$ and $\mu = 55$, and use the mean of this probability distribution for μ as a *Bayesian estimate* of the average daily demand for the new measuring instrument.

8.3 Tests of Hypotheses

There are many problems in which we are not directly concerned with the *actual* value of a parameter; instead we are interested in whether its value exceeds a given number, is less than a given number, falls into a given interval, and so on. Rather than estimate the value of a parameter, we thus want to *decide* whether a statement (or statements) concerning the parameter is true or false; that is, we want to test a hypothesis about the parameter. For example, in quality-control work a random sample may be taken to determine whether the "process mean" (for a given kind of measurement) has remained unchanged or whether it has changed to such an extent that the process has gone "out of control" and adjustments will have to be made.

To illustrate the general concepts involved in this kind of decision problem suppose that a manufacturer claims that a gallon can of his paint will cover on the average 400 square feet, and that a government agency wants to test the validity of this claim. Suppose, furthermore, that in a suitably conducted test a sample of 36 of these one-gallon cans covered on the average 385 square feet. This figure is less than the average of 400 square feet claimed by the manufacturer, but *is it small enough to reject the claim,* that is, is this sufficient evidence to take appropriate action against the manufacturer? Is it not possible that the discrepancy is due entirely to chance and the paint is as good as claimed even though the sample mean turned out to be low?

In testing the manufacturer's claim, the government agency is faced with the problem of establishing a criterion which will enable it to take suitable actions. Surely, if the *true* mean area covered by a gallon can of the paint is 400 square feet or more, there is no cause for any kind of regulatory action. On the other hand, how much leeway should be allowed to the manufacturer if his product is not quite as good as claimed? Should some action be taken if the true mean (area covered) μ is less than 395 square feet, or less than 390 square feet, and so forth? Suppose, for the sake of argument, that it is decided that a practical threat to the consumer's pocketbook exists if the paint covers on the average less than 380 square feet per gallon can. We can then think of the set of all possible values of μ (the set of positive real numbers) as being divided into the three regions shown in Figure 8.1. If μ lies in the rejection interval, some regulatory

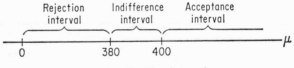

FIG. 8.1 Decision intervals

action should be taken and it would be a serious error not to reject the manufacturer's claim; if μ lies in the acceptance interval, there is certainly no cause for any action and it would be a serious error if, by chance, the agency did reject the manufacturer's claim; if μ lies in the indifference interval, it is difficult to argue whether or not regulatory action should be taken and no serious error is made in either case.

If μ could actually be known, the decision-making problem faced by the government agency would be solved by simply referring to the criterion of Figure 8.1. Since this is not the case in the given problem (or any similar practical situation), the decision will have to be based instead on the results of a random sample, usually the sample mean $\bar{x}$. It is important to realize that $\bar{x}$ might exceed 400 square feet even though μ is less than 380, and that $\bar{x}$ might be less than 380 square feet even though μ exceeds 400. This expresses the fact that *errors are unavoidable* when decisions are based on the results of random samples and, furthermore, that these errors are of two different kinds. The sample data can lead to the rejection of the claim even though μ lies in the acceptance interval, and they can lead to the acceptance of the claim even though μ lies in the rejection interval. Schematically, the situation may be described by means of the following table:

	μ *lies in* *acceptance interval*	μ *lies in* *rejection interval*
Accept the claim	No error	Type II error
Reject the claim	Type I error	No error

Note that if μ lies in the indifference interval, no *serious* error is committed whatever decision is made.

To judge the merits of any decision criterion, it is essential to know the probabilities that it will lead to Type I and Type II errors. Denoting these probabilities by α and β, respectively, that is,

$$\alpha = P(\text{Type I error})$$
$$\beta = P(\text{Type II error})$$

it is desirable to look for decision criteria for which α and β assume pre-assigned values. To illustrate how these probabilities can be calculated for a given criterion, let us suppose that (in our example) the government agency takes a random sample of 36 one-gallon cans of the given kind of paint and decides to reject the manufacturer's claim if $\bar{x}$, the mean of the areas covered by the 36 cans of paint, is less than 385 square feet. To simplify the discussion, we shall also assume that the standard deviation of the areas covered by a can of the paint is $\sigma = 48$ square feet. Now α is the probability of a *false rejection*, namely the probability that $\bar{x} < 385$, given that $\mu \geq 400$. Thus, α cannot be determined unless some value of μ (greater than or equal to 400) is specified. It is easy to see, however, that the probability of committing a Type I error with the given criterion (reject if $\bar{x} < 385$) is *greatest* when $\mu = 400$. In fact, we could think of the acceptance interval as consisting only of the point $\mu = 400$, in which case there is only one possible value of α, namely, the probability of getting an $\bar{x}$ less than 385 when $\mu = 400$.

To calculate this value of α, we approximate the sampling distribution of $\bar{x}$ with a normal distribution having a mean of 400 and a standard deviation of $48/\sqrt{36} = 8$. Thus, α is given by the area under the standard normal curve to the left of

$$z = \frac{385 - 400}{8} = -1.875$$

and it is approximately equal to 0.03.

So far as Type II errors are concerned, we can argue analogously that β is a maximum for $\mu = 380$; that is, for all values in the rejection interval $(\mu \leq 380)$ the probability of a Type II error is greatest for $\mu = 380$. Thinking of the rejection interval as consisting only of the point $\mu = 380$, we can find β by approximating the sampling distribution of $\bar{x}$ with a normal distribution having a mean of 380 and a standard deviation of $48/\sqrt{36} = 8$. Thus, β is given by the area under the standard normal curve to the right of

$$z = \frac{385 - 380}{8} = 0.625$$

and it is approximately equal to 0.27.

Using the method and assumptions illustrated above, it is possible to calculate α and β for testing any hypothesis H_0 of the form $\mu = \mu_0$ against any alternative H_1 of the form $\mu = \mu_1$. (More specifically, the decision procedure involved $\bar{x}$, the sampling distribution of $\bar{x}$ was approximated with a normal curve, and the sample size and the criterion for rejection were specified.) On the other hand, if α and β are to be specified in advance, we can use similar methods to determine the sample size n and an appropriate decision criterion. Another possibility is to specify α and the sample size n in advance, in which case the decision criterion and β are automatically determined. Although statistics other than $\bar{x}$ can be used to test hypotheses concerning population means, it can be shown that the use of $\bar{x}$ usually leads to the smallest value of β for given values of α and n.

To illustrate how the test criterion as well as β are determined in a situation where n and α are given, suppose that in the above example we want to test the hypothesis $\mu = 400$ against the alternative $\mu = 380$, that $\alpha = 0.05$ and $n = 36$, and that the hypothesis $\mu = 400$ is to be rejected if $\bar{x} < C$, where C is a constant to be determined. From Figure 8.2, it can be seen that

$$\frac{C - 400}{8} = -z_{.05} = -1.615$$

and, hence, that $C = 386.8$. Thus, if the hypothesis $\mu = 400$ is rejected whenever $\bar{x} < 386.8$ in a random sample of size 36, we are automatically assured that $\alpha = 0.05$. To find β for this test criterion, we proceed as before, and referring to Figure 8.2 it can be seen that

$$z_\beta = \frac{386.8 - 380}{8} = 0.85$$

so that $\beta = 0.198$.

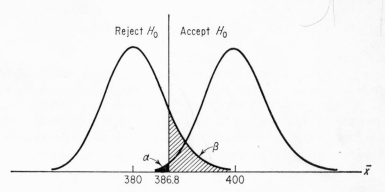

FIG. 8.2 Type I and Type II errors

In making the above test, the choice of H_0, namely, the choice of the hypothesis that $\mu = 400$, was dictated by the manufacturer's claim about the average area covered by a gallon of his paint; on the other hand, the choice of the alternative hypothesis H_1 was arbitrary to some extent. In fact, it would be interesting to see what would happen to the probability of accepting H_0 if the test criterion were the one of the preceding paragraph ($\alpha = 0.05$ and $n = 36$), but H_1 were changed. Denoting the probability of *accepting H_0* for a given value of μ by $L(\mu)$, let us point out first that this is the probability of committing a Type II error for values of μ which should be rejected, and that it is the probability of *not* committing a Type I error for values of μ which should be accepted. It is clear from Figure 8.2 that we can obtain $L(\mu)$ by determining the normal curve area to the right of

$$z = \frac{386.8 - \mu}{8}$$

For example, for $\mu = 370$ we obtain $z = 2.10$ and $L(370) = 0.018$, and for $\mu = 410$ we obtain $z = -2.90$ and $L(410) = 0.998$. Note that for $\mu = 400$ we obtain $z = -1.645$ and $L(400) = 0.95$, which equals $1 - \alpha = 1 - 0.05$ as should have been expected. The graph of $L(\mu)$ for various values of μ, shown in Figure 8.3, is called the *operating characteristic curve* or, simply, the *OC curve* of the test criterion. Note that the probability of accepting H_0 becomes smaller and smaller when μ is decreased.

Ideally, we should want to reject the hypothesis H_0 ($\mu = 400$) in favor of the alternative H_1 ($\mu < 400$) whenever μ is less than 400, and to accept it whenever μ is greater than or equal to 400. Thus, the "ideal" OC curve for testing the given hypothesis against the given alternative is the curve given by the heavy lines of Figure 8.3. In actual practice, an OC curve can only

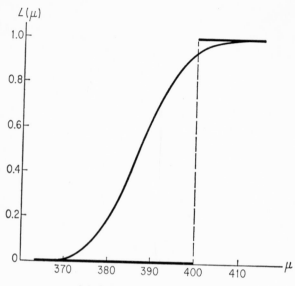

FIG. 8.3 Operating characteristic curve

approximate such an "ideal" curve, with the approximation becoming better as the sample size is increased. To show how an increase in n actually "improves" the OC curve, suppose we let $n = 100$ in our example, while keeping all other values fixed. Since the standard deviation of the sampling distribution of $\bar{x}$ is now $48/\sqrt{100} = 4.8$, the dividing line of the test criterion is given by the solution of

$$\frac{C - 400}{4.8} = -1.645$$

$C = 392.1$

and it is equal to 392.1. Thus, H_0 is accepted if $\bar{x} > 392.1$, $L(\mu)$ is given by the normal curve area to the right of

$$z = \frac{392.1 - \mu}{4.8}$$

and the resulting OC curve is shown in Figure 8.4. Note that the OC curve for $n = 100$ is closer to the "ideal" OC curve than that for $n = 36$, so that by increasing the sample size we have obtained a test which better "discriminates" between $\mu = 400$ and neighboring values of μ. It should be apparent from this discussion that it is impossible to specify α, β, as well as n in advance, and then construct a suitable test. In other words, _given any two of the quantities α, β, and n, the third is automatically determined._

In testing a hypothesis H_0 of the form $\mu = \mu_0$, where μ_0 is a specified constant, we used the test criterion: reject H_0 if $\bar{x} < C$, where C is deter-

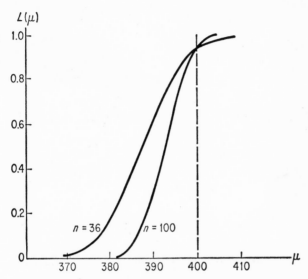

FIG. 8.4 Effect of increasing sample size on OC curve

mined so that the probability of committing a Type I error is equal to α. The set of values of $\bar{x}$ which, thus, leads to the rejection of H_0 in favor of the alternative hypothesis is called the _critical region_ for the test; in our example it was the set of all real numbers less than C. Had the alternative hypothesis been of the form $\mu > \mu_0$, the critical region would change to $\bar{x} > K$, where K must be chosen so that the probability of a Type I error is again equal to α. Using as before $\alpha = 0.05$, $n = 36$, and $\sigma = 48$, we now obtain the OC curve shown in Figure 8.5; it is the mirror image of the one of Figure 8.3, reflected about the vertical line through $\mu = 400$.

So far, the tests we have discussed have been _one-tail tests;_ that is, the hypothesis H_0 has been rejected for values of $\bar{x}$ falling into one "tail" of its sampling distribution. If we now consider the alternative $\mu \neq \mu_0$, we would want to reject H_0 for values of $\bar{x}$ less than or greater than μ_0, and the resulting critical region would be of the form $\bar{x} < C_1$ or $\bar{x} > C_2$. Here C_1 and C_2 would have to be chosen so that the probability of a Type I error is equal to α. (A test like this would arise if the paint manufacturer were concerned about filling the cans with _too little or too much_ paint.) If we choose "equal tails" so that alternative values of μ at the same distance

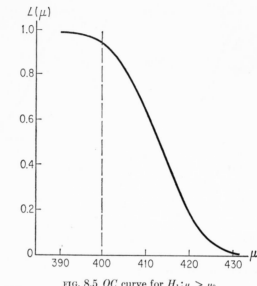

FIG. 8.5 *OC* curve for $H_1 : \mu > \mu_0$

on either side of μ_0 have the same chance of being accepted, and if we fix the probability of a Type I error at α, then C_1 and C_2 can be obtained by solving the equations

$$\frac{C_1 - \mu_0}{\sigma/\sqrt{n}} = -z_{\alpha/2} \quad \text{and} \quad \frac{C_2 - \mu_0}{\sigma/\sqrt{n}} = z_{\alpha/2}$$

For example, if we want to test the hypothesis $H_0: \mu = 400$, against the alternative $H_1: \mu \neq 400$, with $\alpha = 0.05$, $n = 36$, and $\sigma = 48$, we obtain

$$\frac{C_1 - 400}{8} = -1.96 \quad \text{and} \quad \frac{C_2 - 400}{8} = 1.96$$

and, hence, $C_1 = 384.3$ and $C_2 = 415.7$.

To illustrate the calculation of points on the *OC* curve for this two-tail test, let us find $L(420)$. As can be seen from Figure 8.6, this probability is given by the area under the standard normal curve between

$$z_1 = \frac{384.3 - 420}{8} = -4.46 \quad \text{and} \quad z_2 = \frac{415.7 - 420}{8} = -0.54$$

and, hence, it is equal to 0.295. From the symmetry of Figure 8.6 it is evident that $L(380)$ must also equal 0.295 and that, more generally, *the OC curve for this two-tail test is symmetric about $\mu = \mu_0$ with its maximum value being $L(\mu_0) = 1 - \alpha$.* The graph of the *OC* curve for the given two-tail test is shown in Figure 8.7.

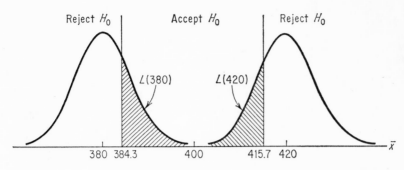

FIG. 8.6 Type II errors for two-tail test

The purpose of this discussion has been to introduce some of the basic problems connected with the testing of statistical hypotheses. Although the methods we have presented are *objective*—that is, two experimenters analyzing the same data under the same conditions would arrive at identical results—their use does entail some arbitrary, or subjective, considerations. For instance, in our illustration it was partially a subjective decision to "draw the line" between satisfactory and unsatisfactory values of μ at 380 square feet. It was also partially a subjective decision to use a sample of 36 one-gallon cans and to reject the claim for values of $\bar{x}$ less than 385 square feet. Equivalently, we could have specified values of α and β, thus controlling the risks to which we are willing to be exposed. The choice

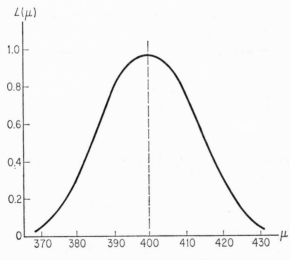

FIG. 8.7 *OC* curve for two-tail test

of α, the probability of a Type I error, could have been based on the consequences of making that kind of error, namely, the manufacturer's cost of having a good product condemned, the possible cost of subsequent litigation, the manufacturer's cost of unnecessarily adjusting his machinery, the cost to the public of not having the product available when needed, and so forth. The choice of β, the probability of a Type II error, could similarly have been based on the consequences of making that kind of error, namely, the cost to the public of buying an inferior product, the manufacturer's savings in paint but loss in good-will, again the cost of possible litigation, and so forth. It should be obvious that it would be extremely difficult to put "cash values" on all these eventualities, but they must nevertheless be considered, at least indirectly, in choosing suitable criteria for testing statistical hypotheses.

In recent years, attempts have been made to incorporate all these matters within a formal theory called *decision theory*. Although many important advances have been made, it should be recognized that such a theory does not eliminate the arbitrariness, or subjectiveness, discussed above; it merely incorporates these matters within the theory. This means that the use of decision theory requires that we actually put cash values on all possible consequences of our decisions. Although this has the advantage that it makes the experimenter (the engineer) more "cost conscious," it also has the disadvantage of requiring information which very often cannot be obtained.

In this text we shall discuss mainly the Neymann-Pearson theory, also called the classical theory of testing hypotheses. This means that we shall consider cost factors and other considerations that are partly arbitrary and partly subjective only insofar as they will affect the choice of a sample size, the choice of an alternative hypothesis, the choice of α and β, and so forth.

EXERCISES

1. Find the probability of a Type I error if the criterion on page 152 is modified so that the manufacturer's claim is rejected for $\bar{x} < 390$. Also find the probability of a Type II error for the modified criterion when $\mu = 380$, and compare with the value 0.27 obtained on page 154.

2. Referring to the two-tail test on page 158, find the values of the OC curve for $\mu = 410$ and 430. Plot these two values together with those for $\mu = 400$ and $\mu = 420$ given in the text, and compare the resulting OC curve with the one shown in Figure 8.7.

3. It is desired to test the hypothesis $\mu = 0$ against the alternative $\mu > 0$ on the bases of a random sample of size 9 from a normal population whose variance is $\sigma^2 = 1$. If the probability of a Type I error is to be 0.05,

(a) verify that the region of rejection is $\bar{x} > 0.548$,

(b) sketch the OC curve after evaluating β for $\mu = 0.5$, 1.0, and 1.5.

4. Repeat Exercise 3 for $n = 25$ and for $n = 100$, selecting in each case three suitable values of μ to get a good over-all picture of the OC curve. Compare the two OC curves obtained in this exercise and the one of Exercise 3 by drawing them on one set of axes.

5. Referring to Exercises 3 and 4, suppose it is desired to test the hypothesis $\mu = 0$ against the alternative $\mu = 0.30$. Which of the three sample sizes would be appropriate (at least approximately), if we did not want the probability of a Type II error to exceed 0.10?

6. Referring to Exercise 4, for each sample size state what alternative value of μ is such that the probability of committing a Type II error is approximately 0.15.

7. It is desired to test the hypothesis $\mu = 0$ against the alternative $\mu > 0$ on the basis of a random sample of size 100 from a normal population having the variance $\sigma^2 = 1$. If the hypothesis is to be rejected for $\bar{x} > 0.233$, (a) show that $\alpha = 0.01$, and (b) sketch the OC curve by evaluating β for $\mu = 0.1, 0.2, 0.3$, and 0.4.

8. Repeat Exercise 7 when (a) the hypothesis is rejected for $\bar{x} > 0.196$, and (b) it is rejected for $\bar{x} > 0.128$. In each case, choose suitable values of μ to calculate the probabilities of Type II errors and plot the corresponding OC curves. Compare the two OC curves of this exercise with the one obtained in Exercise 7 by drawing the three curves on one set of axes.

9. It is desired to test the hypothesis $\mu = 0$ against the alternative $\mu \neq 0$ on the basis of a random sample of size 25 from a normal population having the variance $\sigma^2 = 1$. If $\alpha = 0.05$, find the set of values of $\bar{x}$ for which the hypothesis is to be rejected and plot the OC curve for this criterion.

10. Referring to the OC curve obtained in Exercise 9, for what alternative value or values of μ is the probability of a Type II error approximately 0.10?

11. It is desired to test the hypothesis $\mu = \mu_0$ against the alternative $\mu = \mu_1$ (where $\mu_1 > \mu_0$) on the basis of a random sample of size n from a normal population having the variance σ^2.

(a) If the probabilities of Type I and Type II errors are to assume pre-assigned values α and β, show that the sample size required to attain this degree of precision is

$$n = \frac{\sigma^2(z_\alpha + z_\beta)^2}{(\mu_1 - \mu_0)^2}$$

(b) Use the formula of part (a) to find n when $\sigma = 12$, $\mu_0 = 30$, $\mu_1 = 32$, $\alpha = 0.05$, and $\beta = 0.01$.

8.4 Hypotheses Concerning One Mean

In this section we shall consider more generally the problem of testing the hypothesis that the mean of a population equals a specified value against a suitable alternative; that is, we shall test

$$H_0: \mu = \mu_0$$

against one of the alternatives

$$H_1: \mu < \mu_0, \qquad H_1: \mu > \mu_0, \quad \text{or} \quad H_1: \mu \neq \mu_0$$

and the critical region we shall use will be of the form $\bar{x} < C$, $\bar{x} > C$, or $\bar{x} < C_1$ or $\bar{x} > C_2$, respectively. Since none of these alternative hypotheses actually specifies a unique value of μ, it is impossible to compute β (the probability of a Type II error) for any of these tests, and it would seem reasonable to describe them as tests of whether $\bar{x}$ is *significantly less* than μ_0, *significantly greater* than μ_0, or *significantly different* from μ_0.

A test like this, in which the probability of a false acceptance of H_0 cannot be uniquely determined, is commonly called a *significance test*. The probability α of a Type I error, also called the *level of significance*, can be calculated because μ is uniquely specified by H_0, and the rejection of H_0 is "safe" in this sense. On the other hand, there is a danger inherent in the acceptance of H_0 because the probability of its false acceptance cannot be obtained. Thus, whenever possible, the hypothesis H_0 is chosen so that we shall be willing to "reserve judgment" about its validity, unless there is clear evidence that leads to its rejection. Also for this reason, H_0 will be called a *null hypothesis;* it is set up as a "straw man" with the objective of determining whether or not it can be rejected.

The idea of setting up a null hypothesis is not an uncommon one, even in nonstatistical thinking. In fact, this is exactly what is done in an American court of law, where an accused is assumed to be innocent unless he is proven guilty "beyond a reasonable doubt." The null hypothesis states that the accused is *not guilty*, and the probability expressed subjectively by the phrase "beyond a reasonable doubt" leads to the level of significance α. Thus, the "burden of proof" is always on the prosecution in the sense that the accused is found not guilty unless the null hypothesis of innocence is clearly disproved. Note that this does not imply that the defendant has been proved innocent if found not guilty; it implies only that he has not been proved guilty. Of course, since we cannot legally "reserve judgment" if proof of guilt is not established, the accused is freed and we act as if the null hypothesis of innocence were accepted. Note that this is what we do sometimes in tests of statistical hypotheses, when we cannot afford the luxury of reserving judgment.

To establish a parallel between this argument and the kind of practical problem in which significance tests are ordinarily applied, let us consider the following examples. Suppose a decision has to be made whether to buy an automatic welding machine to do a job formerly done by hand, and it is felt that the machine would be economical only if μ, the average number of defective welds per hundred, were less than 5. Thus, we have a situation which calls for a test of the null hypothesis H_0: $\mu = 5$, although we are not told directly which alternative hypothesis to use. If the burden of proof is to be placed on the machine, it would be appropriate to test H_0 against the *one-sided alternative* H_1: $\mu < 5$, installing the welder only if it can be proved statistically that it produces less than 5 defectives per 100 welds. Note that if $\alpha = 0.05$, there is only a 5 per cent chance of erroneously rejecting H_0 and installing the automatic welder. On the other hand, if the burden of proof were placed on the existing method, the one-sided alternative H_1: $\mu > 5$ would be appropriate. In this case H_0 would be accepted and the automatic welder installed *unless* it were proved (say, with $\alpha = 0.05$) that the automatic welder produces too many defectives. The choice of which one-sided alternative to use in this and in similar situations is a practical rather than a statistical problem; it simply depends on where we wish to place the burden of proof.

To give an example leading to a *two-sided alternative*, suppose a canner wants to test whether the correct amount of fruit juice is being packed in his 20-ounce cans. Since the label reads "20 ounces," the canner cannot afford to pack much less than 20 ounces for fear of losing customer acceptance or running afoul of the law, nor can he afford to pack much more than 20 ounces for fear of losing a substantial part of his profit. Thus, the canner is concerned with the two-sided alternative H_1: $\mu \neq 20$, and the can-filling process will be left undisturbed unless the mean weight of the contents of a sample of cans is significantly different from 20 ounces.

Returning now to the general problem of testing the null hypothesis $\mu = \mu_0$, we find that this problem has already been solved in Section 8.3, provided the sample size is large and the population standard deviation is known. In that case the critical region is given by $\bar{x} < C$ if the alternative hypothesis is $\mu < \mu_0$, $\bar{x} > C$ if the alternative hypothesis is $\mu > \mu_0$, and $\bar{x} < C_1$ or $\bar{x} > C_2$ if the alternative hypothesis is $\mu \neq \mu_0$, and the formulas for computing C, C_1, and C_2 are given on pages 154 and 158. An equivalent, but simpler, method of specifying the critical region is to base it on the statistic

$$z = \frac{\bar{x} - \mu_0}{\sigma/\sqrt{n}}$$

instead of $\bar{x}$. If the level of significance is α, and z_α is, as before, such that the area under the standard normal curve to its right is equal to α, the critical regions for testing H_0: $\mu = \mu_0$ can be expressed as in the following table:

CRITICAL REGIONS FOR TESTING H_0: $\mu = \mu_0$
(Large Sample, σ Known)

Alternative hypothesis	Reject H_0 if
$\mu < \mu_0$	$z < -z_\alpha$
$\mu > \mu_0$	$z > z_\alpha$
$\mu \neq \mu_0$	$z < -z_{\alpha/2}$ or $z > z_{\alpha/2}$

To illustrate, let us return to the problem concerning the automatic welder. The null hypothesis is $\mu = 5$ and we shall use the alternative $\mu < 5$, putting the burden of proof on the automatic welder. Suppose that the decision is to be based on a sample of 64 sets, each of which contains 100 welds, and that the mean and the standard deviation of the number of defective welds per set are, respectively, 4.8 and 1.2. Although σ is actually unknown, the sample is large enough to approximate it with $s = 1.2$, and we thus obtain

$$z = \frac{4.8 - 5}{1.2/\sqrt{64}} = -1.33$$

If the level of significance is to be $\alpha = 0.05$, we find from Table III that the *critical value* is $-z_{.05} = -1.645$; since the calculated value of z is not less than -1.645, the null hypothesis cannot be rejected and we decide, in fact, that the machine is not to be installed. (The reader will be asked to graph the *OC* curve of this test in Exercise 9 on page 172.)

If the sample size is small and σ is unknown, the tests just described cannot be used. However, if the sample comes from a normal population (to within a reasonable degree of approximation), we can make use of the theory discussed in Section 7.3 and base the test of the hypothesis $H_0 \colon \mu = \mu_0$ on the statistic

$$\blacklozenge \qquad t = \frac{\bar{x} - \mu_0}{s/\sqrt{n}} \qquad \blacklozenge$$

The resulting critical regions are as shown in the table on page 165. In this table t_α is as defined on page 137 (the area to its right under the t distribution with $n - 1$ degrees of freedom is equal to α).

To illustrate, let us reconsider the problem of deciding whether changes have to be made in the fruit-juice canning process, namely, the problem in which the null hypothesis $\mu = 20$ is to be tested against the alternative hypothesis $\mu \neq 20$. Suppose that the level of significance is to be $\alpha = 0.01$, and that the net weights of the contents of a sample of 25 cans have a

CRITICAL REGIONS FOR TESTING H_0: $\mu = \mu_0$
(Normal Population, σ Unknown)

Alternative hypothesis	Reject H_0 if for $n - 1$ degrees of freedom
$\mu < \mu_0$	$t < -t_\alpha$
$\mu > \mu_0$	$t > t_\alpha$
$\mu \neq \mu_0$	$t < -t_{\alpha/2}$ or $t > t_{\alpha/2}$

mean of $\bar{x} = 20.03$ and a standard deviation of $s = 0.04$ ounces. To decide whether to adjust the process, we calculate

$$t = \frac{20.03 - 20}{0.04/\sqrt{25}} = 3.75$$

and since this exceeds 2.797, the value of $t_{.005}$ with 24 degrees of freedom (see Table IV), the null hypothesis will have to be rejected. (It is difficult to graph the OC curve for this test, because the sampling distribution of the test statistic is not the t distribution unless $\mu = 20$. However, in the *Biometrika Table* mentioned in the Bibliography there is a special table from which the necessary probabilities can be obtained.)

In spite of the result obtained in this test, the manufacturer may not wish to adjust his machinery, since the loss due to overfilling the cans by a very small amount may actually be less than the cost of experimenting with adjustments. This illustrates the important fact that a result which is *statistically significant* may not be *commercially significant*. Under the circumstances, it might be more appropriate to test the null hypothesis $\mu = 20$ against an alternative such as $\mu < 19.95$ or $\mu > 20.05$, if it is felt that either case will definitely call for an adjustment.

8.5 Hypotheses Concerning Two Means

When dealing with population means, we are frequently faced with the problem of making decisions about the relative values of two or more means. Leaving the general problem until Chapter 13, we shall devote this section to tests concerning the difference between two means. For example, if two kinds of steel are being considered for use in certain structural steel beams, we may take samples and decide which is better by comparing their mean strengths; also, if an achievement test is given to a group of industrial engineers and to a group of civil engineers, we may want to decide whether any observed difference between the means of their scores is significant or whether it may be attributed to chance.

Formulating the problem more generally, we shall consider two populations having the means μ_1 and μ_2 and the variances σ_1^2 and σ_2^2, and we shall want to test the null hypothesis $\mu_1 - \mu_2 = \delta$, where δ is a specified constant, on the basis of independent random samples of size n_1 and n_2. Analogous to the tests concerning one mean, we shall consider tests of this null hypothesis against each of the alternatives $\mu_1 - \mu_2 < \delta$, $\mu_1 - \mu_2 > \delta$, and $\mu_1 - \mu_2 \neq \delta$. The test, itself, will depend on the difference between the sample means, $\bar{x}_1 - \bar{x}_2$, and if both samples are large and the population variances are known, it can be based on the statistic

$$z = \frac{(\bar{x}_1 - \bar{x}_2) - \delta}{\sigma_{\bar{x}_1 - \bar{x}_2}}$$

whose sampling distribution is (approximately) the standard normal distribution. Here $\sigma_{\bar{x}_1 - \bar{x}_2}$ is the standard deviation of the sampling distribution of the difference between the sample means, and its value for random samples from infinite populations may be obtained with the use of the following theorem, which we shall state without proof:

THEOREM 8.1. *If the distributions of two independent random variables have the means μ_1 and μ_2 and the variances σ_1^2 and σ_2^2, then the distribution of their sum (or difference) has the mean $\mu_1 + \mu_2$ (or $\mu_1 - \mu_2$) and the variance $\sigma_1^2 + \sigma_2^2$.*

To find the variance of the difference between the means of two independent random samples of size n_1 and n_2 from infinite populations, note first that the variances of the two means, themselves, are

$$\sigma_{\bar{x}_1}^2 = \frac{\sigma_1^2}{n_1} \qquad \text{and} \qquad \sigma_{\bar{x}_2}^2 = \frac{\sigma_2^2}{n_2}$$

where σ_1^2 and σ_2^2 are the variances of the respective populations. Thus, by Theorem 8.1

$$\sigma_{\bar{x}_1 - \bar{x}_2}^2 = \frac{\sigma_1^2}{n_1} + \frac{\sigma_2^2}{n_2}$$

and the test statistic can be written as

$$z = \frac{(\bar{x}_1 - \bar{x}_2) - \delta}{\sqrt{\dfrac{\sigma_1^2}{n_1} + \dfrac{\sigma_2^2}{n_2}}}$$

Analogous to the table on page 164, the critical regions for testing the null hypothesis $H_0: \mu_1 - \mu_2 = \delta$ are as follows:

CRITICAL REGIONS FOR TESTING H_0: $\mu_1 - \mu_2 = \delta$

(Large Samples, σ_1 and σ_2 Known)

Alternative hypothesis	Reject H_0 if
$\mu_1 - \mu_2 < \delta$	$z < -z_\alpha$
$\mu_1 - \mu_2 > \delta$	$z > z_\alpha$
$\mu_1 - \mu_2 \neq \delta$	$z < -z_{\alpha/2}$ or $z > z_{\alpha/2}$

To illustrate this kind of test, suppose that an achievement test is given to 50 industrial engineers (Group 1) and to 60 civil engineers (Group 2), and that the results are as follows:

$$\bar{x}_1 = 89, \qquad s_1 = 7$$
$$\bar{x}_2 = 87, \qquad s_2 = 5$$

If we wish to test at the 0.05 level of significance whether the observed difference of 2 points between the two means is significant or whether it can be attributed to chance, the appropriate null hypothesis and alternative hypothesis are H_0: $\mu_1 - \mu_2 = 0$ and H_1: $\mu_1 - \mu_2 \neq 0$. Accordingly, we put $\delta = 0$ in the formula for z and the test statistic becomes

$$z = \frac{89 - 87}{\sqrt{\dfrac{49}{50} + \dfrac{25}{60}}} = 1.69$$

(Note that we have approximated the population variances with s_1^2 and s_2^2, which is justifiable since both samples are fairly large.) Since the value which we obtained for the test statistic lies between the critical values of -1.96 and 1.96, the null hypothesis cannot be rejected; thus, we conclude that the observed difference between the means is *not significant* at the 0.05 level or, in other words, that it can well be attributed to chance.

If either (or both) samples are small and the population variances are unknown, we can base tests of the null hypothesis H_0: $\mu_1 - \mu_2 = \delta$ on a suitable t statistic, provided it is reasonable to assume that *both populations are normal with $\sigma_1 = \sigma_2$*. Under these conditions it can be shown that the sampling distribution of the statistic

$$t = \frac{(\bar{x}_1 - \bar{x}_2) - \delta}{s_{\bar{x}_1 - \bar{x}_2}}$$

is the t distribution with $n_1 + n_2 - 2$ degrees of freedom. In this formula the denominator involves a "pooled estimate" of the population variance.

To clarify what we mean here by a "pooled estimate" of the population variance, let us first consider the problem of estimating the variance of the distribution of the difference between two sample means. Under the assumption that $\sigma_1^2 = \sigma_2^2 \, (= \sigma^2)$, this variance is given by

$$\sigma_{\bar{x}_1 - \bar{x}_2}^2 = \frac{\sigma_1^2}{n_1} + \frac{\sigma_2^2}{n_2} = \sigma^2 \left(\frac{1}{n_1} + \frac{1}{n_2} \right)$$

and we now estimate σ^2 by "pooling" the two sums of squared deviations from the respective sample means. In other words, we estimate σ^2 by means of

$$\frac{\Sigma \, (x_1 - \bar{x}_1)^2 + \Sigma \, (x_2 - \bar{x}_2)^2}{n_1 + n_2 - 2} = \frac{(n_1 - 1)s_1^2 + (n_2 - 1)s_2^2}{n_1 + n_2 - 2}$$

where $\Sigma \, (x_1 - \bar{x}_1)^2$ is the sum of the squared deviations from the mean for the first sample, while $\Sigma \, (x_2 - \bar{x}_2)^2$ is the sum of the squared deviations from the mean for the second sample. We divide by $n_1 + n_2 - 2$, since there are $n_1 - 1$ independent deviations from the mean in the first sample, $n_2 - 1$ in the second, and we thus have $n_1 + n_2 - 2$ independent deviations from the mean to estimate the population variance. Substituting this estimate of σ^2 into the above expression for $\sigma_{\bar{x}_1 - \bar{x}_2}^2$ and then substituting the square root of the result into the denominator of the formula for t on page 167, we finally obtain

$$t = \frac{(\bar{x}_1 - \bar{x}_2) - \delta}{\sqrt{(n_1 - 1)s_1^2 + (n_2 - 1)s_2^2}} \sqrt{\frac{n_1 n_2 (n_1 + n_2 - 2)}{n_1 + n_2}}$$

for the statistic on which we shall base the test. The corresponding critical regions for testing the null hypothesis $H_0: \mu_1 - \mu_2 = \delta$ are as shown in the following table:

CRITICAL REGIONS FOR TESTING $H_0: \mu_1 - \mu_2 = \delta$
(Normal Populations, $\sigma_1 = \sigma_2 = \sigma$, σ Unknown)

Alternative hypothesis	Reject H_0 if for $n_1 + n_2 - 2$ degrees of freedom
$\mu_1 - \mu_2 < \delta$	$t < -t_\alpha$
$\mu_1 - \mu_2 > \delta$	$t > t_\alpha$
$\mu_1 - \mu_2 \neq \delta$	$t < -t_{\alpha/2}$ or $t > t_{\alpha/2}$

To illustrate this kind of test, let us assume that a sample of 10 steel beams from Mill A has a mean tensile strength of 54,000 psi with a standard deviation of 2100 psi, and that a sample of 12 beams from Mill B has a mean tensile strength of 49,000 psi with a standard deviation of 1900 psi. The beams from Mill B cost less than those from Mill A, and we are inclined to buy from Mill B unless the beams from Mill A are at least 2000 psi stronger on the average than those from Mill B. Consequently, we shall test the null hypothesis $H_0: \mu_A - \mu_B = 2000$, against the one-sided alternative $H_1: \mu_A - \mu_B > 2000$, and we shall choose a level of significance of $\alpha = 0.01$. The value of the test statistic is

$$ t = \frac{(54{,}000 - 49{,}000) - 2000}{\sqrt{9(2100)^2 + 11(1900)^2}} \sqrt{\frac{10(12)(20)}{22}} = 3.52 $$

and since this exceeds 2.528, the value of $t_{.01}$ for 20 degrees of freedom, the null hypothesis will have to be rejected and the beams purchased from Mill A. (Note that by choosing the alternative hypothesis $\mu_A - \mu_B > 2000$, we place the burden of proof on Mill A.)

In this last example we arbitrarily went ahead and performed a *two-sample t test*, tacitly assuming that the population variances were equal. Fortunately, the test is not overly sensitive to small differences between the population variances, and the procedure used in this instance is quite justifiable. To be on safer grounds, however, we should first have tested whether the difference between the sample variances may be attributed to chance; a procedure for performing such a test will be given in Chapter 9.

If the difference between the sample variances is large or if it is otherwise unreasonable to treat the population variances as being equal, we cannot use the two-sample t test just described. However, there are several alternative methods that can be used instead, which do not require the assumption of equal population variances. One of these, the *paired-sample t test*, applies to two random samples of the same size, which need not be independent. Briefly, the procedure is to work with the differences of paired observations, where the first member of each pair comes from the first sample and the second member comes from the second sample, and to use the one-sample t test described in Section 8.4 to determine whether the mean of the differences is significantly different from δ. Sometimes, as in the case where two examinations are given to each of n persons, the pairing is "natural"; in all other cases the pairing should be random.

To illustrate the paired-sample t test, suppose that a dye is to be tested for resistance to fading by exposing 8 dyed specimens of various kinds to sunlight for a specified period of time. The reflectivity of light of the same color as the dye is measured for each specimen (in arbitrary units) before and after exposure to sunlight, and it will be concluded that the dye is *not* resistant to fading if the difference in reflectivity indices is significantly greater than 1. The following are the results obtained in this experiment:

	Before exposure x_1	After exposure x_2
Specimen 1	19	14
Specimen 2	5	4
Specimen 3	24	20
Specimen 4	8	8
Specimen 5	10	9
Specimen 6	11	9
Specimen 7	7	5
Specimen 8	16	15

The differences between these paired observations are 5, 1, 4, 0, 1, 2, 2, 1, their mean is 2.00, and their standard deviation is 1.69. Assuming that the differences may be treated as a sample from a normal population with $\mu_0 = 1$, the test statistic for the one-sample t test has the value

$$t = \frac{2.00 - 1}{1.69/\sqrt{8}} = 1.67$$

If the level of significance is to be 0.05, we find that $t_{.05}$ for 7 degrees of freedom equals 1.895 and, hence, that the null hypothesis cannot be rejected. We could conclude that the dye is resistant to fading or we could reserve judgment until more data are obtained.

Although this paired-sample t test can be used when sampling from normal populations *regardless of whether the samples are independent or the population variances are equal*, it has two disadvantages. First, the sample sizes must be equal, and second, there is a serious loss of information in the sense that the test is performed as if there were only n observations instead of $2n$ observations. An alternate test which avoids these disadvantages when the samples are independent is given in Exercise 20 below.

EXERCISES

1. The management of a food processing plant is considering the installation of new equipment for sorting eggs. If μ_1 is the average number of eggs sorted per hour by their old machine and μ_2 is the corresponding average for the new machine, the null hypothesis they shall want to test is $\mu_1 - \mu_2 = 0$.

   (a) What alternative hypothesis should they use if the burden of proof is to be put on the new equipment and the old equipment will be kept unless the null hypothesis is rejected?

   (b) What alternative hypothesis should they use if the burden of proof is to be put on the old equipment?

(c) What alternative hypothesis should they use so that the rejection of the null hypothesis could lead either to buying the new machine or keeping the old one?

2. A producer of extruded plastic products finds that his mean daily inventory is 1148 pieces. A new marketing policy has been put into effect and it is desired to test the null hypothesis that the mean daily inventory remains unchanged. What alternative hypothesis should be used if

 (a) it is desired to *prove* that the new policy reduces inventory?

 (b) it is desired to know whether or not the new policy changes the mean daily inventory?

 (c) the new policy will remain in effect unless it can be *proved* that it causes an increase in inventory?

3. A random sample of boots worn by 50 soldiers in a desert region showed an average life of 1.24 years with a standard deviation of 0.55 years. Under standard conditions, such boots are known to have an average life of 1.40 years. Is there reason to assert at a level of significance of 0.05 that use in the desert causes the average life of such boots to decrease?

4. A sample of 9 measurements of the percentage of manganese in ferro-manganese has a mean of 84.0 and a standard deviation of 1.2. Assuming that the sample has been selected at random from a normal population, test the null hypothesis that the true percentage is 80.0 against the alternative that it exceeds 80.0 at the 0.05 level of significance.

5. Test runs with 5 models of an experimental engine showed that they operated, respectively, for 20, 19, 22, 17, and 18 minutes with 1 gallon of a certain kind of fuel. Is this evidence at the 0.01 level of significance that the models are not operating at a desired standard (average) of 22 minutes per gallon? What assumptions are required to perform this test?

6. A quick and inexpensive analytical procedure for the determination of titanium has been developed by a chemist. To show its accuracy, the developer presented 50 independent determinations, having a mean of 0.0095 ppm and a variance of $81.0 \cdot 10^{-8}$. The material tested by the new procedure was carefully checked by a virtually exact but very tedious method, and it was believed that the titanium in this material was in fact 0.0093 ppm. Using a level of significance of 0.05, decide whether there is any reason to doubt the accuracy of the new procedure.

7. A testing laboratory wants to check whether the average lifetime of a certain kind of cutting tool is 2000 pieces against the alternative that it is less than 2000 pieces. What conclusion will they reach at a level of significance of 0.01, if 6 tests showed tool lives of 2010, 1980, 1920, 2005, 1975, and 1950 pieces?

8. A random sample of 100 tires produced by a certain firm lasted on the average 21,000 miles with a standard deviation of 1500 miles. Can it be claimed

that the true mean life of tires produced by this firm exceeds 20,000 miles? Use $\alpha = 0.05$.

9. Calculate some of the necessary probabilities and graph the OC curve for the test used as an illustration on page 164.

10. Graph the OC curve for the test described in Exercise 6.

11. The diameters of rotor shafts in a lot have a mean of 0.249 in. and a standard deviation of 0.003 in. The inner diameters of bearings in another lot have a mean of 0.255 in. and a standard deviation of 0.002 in.

   (a) What are the mean and the standard deviation of the clearances between shafts and bearings selected from these lots?

   (b) If a shaft and a bearing are selected at random, what is the probability that the shaft will not fit inside the bearing? (Assume that both dimensions are normally distributed.)

12. An investigation of the relative merits of two types of flashlight batteries showed that a sample of 100 batteries made by Company A had a mean lifetime of 24 hours with a standard deviation of 4 hours. If a sample of 80 batteries from Company B had a mean lifetime of 40 hours with a standard deviation of 6 hours, can it be concluded at the 0.05 level of significance that the batteries made by Company B have a mean lifetime at least 10 hours longer than those made by Company A?

13. A company wants to compare the lifetimes of two stones used in an abrasive process and it finds that the average lifetime of 10 stones of the first kind is 58 pieces with a standard deviation of 6 pieces, and that the average lifetime of 12 stones of the second kind is 66 pieces with a standard deviation of 4 pieces. Test the null hypothesis that there is no difference between the true average lifetimes of the two stones against the alternative that the second is superior. Use $\alpha = 0.01$. What assumption must be met to perform the test?

14. Members of an army evaluation team are attempting to evaluate the relative merits of two designs of antitank projectiles. A sample of 10 projectiles of type A are fired at maximum range, with a mean target error of 24 feet and a variance of 16 feet. A sample of 8 projectiles of type B are fired, with a mean target error of 30 feet and a variance of 25 feet. Is there a significant difference between the mean target errors of the two kinds of projectiles at the 0.01 level? (Assume that the target errors are normally distributed.)

15. Two randomly selected groups of 50 undergraduate engineering students are taught an assembly operation by two different methods and then tested for performance. The first group averaged 120 points with a standard deviation of 12 points while the second group averaged 112 points with a standard deviation of 9 points. If μ_1 is the true mean performance of students taught by the first method and μ_2 is the true mean performance of students taught by the second method, test the null hypothesis $\mu_1 = \mu_2$ at the 0.05 level against the two-sided alternative $\mu_1 \neq \mu_2$.

16. It is claimed that the resistance of electric wire can be reduced at least 0.050 ohm by alloying. Twenty-five tests each on alloyed wire and standard wire produced the following results:

	Mean	Standard deviation
Alloyed wire	0.089 ohm	0.003 ohm
Standard wire	0.141 ohm	0.002 ohm

Using a level of significance of 0.05, determine whether the claim has been substantiated.

17. Tests are run on the performance of samples of 4 plastic and 4 wooden bowling pins, with special attention paid to the number of lines for which they can be used before showing dents or other imperfections. The results obtained for the 4 plastic pins are 2650, 2770, 2480, and 2660 lines, while those for the 4 wooden pins are 1420, 1600, 1545, and 1395 lines. If μ_1 and μ_2 are the respective true means for the two kinds of pins, test at $\alpha = 0.01$ whether plastic pins last on the average 1000 lines longer. What assumptions are required to perform this test?

18. To determine the effectiveness of an industrial safety program, the following data were collected on lost-time accidents (the figures given are mean man-hours lost per month over a period of 1 year):

Plant no.	1	2	3	4	5	6	7	8
Before program	38.5	69.2	15.3	9.7	120.9	47.6	78.8	52.1
After program	28.7	62.2	28.9	0.0	93.5	49.6	86.5	40.2

Test at the 0.10 level of significance whether the safety program was effective in reducing lost-time accidents.

19. The following data were obtained in an experiment designed to check whether there is a systematic difference in the blood pressure readings yielded by two different instruments:

	Reading obtained with Instrument A	Reading obtained with Instrument B
Patient 1	136	141
Patient 2	115	117
Patient 3	142	141
Patient 4	140	145
Patient 5	123	127
Patient 6	147	146
Patient 7	133	135
Patient 8	150	152
Patient 9	138	135
Patient 10	147	152

Use a level of significance of 0.05 to test whether there is a difference in the true average readings obtained with the two instruments.

20. When dealing with two independent random samples from normal populations whose variances are not necessarily equal, the following *Smith-Satterthwaite* test can be used to test the null hypothesis $\mu_1 - \mu_2 = \delta$. The test statistic is given by

$$t' = \frac{(\bar{x}_1 - \bar{x}_2) - \delta}{\sqrt{\dfrac{s_1^2}{n_1} + \dfrac{s_2^2}{n_2}}}$$

and its sampling distribution can be approximated by the t distribution with

$$\frac{\left(\dfrac{s_1^2}{n_1} + \dfrac{s_2^2}{n_2}\right)^2}{\dfrac{(s_1^2/n_1)^2}{n_1 - 1} + \dfrac{(s_2^2/n_2)^2}{n_2 - 1}}$$

degrees of freedom. Use this test for the data of Exercise 14 and compare the answer with the one previously obtained.

21. Use the formula for t on page 168 to construct a $1 - \alpha$ confidence interval for δ, the difference between the two population means.

22. Use the formula obtained in Exercise 21 to construct a 0.95 confidence interval for the difference between the mean lifetimes of the two abrasive stones of Exercise 13.

9 | INFERENCES CONCERNING VARIANCES

9.1 The Estimation of Variances

There were several instances in the preceding chapter where we estimated a population variance by means of a sample variance as defined by the formula

$$s^2 = \frac{\sum\limits_{i=1}^{n} (x_i - \bar{x})^2}{n - 1}$$

We substituted s^2 for σ^2 in the large-sample confidence interval for μ on page 148, in the large-sample test concerning μ on page 164, and in the large-sample test concerning the difference between two means on page 167. To justify these procedures, let us now prove that s^2 is, in fact, an *unbiased* estimate of σ^2. This means that we shall have to show that the mean of the sampling distribution of s^2 is equal to σ^2.

If $f(x_1, x_2, \ldots, x_n)$ is the joint density of the sample values $x_1, x_2, \ldots,$ and x_n, it follows from the discussion on page 84 that the mean of the sampling distribution of s^2 is given by

$$\int_{-\infty}^{\infty} \int_{-\infty}^{\infty} \cdots \int_{-\infty}^{\infty} s^2 f(x_1, x_2, \ldots, x_n) \, dx_1 \, dx_2 \ldots dx_n$$

$$= \int_{-\infty}^{\infty} \int_{-\infty}^{\infty} \cdots \int_{-\infty}^{\infty} \sum_{i=1}^{n} \frac{(x_i - \bar{x})^2}{n-1} f(x_1, x_2, \ldots, x_n) \, dx_1 \, dx_2 \ldots dx_n$$

If we now write

$$\sum_{i=1}^{n} (x_i - \bar{x})^2 = \sum_{i=1}^{n} x_i^2 - n\bar{x}^2$$

and interchange the operations of summation and integration, the expression for the mean of the distribution of s^2 becomes

$$\frac{1}{n-1} \sum_{i=1}^{n} \int_{-\infty}^{\infty} \int_{-\infty}^{\infty} \cdots \int_{-\infty}^{\infty} x_i^2 f(x_1, x_2, \ldots, x_n) \, dx_1 \, dx_2 \ldots dx_n$$

$$- \frac{n}{n-1} \int_{-\infty}^{\infty} \int_{-\infty}^{\infty} \cdots \int_{-\infty}^{\infty} \bar{x}^2 f(x_1, x_2, \ldots, x_n) \, dx_1 \, dx_2 \ldots dx_n$$

Assuming without loss of generality that the population mean μ is equal to zero, we find that these last two integrals have already been evaluated on page 131, where it was shown that their respective values are σ^2 and σ^2/n. Thus, the mean of the sampling distribution of s^2 is given by

$$\frac{1}{n-1} \sum_{i=1}^{n} \sigma^2 - \frac{n}{n-1} \cdot \frac{\sigma^2}{n} = \frac{n\sigma^2}{n-1} - \frac{\sigma^2}{n-1} = \sigma^2$$

and this completes the proof of the unbiasedness of s^2 as an estimate of σ^2. (Note that, had we divided by n instead of $n-1$ in defining s^2, the resulting estimator would have been biased; the mean of its sampling distribution would have been $\frac{n-1}{n} \cdot \sigma^2$.)

Although the sample *variance* is an unbiased estimator of σ^2, it does not follow that the sample *standard deviation* is also an unbiased estimator of σ; in fact, it is not. However, for large samples the bias is small and it is common practice to estimate σ with s. Besides s, population standard deviations are sometimes estimated in terms of the sample *range R*, which we defined earlier as the difference between the largest and the smallest values in a sample. Given a random sample of size n from a *normal population*, it can be shown that the sampling distribution of R has the mean $d_2\sigma$ and the standard deviation $d_3\sigma$, where d_2 and d_3 are constants which depend on the size of the sample, as shown in the following table:

n	2	3	4	5	6	7	8	9	10
d_2	1.128	1.693	2.059	2.326	2.534	2.704	2.847	2.970	3.078
d_3	0.853	0.888	0.880	0.864	0.848	0.833	0.820	0.808	0.797

Thus, the statistic R/d_2 is an unbiased estimator for σ, and the standard deviation of its sampling distribution is given by $d_3\sigma/d_2$. For very small samples ($n \le 5$), R/d_2 provides nearly as good an estimate of σ as does s, but as the sample size increases it becomes far more efficient to use s. The range is used to estimate σ primarily in problems of quality control, where sample sizes are usually small and computational ease is an important requirement. This application will be discussed in detail in Chapter 15.

Interval estimates of σ or σ^2 are almost always based on the sample variance. Dealing with random samples from *normal populations*, we make use of Theorem 7.4, according to which

$$\frac{(n-1)s^2}{\sigma^2}$$

is a value of a random variable having the chi-square distribution with $n-1$ degrees of freedom. Thus, if χ_1^2 and χ_2^2 cut off left- and right-hand tails of area $\alpha/2$ under the chi-square distribution with $n-1$ degrees of freedom, we can assert with a degree of confidence of $1-\alpha$ that

$$\chi_1^2 < \frac{(n-1)s^2}{\sigma^2} < \chi_2^2$$

Solving this inequality for σ^2, we obtain the following $1-\alpha$ confidence interval for σ^2:

$$\blacklozenge \qquad \frac{(n-1)s^2}{\chi_2^2} < \sigma^2 < \frac{(n-1)s^2}{\chi_1^2} \qquad \blacklozenge$$

If we now take the square root of each member of this inequality, we obtain a corresponding $1-\alpha$ confidence interval for σ. Note that the above confidence intervals, obtained by taking "equal tails," do not actually give the *shortest* confidence intervals for σ^2 and σ, because the chi-square distribution is not symmetrical. Nevertheless, they are used in most applications in order to avoid complicated calculations.

To illustrate the construction of a confidence interval for σ or σ^2, let us return to the example on page 140, and let us suppose that the refractive indices in a random sample of 20 pieces of the glass had a variance of $1.20 \cdot 10^{-4}$. To construct a 0.95 confidence interval for σ^2, we find from Table V that for 19 degrees of freedom

$$\chi_1^2 = \chi_{.975}^2 = 8.907 \qquad \text{and} \qquad \chi_2^2 = \chi_{.025}^2 = 32.852$$

Substituting these values together with $n = 20$ and $s^2 = 1.20 \cdot 10^{-4}$ into the above confidence interval formula, we get

$$\frac{(19)(1.20 \cdot 10^{-4})}{32.852} < \sigma^2 < \frac{(19)(1.20 \cdot 10^{-4})}{8.907}$$

or

$$0.69 \cdot 10^{-4} < \sigma^2 < 2.56 \cdot 10^{-4}$$

Taking square roots, we find that the corresponding 0.95 confidence interval for σ is $0.0083 < \sigma < 0.0160$.

The method which we have discussed applies only to random samples from normal populations (or at least to random samples from populations sufficiently close to normal so that the method provides a good approximation). If the sample size is large, it can be shown that under fairly general conditions the sampling distribution of s can be approximated closely with a normal distribution having the mean σ and the standard deviation $\sigma/\sqrt{2n}$. Hence,

$$z = \frac{s - \sigma}{\sigma/\sqrt{2n}}$$

is a value of a random variable having approximately the standard normal distribution, and solving the inequality

$$-z_{\alpha/2} < \frac{s - \sigma}{\sigma/\sqrt{2n}} < z_{\alpha/2}$$

for σ, we thus obtain the following $1 - \alpha$ large-sample confidence interval for σ:

$$\blacklozenge \qquad \frac{s}{1 + \dfrac{z_{\alpha/2}}{\sqrt{2n}}} < \sigma < \frac{s}{1 - \dfrac{z_{\alpha/2}}{\sqrt{2n}}} \qquad \blacklozenge$$

EXERCISES

1. Use the data of Exercise 7 on page 171 to estimate the standard deviation of the lifetimes of the given kind of cutting tool
   (a) in terms of the sample standard deviation,
   (b) in terms of the sample range.

   Compare the two estimates by expressing their difference as a percentage of the first.

2. The following are the lengths (in inches) of 10 nails produced by a certain machine:

   $$1.14, \ 1.12, \ 1.11, \ 1.10, \ 1.16, \ 1.13, \ 1.18, \ 1.12, \ 1.11, \ 1.15$$

   (a) Find the range of this sample and use it to estimate the standard deviation of the lengths of nails produced by this machine.
   (b) Compare the range estimate obtained in part (a) with the sample standard deviation. (How can coding be used effectively in this case to calculate s?)

3. Using the data of Exercise 5 on page 171, construct a 0.95 confidence interval for the standard deviation of the lengths of time the experimental engine operates with 1 gallon of the given fuel.

4. Using the large-sample formula given on page 178 with the value of s obtained in Exercise 2 substituted for σ, find the minimum sample size needed to estimate σ within ± 0.005 in with a 0.95 degree of confidence.

5. A random sample of 25 executives spent on the average $175.36, with a standard deviation of $16.94, entertaining visiting dignitaries. Find a 0.95 confidence interval for the true standard deviation of such expenses using (a) the small-sample technique based on the chi-square distribution, and (b) the large-sample technique based on the normal distribution. Compare the two confidence intervals.

6. Using the value of s obtained in Exercise 2, construct a 0.90 confidence interval for σ. What assumption must be made about the population of nail lengths?

7. If 50 measurements of the specific gravity of aluminum had a mean of 2.686 and a standard deviation of 0.042, construct a 0.99 confidence interval for the true standard deviation of such measurements.

8. Measurements of the index of refraction of 25 pieces of optical glass had a standard deviation of 0.012. Assuming that the measurements may be treated as a sample from a normal population, find 0.95 confidence limits for σ^2 by the exact method and by the large-sample method. Compare your results.

9.2 Hypotheses Concerning One Variance

In this section we shall consider the problem of testing the null hypothesis that a population variance equals a specified constant against a suitable one- or two-sided alternative; that is, we shall test

$$H_0: \ \sigma^2 = \sigma_0^2$$

against one of the alternatives

$$H_1: \sigma^2 < \sigma_0^2, \qquad H_1: \sigma^2 > \sigma_0^2, \quad \text{or} \quad H_1: \sigma^2 \neq \sigma_0^2$$

Tests like these are important whenever it is desired to control the uniformity of a product or an operation. For example, suppose that a silicon disc, or "wafer," is to be cut into small squares, or "dice," to be used in the manufacture of a semiconductor device. Since certain electrical characteristics of the finished device may depend on the thickness of the die, it is important that all dice cut from a wafer have approximately the same thickness. Thus, not only must the mean thickness of a wafer be kept within specifications, but also the variation in thickness from location to location on the wafer.

Using the same sampling theory as in the preceding section, namely, the fact that for random samples from a normal population with the variance σ_0^2

$$\blacklozenge \qquad \chi^2 = \frac{(n-1)s^2}{\sigma_0^2} \qquad \blacklozenge$$

is a value of a random variable having the chi-square distribution with $n-1$ degrees of freedom, we can use this χ^2-statistic to test the null hypothesis $\sigma^2 = \sigma_0^2$ as shown in the following table:

CRITICAL REGIONS FOR TESTING H_0: $\sigma^2 = \sigma_0^2$

(Normal Population)

Alternative hypothesis	Reject H_0 if for $n-1$ degrees of freedom
$\sigma^2 < \sigma_0^2$	$\chi^2 < \chi^2_{1-\alpha}$
$\sigma^2 > \sigma_0^2$	$\chi^2 > \chi^2_{\alpha}$
$\sigma^2 \neq \sigma_0^2$	$\chi^2 < \chi^2_{1-\alpha/2}$ or $\chi^2 > \chi^2_{\alpha/2}$

In this table χ^2_{α} is as defined on page 139. Note that "equal tails" are used in performing the two-tail test, which is actually not the "best" procedure since the chi-square distribution is not symmetrical.

To illustrate this kind of *chi-square test*, let us assume that the thicknesses of a sample of 15 dice cut from a silicon wafer have a standard deviation of 0.64 mil and that the lapping process which ground the wafers to the proper thickness is acceptable only if σ, the population standard deviation of the dice thicknesses, is at most 0.50 mil. This means that we shall want to test the null hypothesis H_0: $\sigma = 0.50$, against the alternative H_1: $\sigma > 0.50$, and we shall do so at a level of significance of 0.05. Since this is equivalent to testing the null hypothesis $\sigma^2 = (0.50)^2 = 0.25$ against the alternative $\sigma^2 > 0.25$, the value of the test statistic becomes

$$\chi^2 = \frac{(14)(0.64)^2}{0.25} = 22.94$$

Since this does not exceed 23.685, the value of $\chi^2_{.05}$ for 14 degrees of freedom, the null hypothesis cannot be rejected; although the sample standard deviation exceeded 0.50, the evidence is not sufficient to arrive at the conclusion that the lapping process is unsatisfactory.

If the population from which we are sampling is not normal but the sample size is large ($n \geq 30$ is the usual rule of thumb), the null hypothesis H_0: $\sigma = \sigma_0$ can be tested with the use of the statistic

$$z = \frac{s - \sigma_0}{\sigma_0/\sqrt{2n}}$$

whose sampling distribution is approximately the standard normal distribution. The only difference in the tests is that z and z_α replace χ^2 and χ_α^2.

9.3 Hypotheses Concerning Two Variances

The two-sample t test for the difference between two means, described in Section 8.5, requires the assumption that the population variances are equal. Before proceeding with this test, therefore, it would be desirable to put this assumption to a test. In this section we shall describe a test of the null hypothesis $H_0: \sigma_1^2 = \sigma_2^2$ against an appropriate alternative, which applies to independent random samples from two normal populations. As we shall discover in Chapter 13, the test has many other important applications.

If independent random samples of size n_1 and n_2 are taken from normal populations having the same variance, it follows from Theorem 7.5 that the statistic

$$\blacklozenge \qquad F = \frac{s_1^2}{s_2^2} \qquad \blacklozenge$$

is a value of a random variable having the F distribution with $n_1 - 1$ and $n_2 - 1$ degrees of freedom. Thus, if the null hypothesis $\sigma_1^2 = \sigma_2^2$ is true, the ratio of the sample variances s_1^2 and s_2^2 provides a statistic on which tests of the null hypothesis can be based.

The critical region for testing H_0 against the alternative hypothesis $\sigma_1^2 > \sigma_2^2$ is $F > F_\alpha$, where F_α is as defined on page 140, namely, it cuts off a right-hand tail of area α under the F distribution with $n_1 - 1$ and $n_2 - 1$ degrees of freedom. Similarly, the critical region for testing H_0 against the alternative hypothesis $\sigma_1^2 < \sigma_2^2$ is $F < F_{1-\alpha}$, and this causes some difficulties since Table VI only contains values corresponding to right-hand tails of $\alpha = 0.05$ and $\alpha = 0.01$. As a result, we use the reciprocal of the original test statistic and make use of the relation

$$F_{1-\alpha}(\nu_1, \nu_2) = \frac{1}{F_\alpha(\nu_2, \nu_1)}$$

first given on page 141. Thus, we base the test on the statistic $F = s_2^2/s_1^2$ and the critical region for testing $H_0: \sigma_1^2 = \sigma_2^2$ against $H_1: \sigma_1^2 < \sigma_2^2$ becomes $F > F_\alpha$, where F_α is the appropriate critical value of F with $n_2 - 1$ and $n_1 - 1$ degrees of freedom.

For the two-sided alternative $\sigma_1^2 \neq \sigma_2^2$ the critical region is $F < F_{1-\alpha/2}$ or $F > F_{\alpha/2}$, where $F = s_1^2/s_2^2$ and the degrees of freedom are $n_1 - 1$ and $n_2 - 1$. In practice, we modify this test as in the preceding paragraph, so that we can again use the table of F values corresponding to right-hand tails of $\alpha = 0.05$ and $\alpha = 0.01$. To this end we let s_M^2 represent the larger of the two sample variances, s_m^2 the smaller, and we write the corresponding sample sizes as n_M and n_m. Thus, the test statistic becomes $F = s_M^2/s_m^2$ and the critical region is as shown in the following table:

CRITICAL REGIONS FOR TESTING H_0: $\sigma_1^2 = \sigma_2^2$
(Normal Populations)

Alternative hypothesis	Test statistic	Reject H_0 if
$\sigma_1^2 < \sigma_2^2$	$F = s_2^2/s_1^2$	$F > F_\alpha(n_2 - 1, n_1 - 1)$
$\sigma_1^2 > \sigma_2^2$	$F = s_1^2/s_2^2$	$F > F_\alpha(n_1 - 1, n_2 - 1)$
$\sigma_1^2 \neq \sigma_2^2$	$F = s_M^2/s_m^2$	$F > F_{\alpha/2}(n_M - 1, n_m - 1)$

The level of significance of these tests is α and the figures indicated in parentheses are the respective degrees of freedom. Note that, as in the chi-square test, "equal tails" are used in the two-tail test as a matter of mathematical convenience, even though the F distribution is not symmetrical.

To illustrate a one-tail F test for the equality of two variances, suppose that it is desired to determine whether a hand-lapping or an automatic machine-lapping method is better for grinding the silicon wafers mentioned on page 180 to a given thickness. We shall assume that there is essentially no difficulty in controlling the mean wafer thickness by either method, and base the test on the variability of the dice thickness exhibited by dice cut from wafers prepared by each process. If the burden of proof is to be placed on the automatic lapping method (perhaps because it requires new and expensive equipment), the null hypothesis H_0: $\sigma_1^2 = \sigma_2^2$ must be tested against the alternative H_1: $\sigma_1^2 > \sigma_2^2$, where the subscripts 1 and 2 stand, respectively, for the hand-lapping and the automatic-lapping procedures. Given that 31 dice from wafers that were hand lapped have a variance of $s_1^2 = 0.58$ while 35 dice from wafers that were lapped automatically have a variance of $s_2^2 = 0.26$, we find that the appropriate test statistic has the value

$$F = \frac{0.58}{0.26} = 2.23$$

Comparing this value with 1.79, the value of $F_{.05}(30, 34)$ obtained from Table VI by linear interpolation,* we conclude that the null hypothesis

---

* Note that it was really unnecessary to interpolate in this case since 2.23 exceeds both $F_{.05}(30, 30)$ and $F_{.05}(30, 40)$.

must be rejected at the 0.05 level of significance, and the decision is made to install the automatic equipment.

To illustrate a two-tail F test for the equality of two variances, let us return to the problem on page 168, where we tested whether the mean tensile strengths of structural steel beams provided by mills A and B differed by more than 2000 psi. In that example we went ahead and performed a two-sample t test even though there was a difference between the variances of the two samples. To justify that procedure, let us now test whether $\sigma_A^2 = \sigma_B^2$, and let us test this hypothesis against the alternative $\sigma_A^2 \neq \sigma_B^2$, since we are concerned only with the question whether or not these variances are equal. Since

$$s_A = 2100, \qquad s_B = 1900$$
$$n_A = 10, \qquad n_B = 12$$

we shall base the test on the statistic

$$F = \frac{s_A^2}{s_B^2} = \frac{(2100)^2}{(1900)^2} = 1.22$$

Using $\alpha = 0.02$, we find from Table VI that $F_{.01}(9, 11)$ equals 4.63, and it follows that the null hypothesis cannot be rejected. In other words, it was justifiable to use the two-sample t test in the given example.

EXERCISES

1. Referring to the data of Exercise 4 on page 171, test the hypothesis that $\sigma = 1.5$ against the alternative hypothesis that $\sigma < 1.5$. Use $\alpha = 0.05$.

2. Five hundred rounds of ammunition have been fired, and the following frequency table gives the resulting barrel pressures in thousands of pounds per square inch:

Barrel pressure	Frequency
48.0–49.9	21
50.0–51.9	94
52.0–53.9	132
54.0–55.9	155
56.0–57.9	82
58.0–59.9	16

Based on this information, is it reasonable to conclude that the standard deviation of such barrel pressures exceeds 2.2 thousand pounds per square inch? Use a 0.05 level of significance.

3. Test the null hypothesis that $\sigma = 0.01$ in. for the diameters of certain bolts, if in a random sample of size 12 the diameters of the bolts had a variance of $s^2 = 0.000050$. Use a level of significance of 0.01.

4. Referring to the data in Exercise 2 on page 178, test the null hypothesis that $\sigma^2 = 0.0003$ against the alternative that $\sigma^2 > 0.0003$, using the 0.01 level of significance.

5. Referring to Exercise 8 on page 171, test the null hypothesis that $\sigma = 1750$ for the mileages obtained with the given kind of tire. Use $\alpha = 0.05$ and the alternative hypothesis that $\sigma < 1750$.

6. Past data indicate that the variance of measurements made on sheet metal stampings by experienced quality control inspectors is 0.16 in.^{2}. Such measurements made by an inexperienced inspector could have too large a variance (perhaps because of inability to read instruments properly) or too small a variance (perhaps because unusually high or low measurements are discarded). If a new inspector measures 100 stampings with a variance of 0.11 in.^{2}, test at the 0.05 level of significance whether the inspector is making satisfactory measurements.

7. Referring to the data of Exercise 17 on page 173, check whether it is reasonable to claim that there is a greater variability in the lifetimes of plastic bowling pins than there is in the lifetimes of wooden bowling pins. Use $\alpha = 0.05$.

8. Justify the use of the two-sample t test in Exercise 14 on page 172 by testing the hypothesis that the two populations have equal variances. Use a level of significance of 0.02.

9. Referring to Exercise 16 on page 173, test the null hypothesis that $\sigma_1 = \sigma_2$ against the two-sided alternative $\sigma_1 \neq \sigma_2$ at $\alpha = 0.02$. Here σ_1 and σ_2 are the standard deviations of the two populations from which the measurements of the resistance of electric wires were obtained.

10. Two different lighting techniques are compared by measuring the intensity of light at selected locations in areas lighted by the two methods. If 15 measurements in the first area had a standard deviation of 2.5 foot-candles and 21 measurements in the second area had a standard deviation of 4.1 foot-candles, can it be concluded that the lighting in the second area is less uniform? Use a 0.01 level of significance. What assumptions must be made as to how the two samples are obtained?

10 | INFERENCES CONCERNING PROPORTIONS

10.1 Estimation of Proportions

Many engineering problems deal with proportions, percentages, or probabilities. In acceptance sampling we are concerned with the *proportion* of defectives in a lot, and in life testing we are concerned with the *percentage* of certain components which will perform satisfactorily during a stated period of time, or the *probability* that a given component will last at least a given number of hours. It should be clear from these examples that problems concerning proportions, percentages, or probabilities are really equivalent; a percentage is merely a proportion multiplied by 100, and a probability can be interpreted as a proportion "in the long run."

The information that is usually available for the estimation of a proportion is the number of times, x, that an appropriate event has occurred in n trials (or observations). The point estimate, itself, is usually the relative frequency x/n, namely, the proportion of the time that the event has actually occurred. If the n trials satisfy the assumptions underlying the binomial distribution listed on page 39, we know that the mean and the variance of the distribution of the number of "successes" are given by np and $np(1 - p)$. In Exercise 1 on page 190, the reader will be asked to verify that the mean and the variance of the proportion of successes (the relative frequency x/n) are given by

$$\blacklozenge \qquad \mu = p \qquad \text{and} \qquad \sigma^2 = \frac{p(1 - p)}{n} \qquad \blacklozenge$$

This shows that the sample proportion may be regarded as an *unbiased estimator* for the parameter p of a binomial distribution, namely, the "true" proportion we are trying to estimate on the basis of the sample.

In the construction of confidence intervals for the parameter p of the binomial distribution, we meet several obstacles. These are due mainly to the facts that (1) the binomial distribution is discrete, so that it may be impossible to get an interval with a degree of confidence of exactly $1 - \alpha$, and (2) the variance of the sampling distribution of x (or that of the sample proportion x/n) involves the parameter p we are trying to estimate. To construct a confidence interval for p having approximately a degree of confidence of $1 - \alpha$, we first select for a given set of values of p the corresponding quantities x_0 and x_1, where x_0 is the *largest integer* for which

$$\sum_{k=0}^{x_0} b(k; n, p) \leq \alpha/2$$

while x_1 is the *smallest integer* for which

$$\sum_{k=x_1}^{n} b(k; n, p) \leq \alpha/2$$

To emphasize the fact that x_0 and x_1 depend on the value chosen for p, we shall write these quantities as $x_0(p)$ and $x_1(p)$. We can then assert with a probability of approximately $1 - \alpha$ (and *at least* $1 - \alpha$) that

$$x_0(p) < x < x_1(p)$$

for any given value of p.

To change these inequalities into confidence intervals for p, we use a simple graphical method which is illustrated in the following example. Suppose we want to find approximate 0.95 confidence intervals for p for samples of size 20. Using Table I, we first determine x_0 and x_1 for selected values of p such that x_0 is the *largest integer* for which

$$B(x_0; 20, p) \leq 0.025$$

while x_1 is the *smallest integer* for which

$$1 - B(x_1 - 1; 20, p) \leq 0.025$$

Letting p equal 0.1, 0.2, 0.3, . . . , and 0.9, we thus obtain the following table:

p	0.1	0.2	0.3	0.4	0.5	0.6	0.7	0.8	0.9
x_0	—	0	1	3	5	7	9	11	14
x_1	6	9	11	13	15	17	19	20	—

Plotting the points $(p, x_0(p))$ and $(p, x_1(p))$ as we did in Figure 10.1, and drawing smooth curves, one through the x_0 points and one through the x_1 points, we can now "solve" for p. For any given value of x, we obtain approximate 0.95 confidence limits for p by going horizontally to the two curves and marking off the corresponding values of p (see Figure 10.1). Thus, for $x = 4$ we obtain the approximate 0.95 confidence interval $0.05 < p < 0.45$.

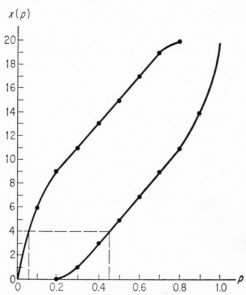

FIG. 10.1 Confidence intervals for proportions

Graphs similar to the one shown in Figure 10.1 are given in Tables VIII(a) and VIII(b) at the end of the book for various values of n and the degrees of confidence of 0.95 and 0.99. These tables differ from the one of Figure 10.1 in that the relative frequency x/n is used instead of x, thus making it possible to graph curves corresponding to various values of n. Also, for increased accuracy, Tables VIII(a) and VIII(b) are arranged so that values of x/n from 0 to 0.50 are marked on the bottom scale while those from 0.50 to 1.00 are marked on the top scale of the diagram. For values of x/n from 0 to 0.50 the confidence limits for p are read off the left-hand scale of the diagram, while for values of x/n from 0.50 to 1.00 they are read off the right-hand scale. Note that with the use of Table VIII(a) we now obtain for $n = 20$ and $x = 4$ the confidence interval $0.06 < p < 0.44$, which is very close, indeed, to the confidence interval we obtained from Figure 10.1.

When n is large and there is no reason to suspect that p is very close to either 0 or 1, we can construct approximate confidence intervals for p making use of the normal curve approximation to the binomial distribution. Since the mean and the standard deviation of the binomial distribution are np and $\sqrt{np(1-p)}$, we can assert with a probability of $1 - \alpha$ that

$$-z_{\alpha/2} < \frac{x - np}{\sqrt{np(1-p)}} < z_{\alpha/2}$$

Solving this quadratic inequality for p, we can obtain a corresponding set of (approximate) confidence limits for p (see Exercise 8 on page 191). However, since the necessary calculations are involved, we shall use the further approximation of substituting the sample proportion x/n for p in $\sqrt{np(1-p)}$. This yields the following $1 - \alpha$ *large-sample confidence interval for p:*

$$\frac{x}{n} - z_{\alpha/2}\sqrt{\frac{\frac{x}{n}\left(1 - \frac{x}{n}\right)}{n}} < p < \frac{x}{n} + z_{\alpha/2}\sqrt{\frac{\frac{x}{n}\left(1 - \frac{x}{n}\right)}{n}}$$

For instance, for $n = 100$ and $x = 36$ we obtain the 0.95 large-sample confidence interval

$$0.36 - 1.96\sqrt{\frac{(0.36)(0.64)}{100}} < p < 0.36 + 1.96\sqrt{\frac{(0.36)(0.64)}{100}}$$

or $0.266 < p < 0.454$

Had we used Table VIII(a) for this example, we would have obtained $0.27 < p < 0.47$.

The magnitude of the error we make when using x/n as an estimate of p is given by $\left|\frac{x}{n} - p\right|$ and using the normal curve approximation to the binomial distribution we can assert with a probability of $1 - \alpha$ that

$$\frac{|x - np|}{\sqrt{np(1-p)}} < z_{\alpha/2} \qquad \text{or} \qquad \left|\frac{x}{n} - p\right| < z_{\alpha/2}\sqrt{\frac{p(1-p)}{n}}$$

In order to use this last formula, we again substitute x/n for p inside the radical and, if we are dealing with a sufficiently large sample, we can assert with a probability of $1 - \alpha$ that the error in using x/n as an estimate of p is less than

$$z_{\alpha/2} \sqrt{\frac{\frac{x}{n}\left(1 - \frac{x}{n}\right)}{n}}$$

For instance, if 65 out of 250 persons attending an automobile show claim that they intend to buy a new car during the current model year and we estimate the true proportion of new-car buyers (attending the show) as $\frac{65}{250} = 0.26$, we can assert with a probability of 0.95 that the error of this estimate does not exceed

$$1.96 \sqrt{\frac{(0.26)(0.74)}{250}} = 0.05$$

The formula on which the above estimate of the error was based can also be used to determine the sample size that is required to attain a desired degree of precision or reliability. Letting E be the maximum error we are willing to risk with a probability of $1 - \alpha$, we have

♦ $$E = z_{\alpha/2} \sqrt{\frac{p(1 - p)}{n}} \quad \text{or} \quad n = p(1 - p)\left[\frac{z_{\alpha/2}}{E}\right]^2$$ ♦

This formula cannot be used as it stands, unless we have some information about the possible size of p on the basis of collateral data, say, a pilot sample. If we have no such information, we can make use of the fact that $p(1 - p)$ is at most equal to $1/4$. Thus, if

♦ $$n = \frac{1}{4}\left[\frac{z_{\alpha/2}}{E}\right]^2$$ ♦

we assert with a probability of *at least* $1 - \alpha$ that the error in using x/n as an estimate of p is less than E.

For instance, if we want to use a sample proportion to estimate the true proportion of defectives in a large shipment of glass bricks, and we want to be able to assert with a confidence of at least 0.95 that the size of the error is less than 0.03, we would have to take a sample of size

$$n = \frac{1}{4}\left[\frac{1.96}{0.03}\right]^2 = 1067.1$$

that is, a sample of size 1068. Had we known from experience with similar glass bricks that the proportion we are trying to estimate is in the neighborhood of 0.12, substitution into the appropriate formula would have yielded a required sample size of only

$$n = p(1 - p)\left[\frac{z_{\alpha/2}}{E}\right]^2 \approx (0.12)(0.88)\left[\frac{1.96}{0.03}\right]^2 = 450.7$$

that is, a sample of size 451. This serves to illustrate how some collateral information about the possible size of p can appreciably reduce the size of the required sample.

If p is very close to 0 or 1, none of the confidence intervals we have described above provides a very satisfactory approximation, even for very large values of n. For example, for $n = 1000$ and $x = 2$, a 0.99 confidence interval for p computed by the above method, which was based on the normal curve approximation to the binomial distribution, is 0.0020 ± 0.0036. Note that the lower confidence limit for p is negative. In cases where p is close to 0 (or 1), such as might be encountered in testing for high reliability, we are really interested more in one-sided confidence intervals of the form $p < C$; that is, we are interested mainly in finding an *upper confidence limit* for p. When p is small and n is large, we approximate the binomial distribution with a Poisson distribution rather than a normal curve (see discussion on page 50), using the relation $\lambda = np$ to obtain an upper confidence limit for p. Without going into any detail, let us merely state the result that such an approximate $1 - \alpha$ upper confidence limit is given by $\dfrac{1}{2n} \cdot \chi_\alpha^2$, where χ_α^2 is as defined on page 139 and the number of degrees of freedom equals $2(x + 1)$. (A discussion of this approximation may be found in the book by A. Hald mentioned in the Bibliography.)

Using this theory for the above example where we had $x = 2$, $n = 1000$, and $\alpha = 0.01$, we obtain the following one-sided confidence interval for p:

$$p < \frac{16.8}{2(1000)} = 0.0084$$

where 16.8 is the value of $\chi_{.01}^2$ for $2(2 + 1) = 6$ degrees of freedom. Had we *erroneously* used the normal distribution rather than the Poisson distribution to approximate the binomial distribution, we would have obtained the much narrower interval $0 < p < 0.0056$.

EXERCISES

1. Verify the formulas given on page 186 for the mean and the variance of the distribution of the *proportion* of successes.

2. Suppose that in a random sample of 200 voters 80 were in favor of a certain piece of legislation and 120 were opposed. Use Table VIII to construct a 0.95 confidence interval for the true proportion of voters favoring the legislation.

3. Among 400 car owners interviewed, 260 stated that the next car they hope to buy will be of the same make as the one they currently own. Use Table

VIII to construct a 0.99 confidence interval for the true proportion of car owners who intend to replace their cars with a new car of the same make.

4. In a random sample of 100 diodes 28 were found to fall in a certain voltage category. Construct 0.99 confidence intervals for the proportion of diodes in the given category by use of Table VIII and by use of the large-sample formula on page 188. Compare results.

5. A company writing industrial accident insurance finds that 138 of 250 policy holders filed at least one claim during the three-year period 1960–1962. Given that this information is based on a random sample taken from the company's files, construct a 0.95 confidence interval for the corresponding true proportion (a) by using Table VIII, and (b) by using the large-sample formula on page 188.

6. What is the size of the smallest sample required to estimate an unknown proportion to within a maximum error of 0.01 with a degree of confidence of 0.95? If the proportion is estimated to be 0.15 on the basis of a small pilot sample, what sample size can then be used?

7. What is the minimum sample size a public opinion poll has to use if it wants to be able to assert with a probability of at least 0.95 that its estimate of the percentage of the vote a certain candidate will get is not "off" by more than 5 per cent? How would the required minimum sample size be affected if it were known that the percentage to be estimated is in the neighborhood of 65 per cent?

8. Show that the double inequality on page 188 leads to the following $1 - \alpha$ confidence limits:

$$\frac{x + \frac{1}{2}z^2_{\alpha/2} \pm z_{\alpha/2}\sqrt{\frac{x(n-x)}{n} + \frac{1}{4}z^2_{\alpha/2}}}{n + z^2_{\alpha/2}}$$

9. Use the confidence-interval formula of Exercise 8 to work Exercise 4 and compare the results.

10. In 5000 firings of an air-to-air rocket there was one instance in which a rocket exploded upon ignition. Construct an upper 0.99 confidence limit for the probability that such a rocket will explode on ignition.

11. Among 500 new units installed by a certain telephone company, 3 required service during the first year. Use the method discussed on page 190 to determine a 0.95 upper confidence limit for the true proportion of new units that require service during the first year of operation.

12. Referring to Exercise 10, find the number of rocket firings without failure that would be required so that one could assert with a degree of confidence of at least 0.995 that the probability of explosion upon ignition is less than 0.0001.

10.2 Hypotheses Concerning One Proportion

Many of the methods used in sampling inspection, quality control, and reliability verification are based on tests of the null hypothesis that a proportion (percentage, or probability) equals some specified constant. The details of the application of such tests to quality control will be discussed in Chapter 15, where we shall also go into some problems of sampling inspection; applications to reliability and life testing will be taken up in Chapter 16.

Although there are exact tests based on the binomial distribution (which can be constructed with the use of Table I), we shall consider here only approximate large-sample tests ($n \geq 100$) based on the normal approximation to the binomial distribution. In other words, we shall test the null hypothesis

$$H_0: p = p_0$$

against one of the alternatives

$$H_1: p < p_0, \qquad H_1: p > p_0, \qquad H_1: p \neq p_0$$

with the use of the following statistic

$$z = \frac{x - np_0}{\sqrt{np_0(1 - p_0)}}$$

If the null hypothesis is true, the sampling distribution of this statistic is approximately the standard normal distribution, and the critical regions for the test are as shown in the following table:

CRITICAL REGIONS FOR TESTING $H_0: p = p_0$
(Large Samples)

Alternative hypothesis	Reject H_0 if
$p < p_0$	$z < -z_\alpha$
$p > p_0$	$z > z_\alpha$
$p \neq p_0$	$z < -z_{\alpha/2}$ or $z > z_{\alpha/2}$

(If the sample size is not large enough to use the normal approximation of the binomial distribution, we have to use the exact test mentioned above. For instance, to test the null hypothesis $p = p_0$ against the alternative $p < p_0$, we use the critical region $x \leq k_\alpha$, where k_α is the *largest integer* such that $B(k_\alpha; n, p_0) \leq \alpha$.)

To illustrate the large-sample test, suppose we want to test an executive's claim that less than 60 per cent of the employees of a very large company are in favor of joining a union. If we place the burden of proof on the executive, the appropriate null hypothesis and alternative hypothesis are, respectively, $p = 0.60$ and $p < 0.60$. If in a random sample of size 400 there were 208 votes for the union and 192 against it, we obtain

$$z = \frac{208 - 400(0.60)}{\sqrt{400(0.60)(0.40)}} = -3.3$$

and it follows that the null hypothesis can be rejected at a level of significance of 0.01. This supports the executive's claim.

10.3 Hypotheses Concerning Several Proportions

When we compare the consumer response (percentage favorable and percentage unfavorable) to two different products, when we decide whether the proportion of defectives of a given process remains constant from day to day, when we judge whether there is a difference in political persuasion among several nationality groups, and in many similar situations, we are interested in testing whether two or more binomial populations have the same parameter p. Referring to these parameters as $p_1, p_2, \ldots,$ and p_k, we are, in fact, interested in testing the null hypothesis

$$H_0: \ p_1 = p_2 = \ldots = p_k$$

against the alternative that at least two of these population proportions are unequal. To perform a suitable large-sample test of this hypothesis, we require independent random samples of size $n_1, n_2, \ldots,$ and n_k from the k populations, and it will be assumed that the corresponding numbers of "successes" are $x_1, x_2, \ldots,$ and x_k. The test we shall use is based on the fact that (1) for large samples, the sampling distribution of

$$z_i = \frac{x_i - n_i p_i}{\sqrt{n_i p_i(1 - p_i)}}$$

is approximately the standard normal distribution, (2) the square of a random variable having the standard normal distribution is a random variable having the chi-square distribution with 1 degree of freedom, and (3) the sum of k independent random variables having chi-square distributions with 1 degree of freedom is a random variable having the chi-square distribution with k degrees of freedom. (Proofs of these last two results may be found in the book by J. E. Freund mentioned in the Bibliography.) Thus, the sampling distribution of the statistic

$$\chi^2 = \sum_{i=1}^{k} \frac{(x_i - n_i p_i)^2}{n_i p_i(1 - p_i)}$$

is approximately the chi-square distribution with k degrees of freedom.

(This approximation is usually quite close so long as $n_i p_i \geq 5$ for all i.)
Now, if the null hypothesis is true, and $p_1 = p_2 = \ldots = p_k = p$, the value
of the above χ^2 statistic becomes

$$\chi^2 = \sum_{i=1}^{k} \frac{(x_i - n_i p)^2}{n_i p (1 - p)}$$

and in actual practice we substitute for p (which, of course, is unknown)
the pooled estimate

$$\hat{p} = \frac{x_1 + x_2 + \ldots + x_k}{n_1 + n_2 + \ldots + n_k}$$

Since the null hypothesis should be rejected if the differences between the
x_i and the $n_i p$ are large, the critical region is $\chi^2 \geq x_\alpha^2$, where χ_α^2 is as defined
on page 139 and the number of degrees of freedom is $k - 1$. The loss of
one degree of freedom results from the fact that p is estimated by $\hat{p}$.

We shall not illustrate this test right away, because in practice it is
convenient to perform the test or express the χ^2 statistic in different (though
equivalent) ways. In the special case where $k = 2$, in which we are testing
the null hypothesis that two population proportions are equal, we base
our decision on the statistic

$$z = \frac{\dfrac{x_1}{n_1} - \dfrac{x_2}{n_2}}{\sqrt{\hat{p}(1 - \hat{p}) \left(\dfrac{1}{n_1} + \dfrac{1}{n_2} \right)}} \quad \text{with } \hat{p} = \frac{x_1 + x_2}{n_1 + n_2}$$

whose sampling distribution is approximately the standard normal distribution. The test based on this statistic is equivalent to the χ^2 test
described above, in the sense that the *square* of this z statistic actually
equals the above χ^2 statistic with $k = 2$ (see Exercise 7 on page 198). It
is preferable to use the z statistic, as it enables us to test the null hypothesis
$p_1 = p_2$ against one-sided or two-sided alternatives; this is not true for the
χ^2 statistic, with which we can only test against the two-sided alternative
$p_1 \neq p_2$. The resulting critical regions based on the above z statistic are

CRITICAL REGIONS FOR TESTING H_0: $p_1 = p_2$
(Large Samples)

Alternative hypothesis	Reject H_0 if
$p_1 < p_2$	$z < -z_\alpha$
$p_1 > p_2$	$z > z_\alpha$
$p_1 \neq p_2$	$z < -z_{\alpha/2}$ or $z > z_{\alpha/2}$

To illustrate this large-sample test for the significance of the difference between two sample proportions, suppose a survey conducted by a market research organization showed that a certain household product was used by 128 of 400 persons interviewed in a city where it was widely advertised, but only by 115 of 500 persons interviewed in a city where the product was not advertised. In order to determine whether the advertising is really effective, it is desired to test the null hypothesis $p_1 = p_2$ against the alternative $p_1 > p_2$, where p_1 and p_2 are the true proportions of persons considered in the two cities who use the product. (In this way, rejection of the null hypothesis implies that the advertising is effective.) Substituting $x_1 = 128$, $n_1 = 400$, $x_2 = 115$, and $n_2 = 500$ into the formulas for $\hat{p}$ and z, we obtain

$$\hat{p} = \frac{128 + 115}{400 + 500} = 0.27$$

and

$$z = \frac{\dfrac{128}{400} - \dfrac{115}{500}}{\sqrt{(0.27)(0.73)\left(\dfrac{1}{400} + \dfrac{1}{500}\right)}} = 3.02$$

This exceeds the critical value for $\alpha = 0.05$, namely, 1.645, and we conclude that the difference in the sample proportions is significant. In other words, the advertising is effective. Whether it is "sufficiently effective" to justify its use depends on the cost of the product, the size of the market, the cost of the advertising, and perhaps other considerations.

When we apply the chi-square criterion on page 194 to the comparison of *several* sample proportions, it is convenient to look at the data as arranged in the following fashion:

	Sample 1	Sample 2	. . .	Sample k	Total
Successes	x_1	x_2	. . .	x_k	x
Failures	$n_1 - x_1$	$n_2 - x_2$	. . .	$n_k - x_k$	$n - x$
Total	n_1	n_2	. . .	n_k	n

where the notation is the same as before, except for the addition of x and n, which represent, respectively, the total number of successes and the total number of trials for all samples combined. With reference to this table, the entry in the cell belonging to the ith row and jth column is called the *observed* cell frequency f_{ij}, with $i = 1, 2$ and $j = 1, 2, \ldots, k$.

Under the null hypothesis that $p_1 = p_2 = \ldots = p_k = p$, we estimate p, as before, as the total number of successes divided by the total number of trials, which we now write as $\hat{p} = x/n$. Hence, the *expected* number of successes for the jth sample is estimated as

$$e_{1j} = n_j \cdot \hat{p} = \frac{n_j \cdot x}{n}$$

while the *expected* number of failures for the jth sample is estimated as

$$e_{2j} = n_j(1 - \hat{p}) = \frac{n_j \cdot (n - x)}{n}$$

The quantities e_{1j} and e_{2j} are referred to as the *expected cell frequencies* e_{ij}, with $i = 1, 2$ and $j = 1, 2, \ldots, k$. *Thus, the expected frequency for any given cell may be obtained by multiplying the totals of the row and column to which the cell belongs, and then dividing by the grand total n.*

Using this new notation, it can be shown (see Exercise 12 on page 198) that the χ^2 statistic on page 194 can be written in the form

♦ $$\chi^2 = \sum_{i=1}^{2} \sum_{j=1}^{k} \frac{(f_{ij} - e_{ij})^2}{e_{ij}}$$ ♦

This formula has the advantage that it can be applied directly to more general problems where each trial permits more than two possible outcomes and where there are, thus, more than two rows in the schematic presentation analogous to the one on page 195. This kind of problem will be discussed in Section 10.4.

To illustrate the use of this χ^2 statistic, suppose it is desired to test at the 0.01 level of significance whether the proportion of purchases brought back and exchanged in a certain department store is subject to *seasonal variations*. The data that are available for this test are shown in the following table:

	First quarter	Second quarter	Third quarter	Fourth quarter	Total
Number of items exchanged	29	12	8	21	70
Number of items not exchanged	81	118	92	139	430
Total	110	130	100	160	500

The expected cell frequencies for the first three cells of the first row are

$$\frac{70 \cdot 110}{500} = 15.4, \qquad \frac{70 \cdot 130}{500} = 18.2, \qquad \frac{70 \cdot 100}{500} = 14.0$$

and, as it can be shown that the expected frequencies for each row or column total the same as the corresponding observed frequencies (see Exercise 16 on page 199), we find by subtraction that e_{14} equals $70 - (15.4 + 18.2 + 14.0) = 22.4$ and that the expected frequencies for the second row equal $110 - 15.4 = 94.6$, $130 - 18.2 = 111.8$, $100 - 14.0 = 86.0$, and $160 - 22.4 = 137.6$. Since the expected frequencies are all 5 or greater, we can substitute these values together with the observed cell frequencies into the appropriate formula for the χ^2 statistic, and we obtain

$$\chi^2 = \frac{(29 - 15.4)^2}{15.4} + \frac{(12 - 18.2)^2}{18.2} + \frac{(8 - 14.0)^2}{14.0} + \frac{(21 - 22.4)^2}{22.4}$$
$$+ \frac{(81 - 94.6)^2}{94.6} + \frac{(118 - 111.8)^2}{111.8} + \frac{(92 - 86.0)^2}{86.0} + \frac{(139 - 137.6)^2}{137.6}$$
$$= 19.49$$

Since this value exceeds 11.345, the value of $\chi^2_{.01}$ with 3 degrees of freedom, we can reject the null hypothesis that the proportion of items exchanged remains constant; in other words, we conclude that there is a definite seasonal pattern.

EXERCISES

1. A medical research worker wants to determine whether a new muscle relaxant will produce beneficial results in a higher proportion of patients suffering from a neurological disorder than the 0.70 receiving beneficial results from standard treatment. How should he interpret an experiment (at the 0.05 level of significance) if 156 of 200 patients obtained beneficial results with the new relaxant?

2. A random sample of size 100 is drawn from a large lot of manufactured items. It is desired to test (at the 0.05 level of significance) whether the proportion of acceptable items in the lot is 0.80 against the alternative that it is less than 0.80.

   (a) What is the maximum number of acceptable items in the sample that will lead to the rejection of the null hypothesis?

   (b) Find the probability of acceptance if the lot actually contains 75 per cent acceptable items.

   (c) Sketch the OC curve of this test.

3. It costs more to test a certain type of ammunition than to manufacture it, and, hence, only three rounds are tested from each large lot. If the lot is rejected unless all three rounds function according to specifications,

   (a) sketch the OC curve for this test,

   (b) find the actual proportion of defectives for which the test procedure will cause a lot to be rejected with a probability of 0.10.

4. A highway official claims that 3 out of 10 cars do not meet state requirements concerning lights, brakes, direction signals, etc. Test this claim at the 0.01

level of significance if among 400 cars stopped at road blocks throughout the state 73 did not meet the above requirements.

5. It is claimed that 30 per cent of all typewriters in use in a certain area were manufactured by a given company. Is this claim substantiated or refuted by a survey showing that 118 out of 500 typewriters were made by that company? Use a level of significance of 0.01.

6. The null hypothesis that $p = 0.35$ for a binomial population is to be tested against the alternative $p > 0.35$ at the level of significance of 0.05. If the decision is to be based on a sample of size $n = 15$, what is the least number of "successes" for which the null hypothesis can be rejected? What is the probability that the null hypothesis $p = 0.35$ will be accepted with this criterion even though p actually equals 0.40?

7. Show that the square of the z statistic on page 194 equals the chi-square statistic on the same page for $k = 2$.

8. Past records show that 150 shipments from Vendor A contained 34 that were unsatisfactory for one reason or another, while 120 shipments from Vendor B contained 46 that were unsatisfactory. Use the χ^2 statistic and a level of significance of 0.05 to test the null hypothesis $p_1 = p_2$, where p_1 and p_2 are true proportions of unsatisfactory shipments from the two vendors. Repeat the test using the z statistic on page 194, and verify that the square of the z statistic equals the value obtained previously for the χ^2 statistic.

9. Repeat Exercise 8, testing the null hypothesis $p_1 = p_2$ against the one-sided alternative $p_1 < p_2$.

10. A manufacturer of electronic equipment wishes to subject two competing brands of transistors to an accelerated environmental test. Of the 80 transistors from the first manufacturer 25 failed the test, and of the 50 transistors from the second manufacturer 21 failed the test. Using a level of significance of 0.05, test whether there is a difference between the two products

(a) on the basis of the chi-square statistic given on page 194,

(b) on the basis of the z statistic given on page 194.

Also verify that the square of the value obtained for the z statistic equals that obtained for the chi-square statistic.

11. Two groups of 50 patients each took part in an experiment in which one group received pills containing an anti-allergy drug, and the other group received a placebo (or a pill containing no drug). In the group given the drug 15 exhibited allergic symptoms, while in the group given the placebo 24 exhibited such symptoms. Is this sufficient evidence to conclude (at the 0.05 level of significance) that the drug is effective in reducing these symptoms?

12. Verify that the two formulas given for the χ^2 statistic on pages 194 and 196 are equivalent.

13. The following are the January, 1964, sales records for three salesmen employed by a certain firm:

	Salesman A	Salesman B	Salesman C
Customers contacted	105	82	138
Number of sales made	11	16	15

   Using a level of significance of 0.05, test whether the differences among the proportions of sales are significant.

14. Tests are made on the proportion of defective castings produced by five different molds. If there were 12 defectives among 100 castings made with mold I, 32 defectives among 200 castings made with mold II, 25 defectives among 180 castings made with mold III, 15 defectives among 120 castings made with mold IV, and 20 defectives among 150 castings made with mold V, test (at the 0.05 level of significance) whether the true proportion of defectives is the same for each mold.

15. Using a level of significance of 0.05, can it be concluded from the following data that the proportion of undergraduates operating automobiles on a certain campus depends on their class?

	Freshmen	Sophomores	Juniors	Seniors
Number of students	450	360	340	300
Students with cars	99	90	102	96

16. Verify that if the expected frequencies are determined as indicated on page 196, the expected frequencies for each row or column total the same as the corresponding observed frequencies.

10.4 Contingency Tables

As we suggested on page 196, the method by which we analyzed the last example of the preceding section lends itself also to the analysis of so-called *r-by-k tables*, that is, tables in which observed frequencies are arranged in r rows and k columns. Such tables arise in essentially two kinds of problems. First, we might again have samples from k populations, with the distinction that now each trial permits more than two possible outcomes. This might happen, for example, if persons belonging to different income groups are asked whether they favor a certain political candidate, whether they are against him, or whether they are indifferent or undecided. The other situation giving rise to an r-by-k table is one in which we sample from one population but classify each item with respect to two (usually qualitative) categories. This might happen, for example, if a consumer testing service rates cars as excellent, superior, average, or poor with regard to performance and also with regard to appearance. Each car tested would then fall into one of the 16 cells of a 4-by-4 table.

The essential difference between the two situations giving rise to r-by-k tables is that in the first case the column totals (the sample sizes) are fixed, while in the second case only the grand total is fixed. In spite of this difference, the method of analysis is the same and we shall treat the two situations as one problem. To illustrate the general approach, let us consider the problem faced by a canner of vegetables, who wants to know whether consumer reaction to his product is the same regardless of the amount of food coloring that is being used—or in other words, whether there is a relationship between the use of different amounts of food coloring and consumer reaction to the product. The data he has available for this study are as shown in the following table:

	No coloring	Lightly colored	Deeply colored	Total
Tastes excellent	18	61	11	90
Tastes fair	48	79	23	150
Tastes poor	34	10	16	60
Total	100	150	50	300

If these data were obtained by taking 100 items without coloring, 150 with light coloring, and 50 with deep coloring, and getting consumer reaction, we have the first kind of situation described above and we shall want to test the null hypothesis

$$p_{i1} = p_{i2} = p_{i3} \qquad \text{for } i = 1, 2, 3$$

where p_{ij} is the probability of obtaining a response belonging to the ith row and jth column. The alternative hypothesis is that the p's are not all alike at least for one row. If the data were obtained by randomly interviewing consumers and classifying each response with regard to the amount of coloring used in the product and the consumer's reaction, we have the second kind of situation described above, and we shall want to test the null hypothesis

$$p_{ij} = (p_{i.})(p_{.j}) \qquad \text{for } \begin{cases} i = 1, 2, 3 \\ j = 1, 2, 3 \end{cases}$$

where $p_{i.}$ is the probability of obtaining an item belonging to the ith row and $p_{.j}$ is the probability of obtaining an item belonging to the jth column.

The alternative to this null hypothesis (which is really a null hypothesis of *independence*) is that the equality does not hold for at least one pair of values of i and j.

No matter how the data were obtained (or how we look at the problem), the method of analysis is the same. We calculate the expected cell frequency e_{ij} by multiplying the ith row total by the jth column total and then dividing by the grand total. (In practice, we make use of the fact that the observed frequencies and the expected frequencies total the same for each row and column, so that only $(r - 1)(k - 1)$ of the e_{ij} have to be calculated for an r-by-k table, while those remaining can be obtained by subtraction from appropriate row or column totals.) We then substitute into the formula

$$\blacklozenge \qquad \chi^2 = \sum_{i=1}^{r} \sum_{j=1}^{k} \frac{(f_{ij} - e_{ij})^2}{e_{ij}} \qquad \blacklozenge$$

and we reject the null hypothesis if the value of this statistic exceeds χ_α^2 with $(r - 1)(k - 1)$ degrees of freedom. (This expression for the number of degrees of freedom is justified by the above observation that after we choose $(r - 1)(k - 1)$ of the expected cell frequencies, the others are automatically determined, that is, they may be obtained by subtraction from appropriate row or column totals.)

Returning to our numerical example, we find that the expected cell frequencies for the first two cells for the first two rows are

$$e_{11} = \frac{(90)(100)}{300} = 30, \qquad e_{12} = \frac{(90)(150)}{300} = 45$$

$$e_{21} = \frac{(150)(100)}{300} = 50, \qquad e_{22} = \frac{(150)(150)}{300} = 75$$

and, by subtraction, that the other expected cell frequencies are $e_{13} = 15$, $e_{23} = 25$, $e_{31} = 20$, $e_{23} = 30$, and $e_{33} = 10$. Thus,

$$\chi^2 = \frac{(18 - 30)^2}{30} + \frac{(61 - 45)^2}{45} + \frac{(11 - 15)^2}{15}$$

$$+ \frac{(48 - 50)^2}{50} + \frac{(79 - 75)^2}{75} + \frac{(23 - 25)^2}{25}$$

$$+ \frac{(34 - 20)^2}{20} + \frac{(10 - 30)^2}{30} + \frac{(16 - 10)^2}{10}$$

$$= 38.74$$

Since this exceeds 9.488, the value of $\chi_{.05}^2$ with $(3 - 1)(3 - 1) = 4$ degrees of freedom, the null hypothesis must be rejected. We conclude that there is some relationship (some dependence) between the amount of food coloring used and customer acceptance of the product.

10.5 Goodness of Fit

We speak of "goodness of fit" when we want to com-
pare an observed distribution with the corresponding values of a theoretical
distribution. To illustrate, suppose that in the manufacture of sheet glass
a quality control engineer inspects samples at regular intervals of time and
that in 250 such samples he observed 0, 1, 2, . . . , and 10 imperfections
with the respective frequencies of 8, 40, 62, 54, 43, 27, 10, 3, 2, 0, and 1.
On the basis of this information he wants to decide whether the data may
be looked upon as values of a random variable having the Poisson distribution, namely, whether a Poisson distribution will give a good fit. The
mean of the given distribution is $740/250 = 2.96$ and we shall, therefore,
attempt to fit a Poisson distribution having $\lambda = 3$ (the value closest to
2.96 in Table II). In the table which follows, the observed frequencies are
given in the second column, the Poisson probabilities with $\lambda = 3$ are given
in the third column, and the expected frequencies in the fourth column
are obtained by multiplying each of the corresponding Poisson probabilities
by 250 and rounding to one decimal.

Number of imperfections	Observed frequencies	Poisson probabilities	Expected frequencies
0	8	0.0498	12.5
1	40	0.1494	37.4
2	62	0.2240	56.0
3	54	0.2240	56.0
4	43	0.1680	42.0
5	27	0.1008	25.2
6	10	0.0504	12.6
7	3	0.0216	5.4
8	2	0.0081	2.0
9	0	0.0027	0.7
10	1	0.0008	0.2

An appropriate test of the null hypothesis that the data come from a
population having a Poisson distribution (against the alternative that the
population has some other distribution) can be based on the statistic

$$\blacklozenge \qquad \chi^2 = \sum_{i=1}^{k} \frac{(f_i - e_i)^2}{e_i} \qquad \blacklozenge$$

where the f_i and e_i are, as before, the corresponding observed and expected
frequencies. The sampling distribution of this statistic is approximately
the chi-square distribution with $k - 2$ degrees of freedom, where k is the
number of terms in the formula for χ^2. In general, the number of degrees
of freedom for the chi-square test of goodness of fit is the number of terms

in the formula for χ^2 *minus* the number of quantities *obtained from the original data* which are required to calculate the expected frequencies. Note that in our example we had to know the mean of the distribution as well as the total frequency to calculate the e_i; therefore, we have $k-2$ degrees of freedom.

In order to follow the rule on page 194, according to which none of the expected frequencies in a chi-square comparison should be less than 5, we shall follow the simple practice of combining adjacent classes as indicated in the table on the preceding page. Combining the last four classes into one class representing 7 or more imperfections, we thus obtain

$$\chi^2 = \frac{(8-12.5)^2}{12.5} + \frac{(40-37.4)^2}{37.4} + \frac{(62-56.0)^2}{56.0} + \frac{(54-56.0)^2}{56.0}$$
$$+ \frac{(43-42.0)^2}{42.0} + \frac{(27-25.2)^2}{25.2} + \frac{(10-12.6)^2}{12.6} + \frac{(6-8.3)^2}{8.3}$$

$$= 3.84$$

Since this is less than 12.592, the value of $\chi^2_{.05}$ for $8-2=6$ degrees of freedom, the null hypothesis cannot be rejected and we conclude that the Poisson distribution provides a *good fit*.

EXERCISES

1. Samples of three kinds of materials, subjected to extreme temperature changes, produced the results shown in the following table.

	Material A	Material B	Material C	
Broke completely	9	15	8	32
Showed slight defects	18	31	27	76
Remained perfect	62	48	51	161
	89	94	86	269

   Test, at a level of significance of 0.05, whether the true proportions of items falling into the three categories are the same for all three materials.

2. A trade journal wants to determine the attitude of executives in various fields toward the value of such "prestige" activities as the sponsorship of research, scholarships, science fairs, and the like. Using the results of the following table, test at the 0.01 level whether there is any relationship between executives' attitude toward such activities and the area of their employment.

	Advertising executives	Personnel executives	Production executives	General administrative executives	
Of little value	60	35	30	25	150
Of some value	50	40	45	20	155
Of great value	100	55	95	45	29
	210	130	170	90	60

3. The following sample data pertain to shipments received by a large firm from four different vendors:

	Number rejected	Number imperfect but acceptable	Number perfect
Vendor A	7	18	65
Vendor B	5	32	83
Vendor C	12	25	103
Vendor D	6	8	86

Test at the 0.05 level of significance whether the four vendors ship products of equal quality.

4. In a random sample of 600 families interviewed concerning their television viewing habits, there were 124 families with low incomes among which 48 liked a certain new comedian while the remaining 76 either did not like him or did not care. There were also 319 families with average incomes and 157 with high incomes; among those with average incomes 115 liked the new comedian while the remaining 204 did not like him or did not care, and among those with high incomes 94 liked the new comedian while 63 did not like him or did not care. Test at the 0.05 level whether there is a relationship between income level and the response to the new comedian.

5. A quality control engineer takes daily samples of 10 electronic components, checking them for imperfections. If on 200 consecutive working days he obtained 112 samples with 0 defectives, 76 samples with 1 defective, and 12 samples with 2 defectives, test at the 0.05 level whether these samples may be looked upon as samples from a binomial population.

6. Referring to the data of Exercise 5, test at the 0.05 level whether they can be looked upon as samples from a binomial population with $p = 0.05$.

7. Roll a die 240 times and use the results to test (at $\alpha = 0.05$) whether the die is really balanced.

8. It is desired to test whether the number of gamma rays emitted per second by a certain radioactive substance has a Poisson distribution with $\lambda = 3.4$. Test this hypothesis at the 0.01 level of significance if the following results were observed for 250 one-second intervals:

Number of gamma rays per second	Frequency
0	3
1	21
2	51
3	60
4	38
5	31
6	26
7 or more	20

9. The following is the distribution of iron-solution indices given first on page 106:

Iron-solution indices	Frequency
0.10–0.29	3
0.30–0.49	13
0.50–0.69	17
0.70–0.89	32
0.90–1.09	23
1.10–1.29	7
1.30–1.49	5

As we showed in Chapter 6, the mean of this distribution is $\bar{x} = 0.795$ and its standard deviation is $s = 0.28$.

(a) Find the probabilities that a random variable having a normal distribution with $\mu = 0.795$ and $\sigma = 0.28$ assumes a value between 0.095 and 0.295, between 0.295 and 0.495, between 0.495 and 0.695, between 0.695 and 0.895, between 0.895 and 1.095, between 1.095 and 1.295, and between 1.295 and 1.495.

(b) Multiply the probabilities obtained in part (a) by the total frequency (in this case $n = 100$), getting thus the *expected normal curve frequencies* corresponding to the seven classes of the given distribution.

(c) Test the null hypothesis that the given data may be looked upon as a random sample from a normal population by comparing the observed and expected frequencies with an appropriate χ^2 statistic (using $\alpha = 0.05$). Explain why the number of degrees of freedom for this χ^2 test is given by $k - 3$, where k is the number of terms in the χ^2 statistic.

10. Among 100 vacuum tubes used in an experiment, 35 had a service life of less than 10 hours, 20 had a service life of more than 10 but less than 20 hours,

18 had a service life of more than 20 but less than 30 hours, 8 had a service life of more than 30 but less than 40 hours, and 19 had a service life of more than 40 hours. Using steps similar to those outlined in Exercise 9, test whether these lifetimes can be regarded as a sample from an exponential population with $\mu = 25$ hours. Use a 0.01 level of significance.

11 | SHORT-CUT METHODS IN INFERENCE

11.1 Introduction

Most of the methods of estimation and of testing hypotheses we have studied so far are based on the assumption that the observations are taken from normal populations. These methods extract all the information that is available in a sample, and they usually attain the best possible precision, that is, the most reliable results. As we have pointed out earlier, the assumption that the samples are taken from normal populations is not really as stringent as it may seem. Most statistical methods based on the normal distribution are fairly *robust*, that is, they will give reasonably accurate answers even when the normality assumption is only satisfied in an approximate sense. In spite of this, there are several reasons why we may wish to use other, less precise methods—the assumption of normality may be grossly incorrect, the labor involved in carrying out the more precise methods may be excessive, or a short-cut method may be desired to determine in advance whether it is worthwhile to carry out the more detailed calculations.

Several short-cut methods have already been introduced, primarily as labor-saving devices. For example, on page 113 we introduced a quick method of estimating the mean and the standard deviation of normally distributed data, using the 50 per cent and 84 per cent points on a "probability" graph. On page 120 we discussed a method of coding which can materially reduce the time required to calculate the mean and the standard deviation of a set of data without any loss in precision. In Chapter 6 we observed that these calculations can further be simplified with only a minor loss in precision by grouping the observations into a frequency table.

Other short-cuts connected with point estimation were introduced in Chapters 8 and 9. We discussed the sample median, which often can be determined more easily and more rapidly than the mean, and, as was pointed out on page 144, the median gives an unbiased estimate for the mean of a symmetric population. Also, the median is superior to the mean as a measure of "location" of a highly skewed population. The sample range was introduced on page 176 as an estimator for the standard deviation of a normal population; it is obtained far more quickly than the sample standard deviation, and its precision is nearly that of s for small samples.

If there is a choice between several statistical methods which can all be used in a given situation, the criterion of *efficiency* is most commonly used as an appropriate guide. If we think of the methods based on the assumption of normality as being fully (100 per cent) efficient, we can use this as a yardstick for measuring the merits of any other method. The most widely used measure of efficiency is based on the sample sizes required to give equally precise results by a given method and by the corresponding method which is fully efficient. For example, in estimating the mean of a normal population, the most efficient method involves use of the sample mean $\bar{x}$. If we wanted to use the median instead of the mean, we would have to take into account that the variance of the sampling distribution of the median is approximately $1.57 \dfrac{\sigma^2}{n}$, so that the efficiency of the median is $1/1.57$ or approximately 64 per cent. In other words, the median based on a sample of size 100 gives as reliable an estimate of the mean of a normal population as the mean based on a sample of size 64. Similarly, it can be shown that the efficiency of the range estimator for the standard deviation of a normal population decreases as the sample size increases; the efficiency is 100 per cent for samples of size 2, 96 per cent for samples of size 5, and 81 per cent for samples of size 15. In the next section we shall introduce other short-cut methods for estimating μ and σ, which are generally more efficient than the median and the range.

Certain methods of inference have the important advantage that they do not require the more stringent assumptions of the methods based on the normal distribution. These methods, which usually have the additional advantage that they require less burdensome calculations, are known as *nonparametric* (or *distribution-free*) methods, since they are generally not related specifically to the parameters of given distributions. The main advantage of nonparametric methods is that exact tests can be performed when the assumptions underlying so-called "standard" methods cannot all be met; essentially, these methods do not depend on the distribution of the population (or populations) from which the samples are obtained. The major disadvantage of nonparametric methods is that they may be wasteful of information, and usually they have a smaller efficiency than the corresponding parametric methods *provided that the assumptions of the standard (parametric) methods* can be met. Thus, if we state that the efficiency of a certain nonparametric method is 80 per cent, we may be understating its relative worth, for the efficiency of the corresponding "standard" method will be somewhat less than 100 per cent if all assumptions are not exactly met.

In this chapter we shall outline a variety of useful short-cut methods of inference, most of which are nonparametric. These methods can be used in place of the corresponding standard methods (described in Chapters 8 through 10) whenever the assumptions are not met or there is a need for greater ease in calculations. Certain other short-cut methods, which can be used in place of "standard" methods not yet introduced, will be described along with the new methods in subsequent chapters.

11.2 Rapid Estimation

The use of $\bar{x}$ to estimate the mean of any population is usually recommended because of its 100 per cent efficiency for normal populations, its usually high efficiency for other populations, and its computational ease. For large samples, where the calculation of $\bar{x}$ becomes lengthy, the median or midrange can be used to give rapid estimates of μ for fairly symmetrical populations. The midrange is obtained by averaging the smallest and largest values in a sample; although it is quickly calculated, its efficiency is generally very low and it is extremely sensitive to outlying sample values (which may or may not represent gross errors).

A variety of rapid point-estimation techniques for μ and σ are based on the *fractiles* of an observed distribution. Dividing the distribution into k equal parts, we define the jth k-tile $F_{j/k}$ to be such that j/k is the fraction of the data that is exceeded by $F_{j/k}$. Specially important fractiles are the three *quartiles* for which $k = 4$ and $j = 1, 2, 3$, the nine *deciles* for which $k = 10$ and $j = 1, 2, \ldots, 9$, and the 99 *percentiles* for which $k = 100$ and $j = 1, 2, \ldots, 99$. To calculate fractiles, we must order the observations either by arranging the individual observations according to size or by constructing a frequency table.

The calculation of fractiles from ungrouped data is facilitated by using the following rule: *given n ordered observations, $F_{j/k}$ is the value of the $\frac{j(n+1)}{k}$ th largest observation.* Note that this rule is consistent with the one given earlier for calculating the median $F_{1/2}$, according to which the median is the value of the observation numbered $(n+1)/2$. To illustrate the calculation of fractiles from ungrouped data, let us find $F_{1/16}$, $F_{1/2}$, and $F_{3/4}$ for the following ordered set of 30 observations:

4	5	7	8	8	9	11	17	19	19
21	21	25	27	28	28	28	29	30	31
31	32	34	36	37	37	40	44	47	51

To calculate $F_{1/16}$, we must find the value of the observation numbered $31/16 = 1.9$, and this means that we must go nine-tenths of the way from the first observation to the second. Thus, $F_{1/16} = 4 + \frac{9}{10}(5 - 4) = 4.9$. To calculate $F_{1/2}$, the median, we must find the value of the observation numbered $31/2 = 15.5$, and this means that we must go half-way from the 15th observation to the 16th. It follows that $F_{1/2} = 28$, since the 15th and 16th values are both equal to 28. To obtain $F_{3/4}$, also called the *third quartile*, we must determine the value of the observation numbered $\frac{3 \cdot 31}{4} = 23.25$, and we obtain $F_{3/4} = 34 + \frac{1}{4}(36 - 34) = 34.5$.

To illustrate the calculation of fractiles from grouped data, let us find the *third decile* of the data grouped in the following table:

x	f
0.5	6
3.5	14
6.5	15
9.5	8
12.5	5
15.5	2
	50

First we must find the class in which the third decile is located. Since there are 50 observations, $F_{3/10}$ exceeds the lowest $\frac{3}{10}(50) = 15$ of the observations, and it is, therefore, located in the second class. Since there are 6 observations in the first class, we need 9 of the 14 observations in the second class; that is, the third decile is located $\frac{9}{14}$ of the way into the second class. Using the fact that the lower boundary of the second class is 2.0 and the class interval is 3.0, we obtain

$$F_{3/10} = 2.0 + \frac{9}{14}\,(3.0) = 3.9$$

Note that for grouped data we count $j \cdot n/k$ observations rather than $j(n + 1)/k$, as we did in the ungrouped case. We do this because we assume that the observations in each class are "spread uniformly" throughout the class interval.

The most commonly used rapid estimates of μ based on fractiles are the *median*, $F_{1/2}$, and the *mid-quartile*, $\frac{1}{2}\,(F_{1/4} + F_{3/4})$; the efficiency of the first is 64 per cent, that of the second is 81 per cent, and they should be used as estimates of μ only for samples from symmetrical populations. For the 30 observations listed above, we find that the median is 28 and the mid-quartile is $\frac{1}{2}\,(15.5 + 34.5) = 25.0$, while $\bar{x}$ equals 25.5.

The following are two useful estimates of σ which are based on the fractiles of a set of data:

$$\frac{1}{3}\,(F_{15/16} - F_{1/16})$$

$$\frac{1}{4}\left(F_{15/16} + \frac{3}{4}\,F_{3/4} - \frac{3}{4}\,F_{1/4} - F_{1/16}\right)$$

The first of these is 62 per cent efficient and it should not be used for highly skewed populations, while the second is 73 per cent efficient and it is fairly insensitive to skewness. For the 30 observations listed above, which have the sample standard deviation $s = 12.7$, we obtain

$$\frac{1}{3}\,(47.4 - 4.9) = 14.2$$

and

$$\frac{1}{4}\left(47.4 + \frac{3}{4}\,(34.5) - \frac{3}{4}\,(15.5) - 4.9\right) = 14.2$$

If a set of data is nearly normally distributed, a very rapid method of estimating σ (even for very large samples) is to calculate one-fourth of the difference between the mean of the highest 5 per cent of the data and the mean of the lowest 5 per cent. This method has an efficiency of 70 per cent for large samples from normally distributed populations. Applying it to the 30 observations on page 210, we find that the means of the highest and lowest $1\frac{1}{2}$ observations are, respectively,

$$\frac{51 + \frac{1}{2}\,(47)}{1 + \frac{1}{2}} = 49.7 \qquad \text{and} \qquad \frac{4 + \frac{1}{2}\,(5)}{1 + \frac{1}{2}} = 4.3$$

and we therefore estimate σ to be $\frac{1}{4}\,(49.7 - 4.3) = 11.4$.

EXERCISES

1. Find $F_{1/4}$, $F_{1/2}$, $F_{3/4}$, $F_{1/10}$, and $F_{19/20}$ for the ungrouped speeds of Exercise 10 on page 115.

2. Referring to the distribution of the number of missing rivets given on page 109, find (a) the median, (b) the first quartile, (c) the ninth decile, and (d) $F_{5/8}$.

3. Use the two fractile estimators to estimate the mean of the population from which the 15 measurements of compressive strength of Exercise 9 on page 115 were obtained.

4. Using the 20 temperature readings given in Exercise 4 on page 123, estimate the population mean on the basis of the mid-quartile.

5. Using the distribution of tin-coating weights obtained in Exercise 3 on page 114, determine the median as well as the mid-quartile, and compare with the mean obtained in Exercise 10 on page 123.

6. Use the distribution of speeds obtained in Exercise 10 on page 115 to calculate the mid-quartile estimate of μ. Compare this result with $\bar{x}$ and with an estimate of μ obtained by plotting the graph on probability paper.

7. Use the two fractile estimators on page 211 to estimate σ for the ungrouped incomes of Exercise 6 on page 114. Compute the sample standard deviation and compare estimates. Also estimate σ by taking one-fourth of the difference between the mean of the highest 5 per cent of the data and the mean of the lowest 5 per cent.

8. Referring to the temperature readings in Exercise 4 on page 123, estimate the population standard deviation by using (a) the sample standard deviation, (b) the two formulas given on page 211, and (c) a probability graph. Compare the resulting estimates.

9. Use the distribution of tin-coating weights obtained in Exercise 3 on page 114 to calculate the two fractile estimators of σ given on page 211. Also compare with the value of the sample standard deviation obtained in Exercise 11 on page 124.

10. Compare the estimate of σ obtained from the probability graph referred to in Exercise 6 with estimates based on the two formulas on page 211. (Calculate the necessary fractiles from the grouped data.)

11.3 The Sign Test

In this section we shall describe nonparametric tests which are based on classifying the data according to two attributes, conveniently represented by *plus signs* and *minus signs*. For example, if we

want to test the null hypothesis $H_0: \mu = \mu_0$ on the basis of a random sample
of size n, we can replace each observation exceeding μ_0 by a plus sign and
each observation exceeded by μ_0 by a minus sign. If the population from
which we are sampling is *continuous and symmetrical*, the probability that
an observation is thus replaced by a plus sign equals $1/2$ when H_0 is true.
Consequently, the test of the null hypothesis $\mu = \mu_0$ becomes equivalent
to a test of the null hypothesis $p = 1/2$, where p is the parameter of a
binomial distribution. The two-sided alternative $\mu \neq \mu_0$ is now equivalent
to $p \neq 1/2$, and the one-sided alternatives $\mu < \mu_0$ and $\mu > \mu_0$ are equivalent
to $p < 1/2$ and $p > 1/2$, respectively, where p is the probability of getting
a plus sign, namely, an observation greater than μ_0.

To illustrate the *one-sample sign test* just described, suppose we want
to test the hypothesis that the mean operating temperature of a thermo-
static switch is 28° C, using the following results obtained for 20 switches:

29.9	28.2	32.0	30.5	29.3	30.1	27.7	31.4	28.6	27.9
+	+	+	+	+	+	−	+	+	−

26.8	30.3	29.0	28.8	28.0	31.4	32.1	27.8	31.7	29.2
−	+	+	+		+	+	−	+	+

Note that there are 15 observations greater than 28.0, 4 observations less
than 28.0, and one observation equal to 28.0. Although the probability is
zero that an observation from a continuous population will equal exactly
28.0, the above figures are rounded, and since we do not know whether
the number 28.0 represents a value greater than or less than 28, we discard
this observation. Thus, we shall determine whether 15 plus signs and 4
minus signs, or 15 "successes" in 19 trials, supports the hypothesis that
$p = 1/2$. Applying the exact test criterion given on page 192 with $\alpha =
0.05$, we find from the table of binomial probabilities that $k_{.025} = 4$ and
$k'_{.025} = 15$; since there were 15 plus signs and 4 minus signs, it follows that
the null hypothesis must be rejected. Note that if the sample size is sufficiently large, we can use the normal curve approximation to the binomial
distribution and the tests given in the table on page 164.

Using paired samples, we can readily extend the sign test to test for
differences between two population means. In this connection, the sign
test can be used as a nonparametric alternative for the paired-sample
t test introduced on page 169. Given n paired observations, with the first
observation coming from Population 1 and the second from Population 2,
we use a *plus sign* to replace each pair for which the observation from the
first population exceeds that from the second, and a *minus sign* to replace
each pair for which the observation from the second population exceeds
that from the first. In case two paired observations are equal, the pair is
omitted from consideration, and the test is carried out as in the one-sample
case already described.

To illustrate the *paired-sample sign test,* suppose two methods for anodizing aluminum are to be compared for general appearance (brightness, depth of color, lack of blemishes, and so forth). Although it would be difficult to assign numerical measures to these qualities, it is not difficult to compare paired specimens and decide which gives the more pleasing result. Suppose that 40 paired specimens are judged, a plus sign or a minus sign being assigned to each pair depending on whether the one anodized by the first method or by the second method was judged superior. Given that there were 24 plus signs, 11 minus signs, and 5 ties, we shall want to test whether the first method is actually superior. Using the normal curve approximation (see page 192) and $\alpha = 0.05$, we first calculate

$$z = \frac{24 - 17.5}{\sqrt{35 \cdot \frac{1}{2} \cdot \frac{1}{2}}} = 2.20$$

and since this exceeds 1.645, the critical value for a one-sided test at the 0.05 level of significance, we conclude that the null hypothesis must be rejected. In other words, we conclude that the first method produces better anodized aluminum.

The efficiency of the sign test is quite high for small samples, 95 per cent for $n = 6$, but declines as the sample size increases to a limiting efficiency of 63 per cent. The assumptions necessary to apply the sign test, either in the one-sample or the paired-sample case, are that the populations under consideration must be continuous and symmetrical. If the population were not continuous, there could be a positive probability that an observation actually equals μ_0 in the one-sample case, or that the paired observations are exactly equal in the paired-sample case. The assumption that $p = 1/2$ would then break down unless we imposed further restrictions. If the population (or populations) were not symmetrical, the probability that an observation is greater than the mean, or that the difference between two paired observations is greater than zero, would not necessarily equal $1/2$ under the null hypothesis that $\mu = \mu_0$ in the one-sample case or $\mu_1 = \mu_2$ in the paired-sample case. It is possible, however, to modify the sign test so that the assumption of symmetry can be dropped. To accomplish this we have only to consider hypotheses concerning the medians of the populations instead of their means.

11.4 Rank-sum Tests

The paired-sample sign test is one of several nonparametric methods for testing the null hypothesis that two samples come from identical continuous populations against the alternative that the populations have unequal means. A highly efficient class of nonparametric tests of this and similar hypotheses is based on *rank sums;* that is, the observations are assigned ranks according to their order of magnitude, and the tests are performed on the basis of certain sums of these ranks. In this section we shall introduce three tests based on rank sums. The *Mann-Whitney U test* will be presented as a substitute for the two-sample t test, and it has a limiting efficiency of 95.5 per cent when the assumptions underlying the corresponding t test are satisfied. A test similar to the U test, which can be used when the alternative hypothesis specifies that the two populations have unequal *dispersions*, will be taken up next. Finally we shall introduce the *Kruskal-Wallis H test*, for testing whether k samples come from identical populations against the alternative that the populations have unequal means. Like the U test, the H test also has a limiting efficiency of 95.5 per cent when compared with the corresponding "standard" procedure, which will be discussed in Chapter 13.

Let us first describe the Mann-Whitney U test by means of the following illustration. Suppose we want to compare two different "getters" used to control moisture content inside a semiconductor device on the basis of the following observed reverse currents in microamperes:

Getter A:	1.3	0.9	0.8	0.2	0.4	0.6	0.1	5.1	0.2	
Getter B:	1.7	3.5	7.8	0.9	0.7	2.6	0.2	1.5	15.3	0.7

First, we *jointly* arrange the 19 observations according to size, retaining the sample identity of each observation. Then, we assign the ranks 1, 2, 3, . . . , and 19 to the observations, as shown in the following table:

Getter:	A	A	A	B	A	A	B	B	A	A	B	A
Observation:	0.1	0.2	0.2	0.2	0.4	0.6	0.7	0.7	0.8	0.9	0.9	1.3
Rank:	1	3	3	3	5	6	7.5	7.5	9	10.5	10.5	12

Getter:	B	B	B	B	A	B	B
Observation:	1.5	1.7	2.6	3.5	5.1	7.8	15.3
Rank:	13	14	15	16	17	18	19

Note that if two or more observations are tied in rank, we assign each of the observations the mean of the ranks they jointly occupy.

If we denote the respective sample sizes by n_1 and n_2 and the sum of the ranks occupied by the first sample by R_1, it can be shown that the mean and the variance of the sampling distribution of the statistic

$$U = n_1 n_2 + \frac{n_1(n_1 + 1)}{2} - R_1$$

are given by

$$\mu_U = \frac{n_1 n_2}{2} \quad \text{and} \quad \sigma_U^2 = \frac{n_1 n_2 (n_1 + n_2 + 1)}{12}$$

(If there are ties in rank, these formulas are only approximately correct.) If both n_1 and n_2 are greater than 8, the distribution of the U statistic can be approximated closely by a normal distribution and, hence, the test can be based on the statistic

$$\blacklozenge \qquad z = \frac{U - \mu_U}{\sigma_U} \qquad \blacklozenge$$

and Table III. There also exist tables on which exact tests can be based when n_1 and n_2 are small (see the table by D. B. Owen mentioned in the Bibliography). Note that it is of no consquence which sample is referred to as the "first," so that we can work with whatever rank sum is most easily obtained.

Returning now to our example, we have $n_1 = 9$, $n_2 = 10$, $R_1 = 66.5$, and, hence,

$$U = 9 \cdot 10 + \frac{9 \cdot 10}{2} - 66.5 = 68.5$$

$$\mu_U = \frac{9 \cdot 10}{2} = 45.0$$

$$\sigma_U^2 = \frac{9 \cdot 10 \cdot 20}{12} = 150.0$$

Thus,

$$z = \frac{68.5 - 45.0}{\sqrt{150.0}} = 1.93$$

and since this value falls between -1.96 and 1.96, the critical values for a two-sided alternative and $\alpha = 0.05$, we conclude that the null hypothesis of identical populations cannot be rejected.

If the ranks are assigned in a somewhat different way, the same U statistic can also be used to test the null hypothesis of identical populations against the alternative that the populations have *unequal dispersions*. The ranks are assigned "from both ends toward the middle" by assigning Rank 1 to the smallest observation, Ranks 2 and 3 to the largest and second largest observation, Ranks 4 and 5 to the second and third smallest, Ranks 6 and 7 to the third and fourth largest, and so on. All other aspects of this test for unequal dispersions are identical with those of the Mann-Whitney U test.

The Kruskal-Wallis H test for deciding whether k independent samples come from identical populations is conducted in a way similar to the U test. As before, the observations are ranked *jointly*, and if R_i is the sum of the ranks occupied by the n_i observations of the ith sample, the test is based on the statistic

$$\blacklozenge \qquad H = \frac{12}{n(n+1)} \sum_{i=1}^{k} \frac{R_i^2}{n_i} - 3(n+1) \qquad \blacklozenge$$

where $n = n_1 + n_2 + \ldots + n_k$. When $n_i > 5$ for all i and the null hypothesis holds, the distribution of the H statistic is well approximated by the chi-square distribution with $k - 1$ degrees of freedom. Special tables applying for selected small values of the n_i and k are referred to in the table by D. B. Owen mentioned in the Bibliography.

To illustrate the Kruskal-Wallis H test, suppose that the experiment described on page 215 is extended to include four different getters, with the results shown in the following table. (Note that tied observations are again assigned the mean of the ranks they jointly occupy.)

Getter A:	0.2	0.3	0.4	0.5	1.7	1.9	2.0
Getter B:	0.8	1.1	1.3	1.9	2.5	7.8	
Getter C:	0.7	0.9	8.2	12.0	12.1	15.3	
Getter D:	0.1	0.1	0.3	0.5	2.9	13.8	

The observations are again reverse currents in microamperes. As can easily be verified, the observations in the first sample occupy Ranks 3, 4.5, 6, 7.5, 14, 15.5, and 17, so that $R_1 = 67.5$. Similarly, the observations in the second sample occupy Ranks 10, 12, 13, 15.5, 18, and 20, so that $R_2 = 88.5$; the observations in the third sample occupy Ranks 9, 11, 21, 22, 23, and 25, so that $R_3 = 111.0$; and the observations in the fourth sample occupy Ranks 1.5, 1.5, 4.5, 7.5, 19, and 24, so that $R_4 = 58.0$. Substituting into the formula for H we thus obtain

$$H = \frac{12}{25 \cdot 26} \left(\frac{67.5^2}{7} + \frac{88.5^2}{6} + \frac{111.0^2}{6} + \frac{58.0^2}{6} \right) - 3(26) = 6.4$$

and if we compare this figure with 7.815, the value of $\chi^2_{.05}$ with 3 degrees of freedom, we find that the null hypothesis cannot be rejected. In other words, we cannot reject the null hypothesis that the samples come from identical populations against the alternative that the population means are not all equal.

EXERCISES

1. Referring to the 100 measurements of the tin-coating weights of electrolytic tin plate of Exercise 3 on page 114, use the sign test with $\alpha = 0.05$ to test the null hypothesis $\mu = 0.33$ against the alternative $\mu < 0.33$, where μ is the mean of the population of weights from which the sample was obtained.

2. Using the one-sample sign test, test the null hypothesis that the mean octane rating of the gasoline from which the following 16 samples were taken is 100 against the alternative that it is greater than 100.

101.6	98.2	104.5	99.0	102.8	105.4	107.7	99.4
103.3	100.0	102.5	97.1	103.6	101.0	98.7	101.0

Use a level of significance of 0.05.

3. Use the sign test and a level of significance of 0.10 to decide on the basis of the data of Exercise 19 on page 173 whether there is a systematic difference in the readings yielded by the two instruments.

4. Structural steel beams are sawed to finished length by two methods, sawing them while they are hot, and sawing them after they have cooled off. The resulting finished lengths (in feet) after all beams have been allowed to cool to ambient temperature are as follows:

Hot-sawed beams:	31.6	30.5	31.1	29.7	27.9	30.2
	30.5	31.8	32.6	28.8	29.6	28.5
	28.9	29.9	31.6	30.7	30.3	31.5
Cold-sawed beams:	30.1	31.0	29.9	29.8	30.0	30.5
	30.6	30.2	31.1	29.8	29.7	29.6
	31.3	30.5	30.1	30.0	30.8	30.3

Randomly pairing the 18 observations in the two samples, use the two-sample sign test to determine at the 0.05 level of significance whether there is a significant difference in the mean finished lengths.

5. In repeated tests, an experimental engine operated, respectively, for 20, 19, 22, 17, 18, 20, 23, 19, 20, 15, 24, 21, 18, 20, 24, 23, 20, 17, 25, and 28 minutes with 1 gallon of a certain kind of fuel. Using the sign test and a level of significance of 0.01, test the null hypothesis $\mu = 20$ against the alternative $\mu \neq 20$.

6. To compare a given soft drink with a competing brand, 50 judges were asked to taste first one brand and then the other and to indicate their preference. (The order of the brands tested was randomly determined for each judge.) If 27 judges preferred the given brand, 18 preferred the competing brand, and 5 could discern no difference in taste, test at the 0.01 level of significance whether the given brand is superior in taste to the competing brand.

7. An experiment designed to compare the tensile strength of two kinds of yarn produced the following results (in pounds):

Yarn A:	143.6	144.8	145.2	144.8	145.6	146.0
	143.0	147.4	144.0	145.6	145.5	144.8
Yarn B:	146.6	147.8	144.4	140.8	143.0	148.8
	153.0	142.4	146.8	143.2	140.9	150.6

Use the U test and a level of significance of 0.05 to test the null hypothesis that the two samples come from identical populations against the alternative that the two populations have unequal means.

8. Repeat Exercise 4 using the Mann-Whitney U test. Also test whether the dispersions of the two populations are equal using the rank-sum test mentioned on page 216.

9. Referring to Exercise 7, use $\alpha = 0.05$ to test the null hypothesis that the samples come from identical populations against the alternative that the two populations have unequal dispersions.

10. So-called Franklin tests were performed to determine the insulation properties of grain-oriented silicon steel specimens that were annealed in five different atmospheres with the following results:

Atmosphere	Test results (amperes)							
1	0.58	0.61	0.69	0.79	0.61	0.59		
2	0.37	0.37	0.58	0.40	0.28	0.44	0.35	
3	0.29	0.19	0.34	0.17	0.29	0.16		
4	0.81	0.69	0.75	0.72	0.68	0.85	0.57	0.77
5	0.26	0.34	0.29	0.47	0.30	0.42		

Use the Kruskal-Wallis H test and a level of significance of 0.05 to decide whether these five samples can be assumed to come from identical populations.

11. To investigate three preventive measures against corrosion, random samples of 10 pieces of wire were tested for each of the three preventive measures, yielding the following results for the depths of maximum pits (in thousandths of an inch):

A:	45	53	60	48	57	62	49	55	53	52
B:	62	58	47	59	63	48	58	52	50	49
C:	57	45	60	54	57	55	48	59	62	60

Test at the 0.05 level of significance whether there is a difference in the effectiveness of the three preventive measures against corrosion.

11.5 Run Tests *Study*

When we discussed random sampling in Chapter 7, we gave several methods which provide some assurance in advance that a sample taken will be random. Nevertheless, it is useful to have a technique for testing whether a sample may be looked upon as random *after it has actually been obtained*. One such technique is based on the order in which the sample values were obtained; more specifically, it is based on the number of *runs* exhibited in the sample results.

Given a sequence of two symbols, such as H and T (which might represent the occurrence of heads and tails in repeated tosses of a coin), a *run* is defined as a succession of identical symbols contained between different symbols or none at all. For example, the sequence

$$T \; \underline{T} \; \underline{H \; H} \; \underline{T \; T} \; \underline{H \; H \; H} \; \underline{T} \; \underline{H \; H \; H} \; \underline{T \; T \; T \; T} \; \underline{H \; H \; H}$$

contains 8 runs, as indicated by the underlines. The total number of runs exhibited in a sequence of n trials gives an indication of whether the sequence may be looked upon as random. Thus, if there had been only two runs, consisting of ten heads followed by ten tails, one might suspect that the probability of a success had not remained constant from trial to trial. On the other hand, had the sequence of twenty tosses consisted of alternating heads and tails, one might suspect that the trials had not been independent. In either case, there are grounds to suspect a lack of randomness. Note that our suspicion is not aroused by the *number* of H's and T's, but by the *order* in which they appeared.

If a sequence contains n_1 symbols of one kind and n_2 of another (and neither n_1 nor n_2 is very small), the sampling distribution of the total number of runs can be approximated closely by a normal distribution having the mean

$$\blacklozenge \qquad \mu_u = \frac{2n_1 n_2}{n_1 + n_2} + 1 \qquad \blacklozenge$$

and the standard deviation

$$\blacklozenge \qquad \sigma_u = \sqrt{\frac{2n_1 n_2 (2n_1 n_2 - n_1 - n_2)}{(n_1 + n_2)^2 (n_1 + n_2 - 1)}} \qquad \blacklozenge$$

where u denotes the total number of runs. Thus, the test of the null hypothesis that the arrangement of the symbols (and, hence, the sample) is random can be based on the statistic

$$\blacklozenge \qquad z = \frac{u - \mu_u}{\sigma_u} \qquad \blacklozenge$$

and Table III. This test gives an excellent approximation so long as neither n_1 nor n_2 is less than 10. Special tables for performing exact tests when n_1 or n_2 is small are given in the tables by D. B. Owen listed in the Bibliography.

To illustrate this test, suppose we examine the following sequence of 32 flight-test results in a missile development program, where S and F stand, respectively, for "success" and "failure":

$$\underline{F \; F \; F} \; \underline{S \; S} \; \underline{F \; F} \; \underline{S \; S \; S} \; \underline{F} \; \underline{S} \; \underline{F} \; \underline{S \; S \; S \; S} \; \underline{F} \; \underline{S \; S \; S} \; \underline{F} \; \underline{S \; S \; S \; S \; S} \; \underline{F} \; \underline{S \; S \; S}$$

Since there are 22 successes, 10 failures, and 14 runs, we substitute $n_1 = 22$, $n_2 = 10$, $u = 14$, and we obtain

$$\mu_u = \frac{2 \cdot 22 \cdot 10}{32} + 1 = 14.75$$

$$\sigma_u = \sqrt{\frac{2 \cdot 22 \cdot 10 (2 \cdot 22 \cdot 10 - 22 - 10)}{(22 + 10)^2 (22 + 10 - 1)}} = 2.38$$

and $\qquad z = \dfrac{14 - 14.75}{2.38} = -0.31$

Since this value falls between -1.96 and 1.96, we cannot reject (at the 0.05 level of significance) the null hypothesis that the arrangement is random. Evidently, not enough evidence is yet available to demonstrate conclusively that there is a real improvement in reliability.

The run test can be used also to test the randomness of samples consisting of numerical data by counting *runs above and below the median*. Denoting an observation exceeding the median of the sample by the letter a and an observation less than the median by the letter b, we can use the resulting sequence of a's and b's to test for randomness by the method just indicated. A frequent application of this test is in quality control, where the means of successive small samples are exhibited on a graph in chronological order. The run test can then be used to check whether there might be a trend in the data, so that it is possible to adjust a machine setting or some other process variable before any serious damage occurs.

To illustrate a test for runs above and below the median, suppose an engineer is concerned about the possibility that too many changes are being made in the settings of an automatic lathe. To test this hypothesis, the following mean diameters (in inches) are obtained for 40 successive shafts turned on the lathe:

0.261	0.258	0.249	0.251	0.247	0.256	0.250	0.247	0.255	0.243
0.252	0.250	0.253	0.247	0.251	0.243	0.258	0.251	0.245	0.250
0.248	0.252	0.254	0.250	0.247	0.253	0.251	0.246	0.249	0.252
0.247	0.250	0.253	0.247	0.249	0.253	0.246	0.251	0.249	0.253

The median of these measurements is 0.250, and, replacing each by the letter a if it exceeds 0.250, by the letter b if it is less than 0.250, and omitting the five which equal 0.250, we obtain the sequence

$$a\,a\,b\,a\,b\,a\,b\,a\,b\,a\,a\,b\,a\,b\,a\,a\,b\,b\,a\,a\,b\,a\,a\,b\,b\,a\,b\,a\,b\,b\,a\,b\,a\,b\,a$$

having 27 runs. Thus, $n_1 = 19$, $n_2 = 16$, $u = 27$, and we obtain

$$\mu_u = \frac{2 \cdot 19 \cdot 16}{35} + 1 = 18.37$$

$$\sigma_u = \sqrt{\frac{2 \cdot 19 \cdot 16(2 \cdot 19 \cdot 16 - 19 - 16)}{(19 + 16)^2(19 + 16 - 1)}} = 2.89$$

and $\qquad z = \dfrac{27 - 18.37}{2.89} = 2.98$

Since this value exceeds 1.96, we can reject the null hypothesis that the sequence of measurements is random. Since the number of runs is larger than one might expect due to chance, it is reasonable to suppose that the lathe is being adjusted too often; it is probably adjusted after each rod is turned, to compensate for any observed discrepancy from a nominal diameter of 0.250 in.

11.6 The Kolmogorov-Smirnov Tests

The Kolmogorov-Smirnov tests are nonparametric tests for differences between two cumulative distributions. The *one-sample test* concerns the agreement between an observed cumulative distribution of sample values and a specified continuous distribution function; thus, it is a test of goodness of fit. The *two-sample test* concerns the agreement between two observed cumulative distributions; it tests the hypothesis whether two independent samples come from identical continuous distributions, and it is sensitive to population differences with respect to location, dispersion, or skewness.

The Kolmogorov-Smirnov one-sample test is generally more efficient than the chi-square test for goodness of fit for small samples, and it can be used for very small samples where the chi-square test does not apply. It must be remembered, however, that the chi-square test of Section 10.5 can be used in connection with discrete distributions whereas the Kolmogorov-Smirnov test cannot.

The one-sample test is based on the maximum absolute difference D between the values of the cumulative distribution of a random sample of size n and a specified theoretical distribution. To illustrate this test, suppose it is desired to check whether pinholes in electrolytic tin plate are distributed uniformly across a plated coil on the basis of the following distances (in inches) of 10 pinholes from one edge of a long strip of tin plate 30 inches wide:

$$4.8 \quad 14.8 \quad 28.2 \quad 23.1 \quad 4.4 \quad 28.7 \quad 19.5 \quad 2.4 \quad 25.0 \quad 6.2$$

Under the null hypothesis that the pinholes are uniformly distributed, the theoretical cumulative distribution with which we want to compare the observed cumulative distribution is given by

$$F(x) = \begin{cases} 0 & \text{for } x \leq 0 \\ x/30 & \text{for } 0 < x < 30 \\ 1 & \text{for } x \geq 30 \end{cases}$$

The graph of this theoretical cumulative distribution, as well as that of the observed cumulative distribution, is shown in Figure 11.1. As indicated on this figure, the maximum difference between the two cumulative distributions is 0.193.

To determine whether this difference is larger than can reasonably be expected, we find the critical value of D in Table IX. For $n = 10$ and $\alpha = 0.05$ the critical value is $D_{05} = 0.410$, and it follows that the null

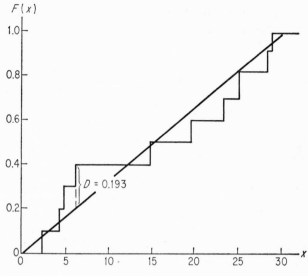

FIG. 11.1 Kolmogorov-Smirnov test

hypothesis (that the pinholes are uniformly distributed) cannot be rejected.

The two-sample Kolmogorov-Smirnov test is based on the maximum absolute difference between the values of the two observed cumulative distributions. In principle, it is very similar to the one-sample test, and the necessary critical values can be obtained from special tables (for example, those by D. B. Owen referred to in the Bibliography).

EXERCISES

1. To test whether a certain radio signal contains a message, an interval of time could be subdivided into a number of very short intervals and it could then be determined whether the signal strength exceeded a certain level (back-ground noise) in each short interval. Suppose that the following is part of such a record, where H denotes a high signal strength and L denotes that the signal strength does not exceed a given noise level.

   $$L L\ H\ L\ H\ L\ H\ L\ H\ H\ H\ H\ L\ H\ H\ H\ H\ L\ H\ H\ H\ L\ H\ L\ H\ L\ H\ L\ L$$
   $$L L\ H\ L\ H\ L\ H\ L\ H\ H\ H\ H\ L\ H\ H\ H\ H\ L\ H\ H\ H\ L\ H\ L\ H\ L\ H\ L\ L$$

   Test this sequence for randomness (using the 0.05 level of significance) and ascertain whether it is reasonable to assume that the signal contains a message.

2. Reading successive rows from left to right, the following is the order in which defective (D) and nondefective (N) pieces were produced by a machine during a certain period of time:

```
N  N  N  N  N  N  N  N  N  D  D  D  N  N  N  N  N  N  N  N
N  N  N  D  N  N  N  N  N  N  N  N  D  D  N  N  D  D  N  N
N  N  N  N  N  N  N  N  N  N  N  N  N  D  D  D  N  N  D  N
D  N  N  D  N  N  N  N  N  N  N  N  D  D  N  N  N  D  N  N
N  N  N  N  N  N  N  N  D  D  D  N  N  N  N  N  N  N  N  N
```

Test at a level of significance of 0.05 whether this arrangement is random.

3. On page 100 a method for generating pseudo-random digits was described, whereby a 4-digit number was squared, the middle four digits of the resulting number was squared, and so on. Starting with the number 3571, use a table of squares or a desk calculator to continue this process until a sequence of 48 digits is obtained. Test the resulting sequence for randomness using runs above and below the median and a 0.05 level of significance.

4. In a factory, the time during working hours in which a machine is not operating because of such difficulties as breakage or failure is called "down time." The following are 50 consecutive down times (in minutes) which a control engineer observed during a certain period of time (read successive rows from left to right):

18	25	28	21	29	30	34	30	25	21
22	29	30	24	35	37	20	27	30	25
30	21	26	33	36	35	31	20	28	39
40	30	36	34	35	39	42	30	35	41
38	35	50	46	34	37	39	42	48	51

Use the method of runs above and below the median and a level of significance of 0.05 to test the hypothesis that the data contain a trend.

5. Hourly oven temperature readings (in degrees centigrade), taken over a period of 24 hours, are as follows:

269, 265, 271, 268, 270, 266, 273, 271, 275, 269, 271, 273
275, 268, 276, 270, 273, 266, 270, 268, 272, 271, 278, 267

Test the randomness of this arrangement at the 0.01 level of significance to investigate whether the oven is "cycling" at two-hour intervals.

6. Exercise 13 on page 116 contains the number of imperfections in samples taken from 50 bolts of cloth. Assuming that the order of the samples is that in which the bolts of cloth were produced, test the hypothesis that the occurrence of samples with no imperfections is random against the alternative that there is a clustering. (Let $\alpha = 0.05$.)

7. Use the Kolmogorov-Smirnov test with $\alpha = 0.01$ to decide whether the compressive strengths of Exercise 9 on page 115 can be assumed to come from a normal distribution having the mean 50,000 psi and the standard deviation 10,000 psi. [*Hint:* Use probability graph paper.]

8. In a vibration study, certain airplane components were subjected to severe vibrations until they showed structural failures. The following are the times obtained (in minutes): 4.1, 0.8, 5.3, 5.0, 8.3, 1.7, 2.5, 6.2, 7.3, 9.0, 1.2, 3.7, 9.5, 10.5. Test whether these data can be looked upon as a sample from an exponential population with a mean of 5 minutes. (Use $\alpha = 0.05$.)

12 | CURVE FITTING

12.1 The Method of Least Squares

One of the major objectives of many engineering investigations is to make predictions, preferably by means of mathematical equations. For instance, an engineer may wish to predict the amount of oxide that will form on the surface of a metal baked in an oven for a specified amount of time at 200° C, or the amount of deformation of a ring subjected to a compressive force of 1000 pounds, or the time between recappings of a tire having a given tread thickness and composition. Usually, such predictions require that a formula be found which relates the dependent variable (whose value one wants to predict) to one or more independent variables. In this section we shall consider the special case where a dependent variable is to be predicted in terms of a single independent variable.

In many problems of this kind the independent variable is observed without error, or with an error which is negligible when compared with the error (chance variation) in the dependent variable. For example, in measuring the amount of oxide on the surface of a metal specimen, the baking temperature can usually be controlled with good precision, but the oxide-thickness measurement may be subject to considerable chance variation. Thus, even though the independent variable may be fixed at x, repeated measurements of the dependent variable may lead to y-values which differ considerably. Such differences among y-values can be attributed to several causes, chiefly to errors of measurement and to the existence of other, uncontrolled variables which may influence the value of y when x is fixed. Thus, measurements of the thickness of oxide layers may vary over several specimens baked for the same length of time at the same temperature because of the difficulty in measuring thickness as well as possible differences in the composition of the oven atmosphere, surface conditions of the specimens, and the like.

It should be apparent from this discussion that in this context y is the value of a random variable whose distribution depends on x. In most situations of this sort we are interested mainly in the relationship between x and the *mean* of the corresponding distribution of y's, and we refer to this relationship as the *regression curve of y on x*. (For the time being we shall assume that x is fixed, that is, not random; in Section 12.5 we shall consider the case where x and y are both values of random variables.)

Let us first treat the case where the regression curve of y on x is *linear*, that is, where, for any given x, the mean of the distribution of the y's is given by $\alpha + \beta x$. In general, an observed y will differ from this mean, and we shall denote this difference by ϵ, writing

$$y = \alpha + \beta x + \epsilon$$

Note that ϵ is a value assumed by a random variable and that we can always choose α so that the mean of its distribution is equal to zero. The value of ϵ for any given observation will depend on a possible error of measurement and on the values of variables other than x which might have an influence on y.

To give an example where the regression curve of y on x can reasonably be assumed to be linear, suppose a thermocouple is to be calibrated by measuring the electromotive force in millivolts at various known temperatures. In the following table (giving the results of 10 measurements) x_i is the ith temperature setting in degrees centigrade and y_i is the corresponding thermocouple reading in millivolts:

i	1	2	3	4	5	6	7	8	9	10
x_i	0	20	40	60	80	100	120	140	160	180
y_i	0.01	0.12	0.24	0.38	0.51	0.67	0.84	1.01	1.15	1.31

It is apparent from Figure 12.1, in which these data have been plotted, that it is reasonable to assume that the relationship (the regression curve) is linear. (If the range of x were extended, it would become evident that

the thermocouple calibration curve is not linear, but a straight line gives
an excellent approximation over the limited range used in our example.)
We now face the problem of using the data plotted in Figure 12.1 to

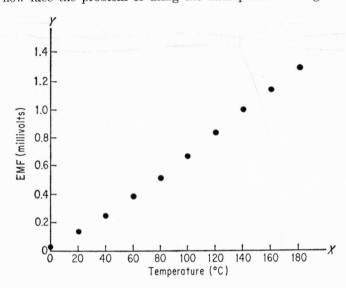

FIG. 12.1 Linear regression

estimate the parameters α and β of the assumed regression line of y on x.
Note that these parameters completely determine the regression line, and
the estimation of α and β is equivalent to finding the equation of the straight
line which "best fits" the data points. In this example it may well be
satisfactory to do this "by eye," and if different experimenters were to fit
a line in this way, they would probably all predict that at 110° C the emf
should be close to 0.75 millivolts. However, if we have to deal with data
such as those plotted in Figure 12.2, the problem of finding a best-fitting
line is not so obvious. To handle problems of this kind, we must seek a
nonsubjective method for fitting straight lines which also has some desirable
statistical properties.

To state the problem formally, we have n paired observations (x_i, y_i)
for which it is reasonable to assume that the regression of y on x is linear,
and we want to determine the line (that is, the equation of the line) which
in some sense provides the "best" fit. There are several ways in which we
can interpret the word "best," and the meaning we shall give it here may
be explained as follows. If we predict y by means of the equation

$$y' = a + bx$$

where a and b are constants, then e_i, the error in predicting the value of y
corresponding to the given x_i, is

$$y_i - y'_i = e_i$$

Note that the equation $y' = a + bx$ provides an *estimate* of the equation of the regression line whose actual, but unknown, equation is $y = \alpha + \beta x$. The actual error in predicting y_i is ϵ_i, and this error is estimated by the quantity $y_i - y'_i = e_i$. We shall attempt to determine a and b so that the estimated errors are in some sense as small as possible.

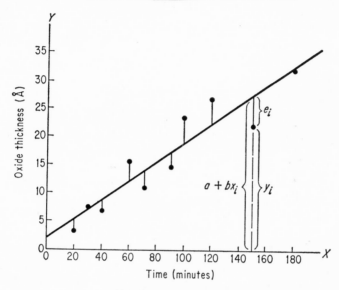

FIG. 12.2 Least-squares criterion

Since we cannot minimize each of the e_i individually, it suggests itself that we might try to make their sum $\sum\limits_{i=1}^{n} e_i$ as close as possible to zero. However, since this sum can be made *equal* to zero by many choices of totally unsuitable straight lines for which the positive and the negative errors cancel, we shall instead minimize the sum of the *squares* of the e_i (see also definition of standard deviation). In other words, we shall choose a and b so that

$$\sum_{i=1}^{n} [y_i - (a + bx_i)]^2$$

is a minimum. Note from Figure 12.2 that this is equivalent to minimizing the sum of the squares of the vertical distances from the points to the line. This criterion, called the *criterion of least squares*, yields values for a and b (estimates for α and β) that have many desirable properties, some of which will be mentioned at the end of this section.

A necessary condition for a relative minimum is the vanishing of the partial derivatives with respect to a and b. We thus have

$$2 \sum_{i=1}^{n} [y_i - (a + bx_i)](-1) = 0$$

$$2 \sum_{i=1}^{n} [y_i - (a + bx_i)](-x_i) = 0$$

and rewriting these equations in a somewhat more convenient form we obtain the following equations, called the *normal equations:*

$$\sum_{i=1}^{n} y_i = an + b \sum_{i=1}^{n} x_i$$

$$\sum_{i=1}^{n} x_iy_i = a \sum_{i=1}^{n} x_i + b \sum_{i=1}^{n} x_i^2$$

The normal equations are a set of two linear equations in the unknowns a and b; their simultaneous solution gives the values of a and b for the line which, thus, provides the best fit to the given data according to the criterion of least squares. Note that they can easily be remembered as follows: we first write down the equation $y_i = a + bx_i$ and then the equation $x_iy_i = ax_i + bx_i^2$, obtained from the first by multiplying both sides by x_i. If we then sum both sides of each of these equations, we get the two normal equations (after some easy algebraic simplifications).

To illustrate the method of least squares, as it is used to fit a straight line to a given set of paired data, let us apply it to the data of Figure 12.2, pertaining to the baking times and oxide thicknesses of certain specimens:

x	20	30	40	60	70	90	100	120	150	180
y	3.5	7.4	7.1	15.6	11.1	14.9	23.5	27.1	22.1	32.9

Here the x's are the baking times in minutes and the y's are the oxide thicknesses in Ångstrom units. Since $n = 10$,

$$\sum_{i=1}^{n} x_i = 860, \qquad \sum_{i=1}^{n} x_i^2 = 98{,}800$$

$$\sum_{i=1}^{n} y_i = 165.2, \qquad \sum_{i=1}^{n} x_iy_i = 18{,}469.0$$

the normal equations are

$$165.2 = 10a + 860b$$

$$18{,}469.0 = 860a + 98{,}800b$$

Solving these two equations we obtain $a = 1.90$, $b = 0.17$, and the equation of the straight line which provides the best fit in the sense of least squares is

$$y' = 1.90 + 0.17x$$

This equation might be used, for example, to predict that the oxide thickness of a specimen baked for 80 minutes will be $y' = 1.90 + (0.17)(80) = 15.5$ Ångstrom units.

It is impossible to make any exact statements about the "goodness" of this prediction unless we make some assumptions about the underlying distribution of the oxide-thickness readings and about the true nature of the regression, namely, that for a given x the true mean of the y's is of the form $\alpha + \beta x$. Looking upon the values of a and b obtained from the normal equations as *estimates* of the *regression coefficients* α and β, the reader will be asked to show in Exercises 13 and 14 on page 239 that these estimates are *linear* in the observations y_i and that they are *unbiased* estimates of α and β. With these properties, we can then refer to the remarkable *Gauss-Markov theorem* which states that among all unbiased estimators for α and β which are linear in the y_i, the least-squares estimators have the smallest variance. In other words, the least-squares estimators are the most reliable in the sense that they are subject to the smallest chance variations. A proof of the Gauss-Markov theorem may be found in the book by F. A. Graybill referred to in the Bibliography.

12.2 Inferences Based on the Least-squares Estimators

The method of the preceding section is used when the relationship between x and the mean of y is linear, or close enough to a straight line so that the least-squares line yields reasonably good predictions. In what follows we shall assume that the regression is linear and furthermore that the n random variables having the values y_i ($i = 1, \ldots, n$) are *independently distributed with normal distributions having the means* $\alpha + \beta x_i$ *and the common variance* σ^2. If we write

$$y_i = \alpha + \beta x_i + \epsilon_i$$

it follows from these assumptions that the ϵ_i are values of independent normally distributed random variables having zero means and the common variance σ^2. The various assumptions we have made here are illustrated in Figure 12.3, showing the distributions of values of y_i for several values of the x_i. Note that these additional assumptions are required to discuss the goodness of predictions based on least-squares equations, the properties of a and b as estimates of α and β, and so on; they were *not* required to obtain the original estimates based on the method of least squares.

Before we state a theorem concerning the distribution of the least-squares estimators of α and β, it will be convenient to introduce some special notation. The following expressions pertaining to the sample values (x_i, y_i) occur so often that it is useful to write them as

$$S_{xx} = n \sum_{i=1}^{n} x_i^2 - \left(\sum_{i=1}^{n} x_i \right)^2$$

$$S_{yy} = n \sum_{i=1}^{n} y_i^2 - \left(\sum_{i=1}^{n} y_i \right)^2$$

$$S_{xy} = n \sum_{i=1}^{n} x_i y_i - \left(\sum_{i=1}^{n} x_i \right) \left(\sum_{i=1}^{n} y_i \right)$$

Using this notation, the reader will be asked to show in Exercise 15 on page 240 that

$$a = \bar{y} - b \cdot \bar{x} \qquad \text{and} \qquad b = S_{xy}/S_{xx}$$

where a and b are the solutions of the two normal equations on page 230, and $\bar{x}$ and $\bar{y}$ are respectively the means of the x_i and y_i. Note also the close

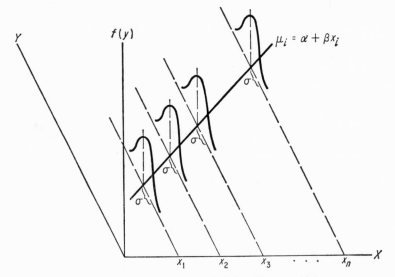

FIG. 12.3 Assumptions underlying Theorem 12.1

relationship between S_{xx} and S_{yy}, respectively, and the sample variances of the x_i and y_i; in fact, $s_x^2 = S_{xx}/n(n-1)$ and $s_y^2 = S_{yy}/n(n-1)$, and we shall sometimes use this alternate notation.

The variance σ^2 defined on page 231 is usually estimated in terms of the vertical deviations of the sample points from the least-squares line. The ith such deviation is $y_i - y_i' = y_i - (a + bx_i)$ and the estimate of σ^2 is

$$s_e^2 = \frac{1}{n-2} \sum_{i=1}^{n} [y_i - (a + bx_i)]^2$$

where s_e is, traditionally, referred to as the *standard error of estimate*. An equivalent formula for this estimate of σ^2, which is more convenient to use in actual applications, is given by

$$s_e^2 = \frac{S_{xx}S_{yy} - (S_{xy})^2}{n(n-2)S_{xx}}$$

In these formulas the divisor $n - 2$ is used to make the resulting estimator for σ^2 *unbiased*. The "loss" of two degrees of freedom is explained by the fact that the two regression coefficients α and β had to be replaced by their least-squares estimates. It can also be shown that under the given assumptions $(n - 2)s_e^2/\sigma^2$ is a value of a random variable having the chi-square distribution with $n - 2$ degrees of freedom.

Based on the assumptions made concerning the distribution of the y's, one can prove the following theorem concerning the distributions of the least-squares estimators of the regression coefficients α and β:

THEOREM 12.1. *Under the assumptions given on page 231, the sampling distributions of the statistics*

$$t = \frac{(a - \alpha)}{s_e}\sqrt{\frac{nS_{xx}}{S_{xx} + (n\bar{x})^2}}$$

and

$$t = \frac{(b - \beta)}{s_e}\sqrt{\frac{S_{xx}}{n}}$$

are t distributions with $n - 2$ degrees of freedom.

Using the first of these statistics, we can construct a confidence interval for α, solving the double inequality $-t_{\alpha/2} < t < t_{\alpha/2}$.* The limits of the resulting confidence interval are

$$a \pm t_{\alpha/2} \cdot s_e \sqrt{\frac{S_{xx} + (n\bar{x})^2}{nS_{xx}}}$$

Similar arguments lead to the following confidence limits for β:

$$b \pm t_{\alpha/2} \cdot s_e \sqrt{\frac{n}{S_{xx}}}$$

To illustrate the construction of such confidence intervals for the regression coefficients α and β, we shall assume that the populations from which the data on oxide thicknesses on page 230 were obtained satisfy the necessary assumptions of independence, normality, and equal variances. Using the numerical results on page 230 together with

$$\sum_{i=1}^{n} y_i^2 = 3563.48$$

we first obtain

---

* Although the symbol α is used here both for a parameter of the regression line and for the level of confidence, the formulas are such that there should be no ambiguity.

$$S_{xx} = 10(98,800) - (860)^2 = 248,400$$

$$S_{yy} = 10(3,563.48) - (165.2)^2 = 8,343.76$$

$$S_{xy} = 10(18,469.0) - (860)(165.2) = 42,618.0$$

and, hence,

$$s_e^2 = \frac{(248,400)(8,343.76) - (42,618.0)^2}{(10)(8)(248,400)} = 12.90$$

Since $t_{.025}$ equals 2.306 for $10 - 2 = 8$ degrees of freedom, we get the following 0.95 confidence intervals for α and β:

$$1.90 \pm (2.306)(3.59) \sqrt{\frac{248,400 + (860)^2}{10(248,400)}}$$

or $-3.32 < \alpha < 7.12$

and $0.17 \pm (2.306)(3.59) \sqrt{\frac{10}{248,400}}$

or $0.12 < \beta < 0.22$

The results of Theorem 12.1 can also be used to establish criteria for testing hypotheses concerning α and β. In this connection, the parameter β is of special importance as it represents the *slope* of the regression line; that is, β gives the change in the mean of y corresponding to a unit increase in x. If $\beta = 0$, the regression line is horizontal and the mean of y does not depend linearly on x.

To test the null hypothesis $H_0: \beta = \beta_0$ we can make use of the second t statistic of Theorem 12.1, namely,

$$\blacklozenge \qquad t = \frac{(b - \beta_0)}{s_e} \sqrt{\frac{S_{xx}}{n}} \qquad \blacklozenge$$

and the resulting critical regions are as shown in the following table:

CRITICAL REGIONS FOR TESTING $H_0: \beta = \beta_0$

Alternative hypothesis	Reject H_0 if
$\beta < \beta_0$	$t < -t_\alpha$
$\beta > \beta_0$	$t > t_\alpha$
$\beta \neq \beta_0$	$t < -t_{\alpha/2}$ or $t > t_{\alpha/2}$

where t_α is obtained from Table IV with $n - 2$ degrees of freedom.

To illustrate this kind of test, let us test for the significance of the linear regression (linear dependence) of oxide thickness on baking time, basing our calculations on the data given on page 230. The null hypothesis to be tested is H_0: $\beta = 0$ and the appropriate alternative is H_1: $\beta \neq 0$. Using the calculations on page 234, we obtain

$$t = \frac{0.17 - 0}{3.59}\sqrt{\frac{248,000}{10}} = 7.46$$

and since this exceeds 2.306, the value of $t_{.025}$ for 8 degrees of freedom, we can reject the null hypothesis at the 0.05 level of significance. In other words, we conclude that there is a relationship between baking time and the average oxide thickness.

Another problem, closely related to the problem of estimating the regression coefficients α and β, is that of estimating $\alpha + \beta x$, namely, the mean of the distribution of the y's for a given value of x. If x is held fixed at x_0, the quantity we want to estimate is $\alpha + \beta x_0$ and it would seem reasonable to use $a + bx_0$, where a and b are again the values obtained by the method of least squares. In fact, it can be shown that this estimator is unbiased, has the variance

$$\sigma^2 \left[\frac{1}{n} + \frac{n(x_0 - \bar{x})^2}{S_{xx}} \right]$$

and that a $1 - \alpha$ confidence interval for $\alpha + \beta x_0$ is given by

$$\blacklozenge \qquad (a + bx_0) \pm t_{\alpha/2} \cdot s_e \sqrt{\frac{1}{n} + \frac{n(x_0 - \bar{x})^2}{S_{xx}}} \qquad \blacklozenge$$

where $t_{\alpha/2}$ is to be obtained from Table IV with $n - 2$ degrees of freedom.

Of even greater importance than the estimation of $\alpha + \beta x_0$ is usually the *prediction* of y', a future value of y when $x = x_0$. For example, although the oxide-thickness experiment did not include a baking time of 80 minutes, it may be important to predict what oxide thickness might be obtained if the baking time were 80 minutes. On page 231 we already obtained an estimate of 15.5 for this oxide thickness by substituting $x = 80$ into the equation of the least-squares line. Now let us construct an interval in which y can be expected to lie with a given probability when $x = x_0$. If α and β were known, we could use the fact that y is a value of a random variable having a normal distribution with the mean $\alpha + \beta x_0$ and the variance σ^2 (or that $y - \alpha - \beta x_0$ is a value of a random variable having a normal distribution with zero mean and the variance σ^2). However, if α and β are not known, we must consider the quantity $y - a - bx_0$, where y, a, and b are all values of random variables, and the resulting theory leads to the following *limits of prediction* for y when $x = x_0$:

$$\blacklozenge \qquad (a + bx_0) \pm t_{\alpha/2} \cdot s_e \sqrt{1 + \frac{1}{n} + \frac{n(x_0 - \bar{x})^2}{S_{xx}}} \qquad \blacklozenge$$

where the number of degrees of freedom for $t_{\alpha/2}$ is again $n - 2$.

To illustrate the construction of confidence limits for $\alpha + \beta x_0$ and limits of prediction for a future value of y, let us again refer to the oxide-thick-nesses of our numerical example. When $x = 80$, we can write 0.95 confidence limits for $\alpha + 80\beta$ as

Confidence

$$15.5 \pm (2.306)(3.59) \sqrt{\frac{1}{10} + \frac{(10)(80 - 86)^2}{248,400}}$$

and, hence, $12.9 < \alpha + 80\beta < 18.1$

Correspondingly, 0.95 limits of prediction for a future value of y when $x = 80$ are given by

Prediction Interval

$$15.5 \pm (2.306)(3.59) \sqrt{1 + \frac{1}{10} + \frac{(10)(80 - 86)^2}{248,400}}$$

or 15.5 ± 8.7.

Note that although the *mean* of the distribution of y's when $x = 80$ can be estimated fairly closely, the value of a single future observation cannot be predicted with good precision. Observe from the formula for the limits of prediction that even as $n \to \infty$ the width of the interval does not approach zero. The limiting width depends on s_e, which expresses the inherent variability of the data. Note, further, that if we wish to *extrapolate*, that is, to predict a future value of y' corresponding to a value of x outside the range of the observations, the limits of prediction (and also the confidence limits for $\alpha + \beta x$) become increasingly wide. For example, 0.95 limits of prediction for y' corresponding to $x = 240$ minutes are given by

$$42.7 \pm (2.306)(3.59) \sqrt{1 + \frac{1}{10} + \frac{(10)(240 - 86)^2}{248,400}}$$

or 42.7 ± 11.8. In other words, we can assert with a probability of 0.95 that the oxide thickness of a specimen baked for 240 minutes falls between 30.9 and 54.5 Ångstrom units. Poor as it is, this prediction is also based on the assumption that the true regression is linear even if we go beyond the range of the observations.

EXERCISES

1. The following table shows the results of measurements of the electrical resistivity in ohm-cm $\cdot 10^{-6}$ of platinum at several temperatures in degrees Kelvin.

Temperature, x	100	200	300	400	500
Resistivity, y	4.1	8.0	12.6	16.3	19.4

(a) Assuming the regression of y on x to be of the form $y = \alpha + \beta x$, find the normal equations for estimating the parameters α and β and solve for a and b.

(b) Graph the data and the straight line obtained in (a) on the same set of coordinate axes. What is your estimate of the resistivity of platinum when its temperature is 350 degrees Kelvin?

2. Solving the normal equations on page 230 symbolically, show that

$$a = \frac{(\Sigma x^2)(\Sigma y) - (\Sigma x)(\Sigma xy)}{n(\Sigma x^2) - (\Sigma x)^2}$$

$$b = \frac{n(\Sigma xy) - (\Sigma x)(\Sigma y)}{n(\Sigma x^2) - (\Sigma x)^2}$$

(The indices and limits of summation have been omitted for simplicity.) Use these formulas to verify the results obtained in part (a) of Exercise 1.

3. In the accompanying table, x is the tensile force applied to a steel specimen in thousands of pounds and y is the resulting elongation in thousandths of an inch. Assuming the regression of y on x to be linear, estimate the parameters of the regression line and construct a 0.95 confidence interval for β, the elongation of the specimen per thousand pounds of tensile stress.

x	1	2	3	4	5	6
y	15	35	41	63	77	84

4. A student obtained the following data concerning the amount of potassium bromide, y, which will dissolve in 100 grams of water at various temperatures, x.

x (°C)	0	10	20	30	40	50
y (grams)	52	60	64	73	76	81

(a) Estimate α and β, the coefficients of the regression line of y on x.

(b) Test the null hypothesis $\beta = 0.5$ at a level of significance of 0.05.

5. The cost of manufacturing a lot of a certain product depends upon the lot size as shown in the following table:

Cost (dollars)	30	80	130	270	520	1050	2500	5025
Lot size	1	5	10	25	50	100	250	500

Fit a straight line to these data by the method of least squares, using lot size as the independent variable. Also, find a 0.90 confidence interval for α, which can here be interpreted as the fixed overhead cost of manufacturing.

6. Raw material used in the production of a synthetic fibre is stored in a place which has no humidity control. Measurements of the relative humidity in the storage place and the moisture content of a sample of the raw material (both in percentages) on 12 days yielded the following results:

x Humidity	y Moisture content
43	12
35	8
51	14
47	9
46	11
62	16
32	7
36	9
41	12
39	10
53	13
48	11

(a) Estimate α and β, the coefficients of the regression line of y on x.

(b) Find a 0.99 confidence interval for the mean moisture content of the raw material when the humidity of the storage place is 40 per cent.

(c) Find 0.95 limits of prediction for the moisture content of the raw material when the humidity of the storage place is 40 per cent.

(d) Referring to part (c), indicate to what extent the width of the interval is affected by the size of the sample and to what extent it is affected by the inherent variability of the data.

7. Referring to the data of Exercise 3,

(a) find a 0.95 confidence interval for the mean of the distribution of the y's when $x = 3.5$,

(b) express the 0.95 confidence limits for the mean of the distribution of the y's in terms of x_0; plot a graph of the estimated regression line and, choosing suitable values of x_0, sketch graphs of the loci of the upper and lower confidence limits on the same set of coordinate axes. (The resulting "confidence bands" do *not* give confidence intervals for the line itself; in fact, since any two confidence intervals obtained from these bands are dependent, they should be used only *once* in connection with some fixed value x_0.)

8. Referring to the data of Exercise 4, express 0.95 limits of prediction for the amount of potassium bromide that will dissolve in 100 grams of water in terms of x_0; choosing suitable values of x_0, sketch graphs of the loci of the upper and lower limits of prediction on the same set of coordinate axes. (Note that, as in Exercise 7, such bands should be used only once in connection with some fixed value x_0.)

9. Referring to Exercise 3, it is entirely reasonable to impose the condition that there will be no elongation when no tensile force is applied.

(a) Using the method of least squares, derive a formula for estimating β when the regression line is assumed to have the form $y = \beta x$.

(b) Using the data of Exercise 3 and the formula obtained in (a), estimate β and compare your result with the estimate previously obtained without the condition that the line must pass through the origin.

10. Referring to Exercise 4, suppose it is known that at 10 degrees centigrade 60 grams of potassium bromide will dissolve in 100 grams of water.

(a) Using the method of least squares, derive a formula for estimating β when the regression line is assumed to have the form $y = 60 + \beta(x - 10)$, that is, when the line is assumed to pass through the point $(10, 60)$.

(b) Using the data of Exercise 4 and the formula obtained in (a), estimate β and compare your result with that previously obtained without the condition that the line must pass through the point $(10, 60)$.

11. Referring to the data of Exercise 5, fit a straight line using the cost as the independent variable. Graph the resulting line and that found in Exercise 5 on the same set of coordinate axes and note that the two regression lines do *not* coincide.

12. When the sum of the x-values is equal to zero, the calculation of the coefficients of the regression line of y on x is greatly simplified; in fact, their estimates are given by

$$a = \frac{\Sigma y}{n} \quad \text{and} \quad b = \frac{\Sigma xy}{\Sigma x^2}$$

This simplification can also be attained when the x's are *equally spaced*, that is, when they are in arithmetic progression. We then "code" the data by substituting for the x's the values $\ldots, -2, -1, 0, 1, 2, \ldots$, when n is *odd*, or the values $\ldots, -3, -1, 1, 3, \ldots$, when n is *even*. The above formulas are then used in connection with the coded data.

(a) Use this technique to fit a least-squares trend line to the following data on a company's profits in millions of dollars:

x Year	y Profit
1957	6.7
1958	7.5
1959	8.3
1960	10.2
1961	11.1
1962	12.5
1963	14.6

(b) Use the result obtained in (a) to estimate the company's profit for 1965.

13. Using the formulas obtained in Exercise 2, show that

(a) the expression for a is linear in the y_i,

(b) a is an unbiased estimate of α.

14. Using the formulas obtained in Exercise 2, show that
    (a) the expression for b is linear in the y_i,
    (b) b is an unbiased estimate of β.

15. Show that the least-squares estimates of the coefficients of the regression line of y on x can be written in the form
$$a = \bar{y} - b \cdot \bar{x} \quad \text{and} \quad b = S_{xy}/S_{xx}$$

12.3 Curvilinear Regression

So far we have studied only the case where the regression curve of y on x is linear, that is, where for any given x, the mean of the distribution of the y's is given by $\alpha + \beta x$. In this section, we shall first investigate cases where the regression curve is nonlinear, but where the methods of Section 12.1 can nevertheless be applied; then we shall take up the problem of polynomial regression, that is, problems where for any given x the mean of the distribution of the y's is given by $\beta_0 + \beta_1 x + \beta_2 x^2 + \ldots + \beta_p x^p$. This last technique is also used to obtain approximations when the functional form of the regression curve is unknown.

It is common practice for engineers to plot paired data on various kinds of graph paper, in order to determine whether for suitably transformed scales the points will fall close to a straight line. If that is the case, the nature of the transformation used leads to a functional form of the regression equation, and the necessary constants (parameters) can be determined by applying the method of Section 12.1 to the transformed data. If a set of paired data consisting of n points (x_i, y_i) "straightens out" when plotted on semi-log paper, for instance, this indicates that the regression curve of y on x is *exponential*, namely, that for any given x, the mean of the distribution of the y's is given by $\alpha \cdot \beta^x$. Taking logarithms to the base 10 of both sides of the *predicting equation**
$$y' = \alpha \cdot \beta^x$$
we obtain
$$\log y' = \log \alpha + x \cdot \log \beta$$

and we can now get estimates of $\log \alpha$ and $\log \beta$, and hence of α and β, by applying the method of Section 12.1 to the n pairs of values $(x_i, \log y_i)$.

To illustrate this least-squares fitting of an exponential curve, let us refer to the following observations of the weights of 8 metal specimens exposed to a corrosive atmosphere for different periods of time:

y, Weight (grams)	92.7	58.3	59.5	41.7	45.6	31.8	38.3	19.9
x, Exposure time (days)	5	10	15	20	25	30	35	40

* Any other base could have been used.

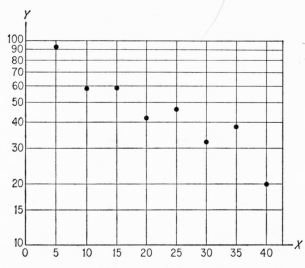

FIG. 12.4 Exponential regression

When plotting the data on semi-log graph paper as in Figure 12.4, we observe that the points fall fairly close to a straight line and that it is, therefore, justifiable to fit an exponential curve to the original data. Determining first the logarithms of the eight y's we obtain, respectively, 1.967, 1.766, 1.775, 1.620, 1.659, 1.502, 1.583, 1.299, and the summations required for substitution into the normal equations are

$$\Sigma \, x = 180, \qquad\qquad \Sigma \, x^2 = 5100$$
$$\Sigma \log y = 13.171 \qquad \Sigma \, x \cdot \log y = 280.420$$

where the indices and limits of summation have been omitted for simplicity. Again using a and b for the least-squares estimates of α and β, we obtain the normal equations

$$13.171 = 8(\log a) + 180(\log b)$$
$$280.420 = 180(\log a) + 5100(\log b)$$

and, solving this system, we have

$$\log a = 1.986, \qquad \log b = -0.0151$$

Hence, $a = 96.8$, $b = 0.966$, and the least-squares exponential curve has the equation

$$y' = (96.8)(0.966)^x$$

This last equation can also be written as

$$y' = (96.8)10^{-0.0151x} \qquad \text{or} \qquad y' = (96.8)e^{-0.0346x}$$

making use of the fact that $0.966 = 10^{-0.0151} = e^{-0.0346}$.

If we want to base a prediction on an exponential equation fitted to a set of data, it is usually more convenient to use it in its logarithmic form. Thus, if we want to predict the weight of a specimen exposed to a corrosive atmosphere for, say, 12 days in our example, we obtain

$$\log y = 1.986 - 0.0151(12)$$
$$= 1.805$$

and, hence, a weight of 63.8 grams.

Two other relationships, fequently arising in engineering practice, that can be fitted by the method of Section 12.1 after suitable transformations are the *reciprocal function* given by $y' = \dfrac{1}{\alpha + \beta x}$, and the *power function* $y' = \alpha \cdot x^{\beta}$. The first of these represents a linear relationship between x and $1/y'$, namely,

$$\frac{1}{y'} = \alpha + \beta x$$

and we obtain estimates of α and β by applying the method of Section 12.1 to the points $(x_i, 1/y_i)$. The second represents a linear relationship between $\log x$ and $\log y'$, namely,

$$\log y' = \log \alpha + \beta \cdot \log x$$

and we obtain estimates of $\log \alpha$ and β, and hence of α and β, by applying the method of Section 12.1 to the points $(\log x_i, \log y_i)$. Examples of other curves that can be fitted by the method of least squares after a suitable transformation are given in Exercises 6 and 7 on page 251.

If there is no clear indication about the functional form of the regression of y on x, we often assume that the underlying relationship is at least "well behaved" to the extent that it has a Taylor series expansion and that the first few terms of this expansion will yield a fairly good approximation. We thus fit to our data a polynomial, that is, a predicting equation of the form

$$y' = \beta_0 + \beta_1 x + \beta_2 x^2 + \ldots + \beta_p x^p$$

where the degree is determined by inspection of the data or by more "scientific" methods to be discussed below.

Given a set of data consisting of n points (x_i, y_i), we estimate the coefficients $\beta_0, \beta_1, \beta_2, \ldots, \beta_p$ of the pth-degree polynomial by minimizing

$$\sum_{i=1}^{n} [y_i - (\beta_0 + \beta_1 x_i + \beta_2 x_i^2 + \ldots + \beta_p x_i^p)]^2$$

In other words, we are now applying the least-squares criterion by minimizing the sum of the squares of the vertical distances from the points

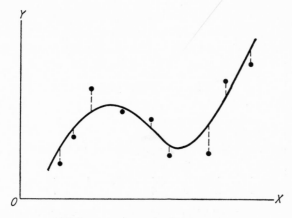

FIG. 12.5 Least-squares criterion for polynomials

to the curve (see Figure 12.5). Differentiating partially with respect to $\beta_0, \beta_1, \beta_2, \ldots, \beta_p$, equating these partial derivatives to zero, rearranging some of the terms, and letting b_i be the estimate of β_i, we obtain the $p + 1$ *normal equations*

$$\Sigma\, y = nb_0 + b_1 \Sigma\, x + \ldots + b_p \Sigma\, x^p$$

$$\Sigma\, xy = b_0 \Sigma\, x + b_1 \Sigma\, x^2 + \ldots + b_p \Sigma\, x^{p+1}$$

$$\cdots\cdots\cdots\cdots\cdots\cdots\cdots\cdots\cdots\cdots\cdots\cdots\cdots\cdots$$

$$\Sigma\, x^p y = b_0 \Sigma\, x^p + b_1 \Sigma\, x^{p+1} + \ldots + b_p \Sigma\, x^{2p}$$

where the indices and limits of summation are omitted for simplicity. Note that this is a system of $p + 1$ *linear* equations in the $p + 1$ unknowns, $b_0, b_1, \ldots, b_p$. Unless the choice of the x values is very unusual, this system of equations will have a unique solution.

To illustrate the fitting of a polynomial by the method of least squares, we shall fit a quadratic (second-degree) polynomial to the following data, relating the drying time of a varnish to the amount of a certain additive:

x Amount of varnish additive (grams)	y Drying time (hours)
0	12.0
1	10.5
2	10.0
3	8.0
4	7.0
5	8.0
6	7.5
7	8.5
8	9.0

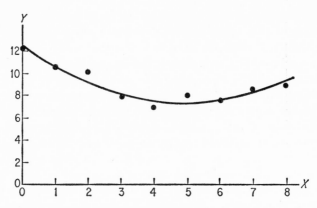

FIG. 12.6 Polynomial regression curve

Inspection of these data plotted in Figure 12.6 indicates that a second-degree polynomial, having one relative minimum, should yield a fairly good fit. First calculating the sums required for substitution into the normal equations, we obtain

$$\Sigma\, x = 36, \quad \Sigma\, x^2 = 204, \quad \Sigma\, x^3 = 1296, \quad \Sigma\, x^4 = 8772$$

$$\Sigma\, y = 80.5, \quad \Sigma\, xy = 299.0, \quad \Sigma\, x^2 y = 1697.0$$

and we thus have to solve the following system of three linear equations in three unknowns:

$$80.5 = 9b_0 + 36b_1 + 204b_2$$

$$299.0 = 36b_0 + 204b_1 + 1296b_2$$

$$1697.0 = 204b_0 + 1296b_1 + 8772b_2$$

Getting $b_0 = 12.2$, $b_1 = -1.85$, and $b_2 = 0.183$, we find that the equation of the least-squares polynomial is

$$y' = 12.2 - 1.85x + 0.183x^2$$

The graph of this equation is also shown in Figure 12.6.

Having obtained this equation, we might now use it to predict the drying time when the amount of additive used is 6.5 grams. Substituting $x = 6.5$ into the equation, we obtain

$$y' = 12.2 - 1.85(6.5) + 0.183(6.5)^2 = 7.9$$

that is, a predicted drying time of approximately 7.9 hours. Note that it would have been rather dangerous to use the above equation to predict, say, the drying time which corresponds to 24.5 grams of additive. The risks inherent in extrapolation discussed on page 236, in connection with fitting straight lines, are greatly increased when polynomials are used to approximate unknown regression functions.

In actual practice, it may be difficult to determine the degree of the polynomial to fit to a given set of paired data. As it is always possible to find a polynomial of degree at most $n - 1$ that will pass through each of n points corresponding to n distinct values of x, it should be clear that what we actually seek is a polynomial of *lowest possible degree* that "adequately" describes the data. As we did in our example, it is often possible to determine the degree of the polynomial by inspection of the data.

There also exists a more rigorous method for determining the degree of the polynomial to be fitted to a given set of data. Essentially, it consists of first fitting a straight line as well as a second-degree polynomial and testing the null hypothesis $\beta_2 = 0$, namely, that nothing is gained by including the quadratic term. If this null hypothesis can be rejected, we then fit a third-degree polynomial and test the hypothesis $\beta_3 = 0$, namely, that nothing is gained by including the cubic term. This procedure is continued until the null hypothesis $\beta_i = 0$ cannot be rejected in two successive steps and there is, thus, no apparent advantage to carrying the extra terms. Note that in order to perform these tests it is necessary to impose the assumptions of normality, independence, and equal variances introduced in Section 12.2. Also, these tests should never be used "blindly," that is, without inspection of the over-all pattern of the data.

The use of this technique is fairly tedious and we shall not illustrate it in the text. In Exercise 10 on page 252 the reader will be asked to apply it to the varnish-additive, drying-time data in order to check whether it is worthwhile to carry the quadratic term. (If the x values are equally spaced, it is possible to simplify the necessary calculations with the use of *orthogonal polynomials*, as is explained in the book by R. L. Anderson and T. A. Bancroft referred to in the Bibliography.)

12.4 Multiple Regression

Before we extend the methods of the preceding sections to problems involving more than one independent variable, let us point out that the curves obtained (and the surfaces we will obtain) are not used only to make predictions. They are often used also for purposes of *optimization*, namely, to determine for what values of the independent variable (or variables) the dependent variable is a maximum or minimum. For instance, in the example on page 244 we might use the polynomial fitted to the data to conclude that the drying time is a minimum when the amount of varnish additive used is 5.1 grams (see Exercise 11 on page 252).

Statistical methods of prediction and optimization are often referred to under the general heading of *response surface analysis*. Within the scope of this text, we shall be able to introduce two further methods of response surface analysis: *multiple regression* in this section and related problems of *factorial experimentation* in Chapter 14.

In multiple regression, we deal with data consisting of n $(r + 1)$-tuples $(x_{1i}, x_{2i}, \ldots, x_{ri}, y_i)$, where the x's are again assumed to be known without error while the y's are values of random variables. Data of this kind arise, for example, in studies designed to determine the effect of various climatic conditions on a metal's resistance to corrosion, the effect of kiln temperature, humidity, and iron content on the strength of a ceramic coating, or the effect of factory production, consumption level, and stocks in storage on the price of a product.

As in the case of one independent variable, we shall first treat the problem where the regression equation is linear, namely, where for any given set of values $x_1, x_2, \ldots,$ and x_r the mean of the distribution of the y's is given by

$$\beta_0 + \beta_1 x_1 + \beta_2 x_2 + \ldots + \beta_r x_r$$

For two independent variables, this is the problem of fitting a *plane* to a set of n points with coordinates (x_{1i}, x_{2i}, y_i) as is illustrated in Figure 12.7.

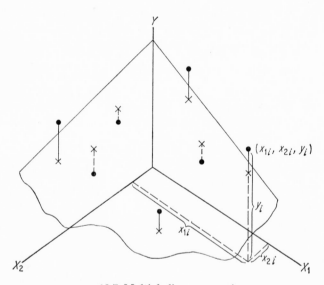

FIG. 12.7 Multiple linear regression

Applying the method of least squares to obtain estimates of the coefficients β_0, β_1, and β_2, we minimize the sum of the squares of the vertical distances from the points to the plane (see Figure 12.7); symbolically, we minimize

$$\sum_{i=1}^{n} [y_i - (\beta_0 + \beta_1 x_{1i} + \beta_2 x_{2i})]^2$$

and it will be left to the reader to verify in Exercise 12 on page 252 that the resulting normal equations are

$$\Sigma y = nb_0 + b_1 \Sigma x_1 + b_2 \Sigma x_2$$
$$\Sigma x_1 y = b_0 \Sigma x_1 + b_1 \Sigma x_1^2 + b_2 \Sigma x_1 x_2$$
$$\Sigma x_2 y = b_0 \Sigma x_2 + b_1 \Sigma x_1 x_2 + b_2 \Sigma x_2^2$$

As before, we write the least-square estimates of β_0, β_1, and β_2 as b_0, b_1, and b_2. Note that in the abbreviated notation used Σx_1 stands for $\sum_{i=1}^{n} x_{1i}$, $\Sigma x_1 x_2$ stands for $\sum_{i=1}^{n} x_{1i} x_{2i}$, $\Sigma x_1 y$ stands for $\sum_{i=1}^{n} x_{1i} y_i$, and so forth.

To illustrate this method of fitting a plane to a set of data, let us consider the following data relating the number of twists required to break a forged alloy bar to the percentage of each of two alloying elements present in a metal.

y Number of twists	x_1 Per cent of element A	x_2 Per cent of element B
38	1	5
40	2	5
85	3	5
59	4	5
40	1	10
60	2	10
68	3	10
53	4	10
31	1	15
35	2	15
42	3	15
59	4	15
18	1	20
34	2	20
29	3	20
42	4	20

Substituting

$$\Sigma x_1 = 40, \quad \Sigma x_2 = 200, \quad \Sigma x_1^2 = 120, \quad \Sigma x_1 x_2 = 500, \quad \Sigma x_2^2 = 3000$$
$$\Sigma y = 733, \quad \Sigma x_1 y = 1989, \quad \Sigma x_2 y = 8285$$

into the normal equations, we obtain

$$733 = 16b_0 + 40b_1 + 200b_2$$
$$1989 = 40b_0 + 120b_1 + 500b_2$$
$$8285 = 200b_0 + 500b_1 + 3000b_2$$

The unique solution of this system of equations is $b_0 = 48.2$, $b_1 = 7.83$, $b_2 = -1.76$, and we can thus estimate (predict) the number of twists required to break one of these bars by means of the equation

$$y' = 48.2 + 7.83x_1 - 1.76x_2$$

for any given pair of values of x_1 and x_2. Note that b_1 and b_2 are estimates of the average change in y resulting from a unit increase in the corresponding independent variable when the other independent variable is held fixed.

When a regression problem involves many variables and (or) the fitting of polynomials, the necessary calculations can become quite tedious. However, if the values of the independent variables can be controlled, it is possible to attain considerable simplifications by using appropriate spacings and subsequent coding (similar to that used in Exercise 8 on page 251). Observe that in the preceding example the x_1's as well as the x_2's are equally spaced and that, furthermore, each value (level) of x_1 occurs once in combination with each value (level) of x_2. This arrangement makes it possible to reduce the labor of obtaining and solving the normal equations. Coding the x_1 values as well as the x_2 values -3, -1, 1, and 3,* and calling them z_1 and z_2, we can write the original data as

y	z_1	z_2
38	-3	-3
40	-1	-3
85	1	-3
59	3	-3
40	-3	-1
60	-1	-1
68	1	-1
53	3	-1
31	-3	1
35	-1	1
42	1	1
59	3	1
18	-3	3
34	-1	3
29	1	3
42	3	3

We now get $\Sigma z_1 = 0$, $\Sigma z_2 = 0$, $\Sigma z_1^2 = 80$, $\Sigma z_1 z_2 = 0$, $\Sigma z_2^2 = 80$, $\Sigma y = 733$, $\Sigma z_1 y = 313$, $\Sigma z_2 y = -351$, and the normal equations become

---

* Had there been five values of x_1, we would have coded them -2, -1, 0, 1, and 2. In this kind of coding the values must always be equally spaced and their sum must equal zero.

$$733 = 16b_0$$
$$313 = 80b_1$$
$$-351 = 80b_2$$

Thus, in terms of these coded variables, we have

$$y' = 45.8 + 3.91z_1 - 4.39z_2$$

and the reader will be asked to verify in Exercise 15 on page 253 that (except for rounding errors) this result is equivalent to the one previously obtained.

The same coding would have produced even greater simplifications if we had wanted to fit a second-degree polynomial to our data, that is, if we had used an equation of the form

$$y' = \beta_0 + \beta_1 x_1 + \beta_2 x_2 + \beta_3 x_1 x_2 + \beta_4 x_1^2 + \beta_5 x_2^2$$

Without coding, the method of least squares would have led to a system of normal equations consisting of six simultaneous linear equations in six unknowns. As the reader will be asked to verify in Exercise 16 on page 253, the same coding as used above reduces this problem, essentially, to that of solving three simultaneous linear equations in three unknowns.

The example of this section served to illustrate how a careful choice of the values of the independent variables can simplify the calculations required in a problem of multiple regression. The principles and procedures for making this choice, whenever possible, are part of the important subject of *experimental design*. In Chapter 13 we shall consider some of the simpler, but nevertheless widely used, experimental designs. We shall focus our attention on what is called the *analysis of variance*, where tests are made concerning the significance of the effects of certain combinations of levels of the independent variables. In Chapter 14 we shall introduce the related problem of *factorial experimentation*.

EXERCISES

1. In the following table y is barometric pressure measured at a distance x above sea level:

y (inches)	29.9	29.4	29.0	28.4	27.7
x (feet)	0	500	1000	1500	2000

Use the method of least squares to fit an exponential curve of the form $y = \alpha \cdot e^{-\beta x}$.

2. The following data pertain to the amount of a substance remaining in a reacting chemical system after x minutes:

y (grams)	96	75	63	30	9	2
x (minutes)	1	5	10	25	50	100

(a) Plot the data on semi-log paper and use the method of least squares to fit an exponential curve of the form $y = \alpha \cdot \beta^x$.

(b) Use the result obtained in (a) to estimate what amount of the substance will remain after 8 minutes.

√3. A test was conducted in which five different groups of rats were maintained on a diet deficient in Vitamin A, and then given supplementary rations of Vitamin A in the form of cod-liver oil. The dosage of cod-liver oil given to each group of rats and the corresponding mean weight gains are as follows:

Dosage (mg)	0.25	1.00	1.50	2.50	7.50
Weight gain (g)	−10.8	13.5	16.4	28.7	51.3

(a) Graph these data in two ways—using ordinary (arithmetic) graph paper, and using semi-logarithmic graph paper with the dosages plotted on the logarithmic scale.

(b) Fit a curve of the form $y = \alpha + \beta \log x$, where x is the dosage and y is the corresponding weight gain.

4. The ion concentration n, remaining in a gas after the ionization agent is turned off, is given by

$$n = \frac{n_0}{1 + n_0 \alpha t}$$

where n_0 is the initial concentration of ions and α is a constant called the "coefficient of recombination." In an experiment to determine α, a gas is ionized by X-radiation and the following data are obtained:

$n \cdot 10^{-4}$	5.03	4.71	4.40	3.97	3.88	3.62	3.30	3.15	3.08	2.92	2.70
t (sec)	0	1	2	3	4	5	6	7	8	9	10

Using these data, estimate α and n_0 by the method of least squares. Why is it preferable to use the least-squares estimate of n_0 thus obtained rather than the observed value of 5.03? Graph the data as well as the fitted curve.

5. In an experiment designed to determine the specific heat ratio γ for a certain gas, the gas was compressed adiabatically to several predetermined volumes V, and the corresponding pressure p was measured with the following results:

p (lb/in.²)	16.8	39.7	78.6	115.5	195.0	546.1
V (in.³)	50	30	20	15	10	5

Assuming the ideal gas law $p \cdot V^\gamma = C$, use these data to

(a) estimate γ for this gas.

(b) construct a 0.95 confidence interval for γ. (State what assumptions will have to be made.)

6. Fit a Gompertz curve of the form

$$y = e^{e^{\alpha x + \beta}}$$

to the data of Exercise 2 and compare the fit with that of the exponential curve obtained in part (a) of Exercise 2.

7. The rise of current in an inductive circuit having the time constant τ is given by

$$I = 1 - e^{-t/\tau}$$

where t is the time measured from the instant the switch is closed, and I is the ratio of the current at time t to the full value of the current given by Ohm's law. Given the measurements

I	0.110	0.330	0.450	0.555	0.630	0.700	0.775	0.865
t (sec)	0.2	0.4	0.6	0.8	1.0	1.2	1.5	2.0

estimate τ. [*Hint:* See Exercise 9 on page 238.]

8. The following figures show the per capita consumption (in pounds) of tobacco in the United States for the 25-year period 1931–1955:

Year	Consumption	Year	Consumption
1931	8.4	1944	11.2
1932	7.6	1945	12.5
1933	7.8	1946	12.2
1934	8.3	1947	12.0
1935	8.2	1948	12.1
1936	8.8	1949	11.9
1937	9.0	1950	12.0
1938	8.8	1951	12.5
1939	8.8	1952	12.9
1940	9.1	1953	12.9
1941	9.8	1954	12.2
1942	10.7	1955	12.3
1943	11.5		

Coding the years $-12, -11, \ldots, 11$, and 12, fit a parabolic trend to these data.

9. The following are measurements of the elevation of a straight (but hilly) road above a fixed reference point on the road, made at increasing horizontal distances along the road from that point:

Elevation (ft)	0	6	12	19	16	9	10	11	15	20
Distance (100 ft)	0	1	2	3	4	5	6	7	8	9

(a) Graph this set of data and determine by inspection the degree of the polynomial that would adequately describe the road elevation in terms of the distance.

(b) Fit such a polynomial to the given data, and use the result to estimate the location of the crest of the hill and the bottom of the dip in this road.

10. When fitting a polynomial to a set of paired data, we usually begin by fitting a straight line and using the method on page 234 to test the null hypothesis $\beta_1 = 0$. Then we fit a second-degree polynomial and test whether it is worthwhile to carry the quadratic term by comparing $\hat{\sigma}_1^2$, the *residual variance* after fitting the straight line, with $\hat{\sigma}_2^2$, the *residual variance* after fitting the second-degree polynomial. Each of these residual variances is given by the formula

$$\frac{\Sigma \, (y - y')^2}{\text{degrees of freedom}}$$

with y' computed, respectively, from the equation of the line and the equation of the second-degree polynomial. The decision whether to carry the quadratic term is based on the statistic

$$F = \frac{\hat{\sigma}_1^2 - \hat{\sigma}_2^2}{\hat{\sigma}_2^2}$$

which (under the assumptions of Section 12.2) is a value of a random variable having the F distribution with 1 and $n - 3$ degrees of freedom.

(a) Fit a straight line to the varnish-additive and drying-time data on page 243, test the null hypothesis $\beta_1 = 0$ at the 0.05 level of significance, and calculate $\hat{\sigma}_1^2$.

(b) Using the result on page 244 calculate $\hat{\sigma}_2^2$ for the given data and test at the 0.05 level whether we should carry the quadratic term. (Note that we could continue this procedure and test whether to carry a cubic term by means of a corresponding comparison of residual variances. Then we could test whether to carry a fourth-degree term, and so on. It is customary to terminate this procedure after two successive steps have not produced significant results.)

11. Referring to the example on page 244, verify that the drying time is a minimum when the amount of varnish additive used is 5.1 grams.

12. Verify that the method of least squares leads to the system of normal equations on page 247.

13. Twelve samples of cold-reduced sheet steel, having differing copper contents and annealing temperatures, are measured for hardness with the following results:

Hardness (Rockwell 30-T)	Copper content (per cent)	Annealing temperature (degrees F)
78.8	0.02	1000
65.1	0.02	1100
55.4	0.02	1200
56.2	0.02	1300
80.9	0.10	1000
69.5	0.10	1100
57.4	0.10	1200
55.2	0.10	1300
85.6	0.18	1000
71.8	0.18	1100
60.2	0.18	1200
58.7	0.18	1300

Fit an equation of the form $y = \beta_0 + \beta_1 x_1 + \beta_2 x_2$, where x_1 represents the copper content, x_2 represents the annealing temperature, and y represents the hardness.

14. The following data were collected to determine the relationship between two processing variables and the current gain of a certain kind of transistor:

y Current gain	x_1 Diffusion time (hours)	x_2 Sheet resistance (ohm-cm)
5.3	1.5	66
7.8	2.5	87
7.4	0.5	69
9.8	1.2	141
10.8	2.6	93
9.1	0.3	105
8.1	2.4	111
7.2	2.0	78
6.5	0.7	66
12.6	1.6	123

Fit an equation of the form $y = \beta_0 + \beta_1 x_1 + \beta_2 x_2$ to the data and use it to estimate the current gain corresponding to a diffusion time of 2.2 hours and a sheet resistance of 90 ohm-cm.

15. Referring to the example involving the number of twists required to break a forged bar, verify that the result given on page 249, obtained by coding, is equivalent to the original result shown on page 248.

16. Verify that if the x's are coded as on page 248, the normal equations for estimating the coefficients of

$$y' = \beta_0 + \beta_1 x_1 + \beta_2 x_2 + \beta_3 x_1 x_2 + \beta_4 x_1^2 + \beta_5 x_2^2$$

become

$$733 = 16b_0 \qquad\qquad\qquad + 80b_4 + 80b_5$$
$$315 = \qquad 80b_1$$
$$351 = \qquad\qquad 80b_2$$
$$-79 = \qquad\qquad\qquad 400b_3$$
$$3453 = 80b_0 \qquad\qquad\qquad + 656b_4 + 400b_5$$
$$3493 = 80b_0 \qquad\qquad\qquad + 400b_4 + 656b_5$$

17. Code the values of x_1 in Exercise 13 as $z_1 = -1, 0, +1$, and the values of x_2 as $z_2 = -3, -1, +1, +3$. Then write down the resulting normal equations, solve, and show that the resulting regression equation is equivalent to the one obtained in Exercise 13.

12.5 Correlation

Until now we have studied problems where the independent variable (or variables) was assumed to be known without error. Although this applies to many experimental situations, there are also problems where the x's as well as the y's are values assumed by random variables. This would be the case, for instance, if we studied the relationship between rainfall and the yield of a certain crop, the relationship between the tensile strength and the hardness of aluminum, or the relationship between impurities in the air and the incidence of a certain disease. Problems like these are referred to as problems of *correlation analysis*, where it is assumed that the data points (x_i, y_i) for $i = 1, 2, \ldots, n$ are values of a pair of random variables whose joint density is given by $f(x, y)$.

The bivariate density which is most commonly used in problems of correlation analysis is the bivariate normal density. To introduce this bivariate density, let us first define what is meant by a *conditional density*. Analogous to the formula $P(A \cap B) = P(A) \cdot P(B \mid A)$ which we used to find joint probabilities, we write

$$f(x, y) = g(x)f(y \mid x)$$

where $f(y \mid x)$ defines the conditional density of the second random variable for fixed x. Here $g(x)$ is a marginal density, as defined on page 83.

So far as the bivariate normal density is concerned, the conditions we shall impose on $f(y \mid x)$ are practically identical with the ones we used in connection with the sampling theory of Section 12.2. For any given x, it will be assumed that $f(y \mid x)$ is a normal distribution with the mean $\alpha + \beta x$ and the variance σ^2. Thus, the regression of y on x is linear and the variance of the conditional density does not depend on x. Furthermore, we shall assume that the marginal density $g(x)$ is normal with the mean μ_1 and the variance σ_1^2. Substituting the appropriate expressions for $f(y \mid x)$ and $g(x)$, we thus obtain

$$f(x, y) = \frac{1}{\sqrt{2\pi}\,\sigma_1} e^{-(x-\mu_1)^2/2\sigma_1^2} \cdot \frac{1}{\sqrt{2\pi}\,\sigma} e^{-[y-(\alpha+\beta x)]^2/2\sigma^2}$$

$$= \frac{1}{2\pi \cdot \sigma \cdot \sigma_1} e^{-\{[y-(\alpha+\beta x)]^2/2\sigma^2 + (x-\mu_1)^2/2\sigma_1^2\}}$$

for $-\infty < x < \infty$ and $-\infty < y < \infty$. Note that this joint distribution involves the *five* parameters μ_1, σ_1, α, β, and σ.

For reasons of symmetry and other considerations to be explained below, it is customary to express the bivariate normal density in terms of the parameters μ_1, σ_1, μ_2, σ_2, and ρ. Here μ_2 and σ_2^2 are the mean and the variance of the marginal distribution $h(y)$, while ρ, called the *correlation coefficient*, is defined by

$$\rho^2 = 1 - \frac{\sigma^2}{\sigma_2^2}$$

with ρ taken to be positive when β is positive (and negative when β is negative). Leaving it to the reader to show in Exercise 4 on page 259 that

$$\mu_2 = \alpha + \beta\mu_1 \qquad \text{and} \qquad \sigma_2^2 = \sigma^2 + \beta^2\sigma_1^2$$

we then substitute into the above expression for $f(x, y)$ and finally obtain the following form of the bivariate normal distribution:

$$f(x, y) = \frac{1}{2\pi \cdot \sigma_1\sigma_2\sqrt{1-\rho^2}} e^{-\left[\left(\frac{x-\mu_1}{\sigma_1}\right)^2 - 2\rho\left(\frac{x-\mu_1}{\sigma_1}\right)\left(\frac{y-\mu_2}{\sigma_2}\right) + \left(\frac{y-\mu_2}{\sigma_2}\right)^2\right]/2(1-\rho^2)}$$

for $-\infty < x < \infty$ and $-\infty < y < \infty$ (see Exercise 5 on page 259).

Concerning the correlation coefficient ρ, note that $-1 \le \rho \le +1$ since $\sigma_2^2 = \sigma^2 + \beta^2\sigma_1^2$ and, hence, $\sigma_2^2 \ge \sigma^2$. Furthermore, ρ can equal -1 or $+1$ only when $\sigma^2 = 0$, which represents the *degenerate case* where all the probability is concentrated along the line $y = \alpha + \beta x$ and there is, thus, a perfect linear relationship between the two random variables. (That is, for a given value of x, y *must* equal $\alpha + \beta x$.) The correlation coefficient is equal to zero if and only if $\sigma^2 = \sigma_2^2$, and it follows from the identity $\sigma_2^2 = \sigma^2 + \beta^2\sigma_1^2$ that this can happen only when $\beta = 0$. Thus, $\rho = 0$ implies that the regression line of y on x is a horizontal line and, hence, that knowledge of x does not help in the prediction of y. Thus, when $\rho = \pm 1$ we say that there is a perfect linear correlation (relationship, or association) between the two random variables; when $\rho = 0$ we say that there is no correlation (relationship, or association) between the two random variables. In fact, $\rho = 0$ implies for the bivariate normal density that the two random variables are *independent* (see Exercise 6 on page 259).

For values between 0 and $+1$ or 0 and -1, we interpret ρ by referring back to the identity

$$\rho^2 = 1 - \frac{\sigma^2}{\sigma_2^2} = \frac{\sigma_2^2 - \sigma^2}{\sigma_2^2}$$

on page 255. Since σ^2 is a measure of the variation of the y's when x is *known* while σ_2^2 is a measure of the variation of the y's when x is *unknown*, $\sigma_2^2 - \sigma^2$ measures the variation of the y's that is accounted for by the linear relationship with x. Hence, ρ^2 tells us what *proportion* of the variation of the y's can be attributed to the linear relationship with x.

Given a random sample of size n—that is, n pairs of values (x_i, y_i)—it is customary to estimate ρ by means of the *sample correlation coefficient*

$$\blacklozenge \qquad r = \frac{S_{xy}}{\sqrt{S_{xx} \cdot S_{yy}}} \qquad \blacklozenge$$

where S_{xy}, S_{xx}, and S_{yy} are as defined on page 232. This estimator is not unbiased and, except for the factor $\sqrt{\dfrac{n-1}{n-2}}$, it may be obtained by substituting for σ_2^2 the sample variance of the y's and for σ^2 the estimator on page 233, namely, s_e^2 (see also Exercise 7 on page 259). Note that the sample correlation coefficient r is often used to measure the strength of a linear relationship exhibited by sample data even if the data do not necessarily come from a bivariate normal population.

To illustrate the calculation of r, consider the following paired measurements of the modulus of rupture and the modulus of elasticity of 12 common woods:

x Modulus of rupture	y Modulus of elasticity	x Modulus of rupture	y Modulus of elasticity
8.76	889	6.49	908
7.08	808	11.83	1654
11.35	1513	15.08	1502
5.25	550	7.13	1216
10.91	1008	9.08	1315
13.56	1952	3.86	497

The calculations required to find r are as follows, where the indices of summation and the limits of summation are omitted for the sake of simplicity:

$$\Sigma\, x = 110.38, \qquad \Sigma\, x^2 = 1143.8090$$

$$\Sigma\, y = 13{,}812, \qquad \Sigma\, xy = 141{,}673.33 \qquad \Sigma\, y^2 = 18{,}132{,}296$$

$$S_{xx} = 12(1143.8090) - (110.38)^2 = 1541.9636$$

$$S_{xy} = 12(141{,}673.33) - (110.38)(13{,}812) = 175{,}511.40$$

$$S_{yy} = 12(18{,}132{,}296) - (13{,}812)^2 = 26{,}816{,}208$$

$$r = \frac{175{,}511.40}{\sqrt{(1541.9636)(26{,}816{,}208)}} = 0.86$$

This means that $100r^2 = 74$ per cent of the variation in modulus of elasticity is explained by (is accounted for or may be attributed to) differences in modulus of rupture.

Whenever a value of r is based on sample data, it is customary to perform a test of significance (a test of the null hypothesis $\rho = 0$), in order to determine whether we might not have a spuriously high sample value even though there is no relationship between the two variables. For random samples from a bivariate normal population, this test is usually based on the statistic

$$\frac{1}{2} \ln \frac{1 + r}{1 - r}$$

as it can be shown that the sampling distribution of this statistic is approximately normal with the mean $\frac{1}{2} \ln \frac{1 + \rho}{1 - \rho}$ and the variance $\frac{1}{n - 3}$. Thus, we test the null hypothesis $\rho = 0$ with the statistic

$$\blacklozenge \qquad z = \frac{\sqrt{n - 3}}{2} \ln \frac{1 + r}{1 - r} \qquad \blacklozenge$$

whose sampling distribution is approximately the standard normal distribution.

Returning to our numerical example, for which we obtained $r = 0.86$, we now have

$$z = \frac{\sqrt{9}}{2} \ln \frac{1 + 0.86}{1 - 0.86} = 3.88$$

Since this exceeds $z_{.005} = 2.58$ we conclude that the sample value is significant, namely, that there exists a linear relationship between the modulus of rupture and the modulus of elasticity of the woods.

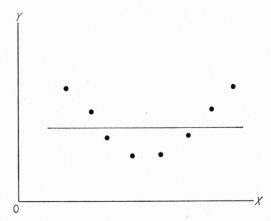

FIG. 12.8 Non-linear relationship where correlation coefficient is zero

There are several serious pitfalls in the interpretation of the coefficient of correlation. First, it must be emphasized that r is an estimate of the strength of the *linear* association between the random variables; thus, as illustrated in Figure 12.8, r may be close to zero when there is actually a strong (but nonlinear) relationship between the two random variables. Second, and perhaps of greatest importance, a significant correlation does not necessarily imply a *causal* relationship between the two random variables. Although it would not be surprising, for example, to obtain a high positive correlation between the annual sales of chewing gum and the incidence of crime in the United States, one cannot conclude that crime might be reduced by prohibiting the sale of chewing gum. Both variables depend upon the size of the population, and it is this mutual relationship with a third variable (population size) which produces the positive correlation. The initial controversy surrounding the evidence linking smoking to lung cancer was brought about by a similar confusion between correlation and causation.

EXERCISES

1. The following are measurements of the carbon content and the permeability of twenty sinter mixtures:

Carbon content (%)	Permeability index	Carbon content (%)	Permeability index
4.1	13	5.1	22
4.9	12	4.5	21
4.4	11	5.1	13
4.7	10	3.0	37
5.1	13	4.8	13
5.0	14	4.2	19
4.7	21	5.2	12
4.6	14	5.5	14
3.6	26	5.2	21
4.9	25	4.4	29

   (a) Calculate the coefficient of correlation.

   (b) Test the null hypothesis that these two variables are uncorrelated, using the 0.05 level of significance.

2. Calculate r for the humidity and moisture-content data of Exercise 6 on page 237. Assuming that the necessary conditions can be met, test for significance at $\alpha = 0.01$.

3. Using the statement on page 257 about the approximate sampling distri-

bution of the statistic $\frac{1}{2} \ln \frac{1+r}{1-r}$, it can be shown that the following formula gives $1 - \alpha$ confidence limits for ρ:

$$\frac{1 + r - (1 - r)e^{\pm 2z_{\alpha/2}/\sqrt{n-3}}}{1 + r + (1 - r)e^{\pm 2z_{\alpha/2}/\sqrt{n-3}}}$$

Using this formula and the result obtained in part (a) of Exercise 1, construct a 0.95 confidence interval for the correlation between the carbon content and the permeability index.

4. Evaluating the necessary integrals, verify the identities

$$\mu_2 = \alpha + \beta\mu_1 \qquad \text{and} \qquad \sigma_2^2 = \sigma^2 + \beta^2\sigma_1^2$$

on page 255.

5. Substitute $\mu_2 = \alpha + \beta\mu_1$ and $\sigma_2^2 = \sigma^2 + \beta^2\sigma_1^2$ into the formula for the bivariate density given at the top of page 255, and show that this gives the final form shown on that same page.

6. Show that for the bivariate normal distribution (a) independence implies zero correlation, and (b) zero correlation implies independence.

7. By substituting the sample variance of the y's for σ_2^2 and s_e^2 for σ^2 in the formula $\rho^2 = 1 - \sigma^2/\sigma_2^2$, verify the formula for r given on page 256 (except for a multiplicative constant).

8. Instead of using the computing formula on page 256, the correlation coefficient r may be obtained from the formula

$$r = \pm\sqrt{1 - \frac{\Sigma (y - y')^2}{\Sigma (y - \bar{y})^2}}$$

which is analogous to the formula used to define ρ. Although the computations required by the use of this formula are tedious, the formula has the advantage that it can be used also to measure the strength of nonlinear relationships or relationships in several variables. For instance, in the multiple linear regression example on page 247, one could calculate the predicted values by means of the equation

$$y' = 48.2 + 7.83x_1 - 1.76x_2$$

and then determine r as a measure of how strongly y, the twist required to break one of the forged alloy bars, depends on *both* percentages of alloying elements present.

(a) Using the data on page 247, find $\Sigma (y - \bar{y})^2$ by means of the formula $\Sigma (y - \bar{y})^2 = \Sigma y^2 - n\bar{y}^2$.

(b) Using the regression equation obtained on page 248, calculate y' for the sixteen points and then determine $\Sigma (y - y')^2$.

(c) Substitute the results obtained in (a) and (b) into the above formula for r. The result is the so-called *multiple correlation coefficient*.

9. By substituting for the actual values of paired data the *ranks* which the values occupy in the respective samples, the correlation coefficient can be written in the form

$$r' = 1 - \frac{6 \Sigma d_i^2}{n(n^2 - 1)}$$

in which form it is called the *rank correlation coefficient*. In this formula, d_i is the difference between the *ranks* of the paired observations (x_i, y_i) and n is the number of pairs in the sample. (In case of ties, substitute for each of the observations the mean of the ranks that they would otherwise occupy, as in Section 11.4.) Calculate r' for the data of Exercise 1 and compare with the value of r previously obtained.

10. Calculate the rank correlation coefficient (see Exercise 9) for the varnish-additive and drying-time data on page 243.

13 | ANALYSIS OF VARIANCE

13.1 Introduction

Some of the examples of Chapter 12 have already taught us that considerable economies in calculation can result by appropriately planning an experiment in advance. What is even more important, proper experimental planning can give a reasonable assurance that the results of an experiment will provide clear-cut answers to questions under investigation. While it is impossible to give in this chapter a complete discussion of *experimental design*, including the many pitfalls to which the experimenter is exposed, we shall begin by presenting in this section some of the general principles of experimental design. Several of the designs most frequently used in engineering and other applied research will be given in subsequent sections.

To illustrate some of the most important aspects of experimental design, let us consider the following situation. Suppose a steel mill supplies tin plate to three can manufacturers, the major specification being that the tin-coating weight should be at least 0.25 pound per base box. The mill and each can manufacturer has a laboratory where measurements are made of the tin-coating weights of samples taken from each shipment. Suppose, also, that some disagreement has arisen about the actual tin-coating weights of the tin plate being shipped, and it is decided to plan an experiment to determine whether the four laboratories are making consistent measurements. A complicating factor is that part of the measuring process consists of the chemical removal of the tin from the surface of the base metal; thus, it is impossible to have the identical sample measured by each laboratory to determine how closely the measurements correspond.

One possibility is to send several samples (in the form of circular discs having equal areas) to each of the laboratories. Although these discs may not actually have identical tin-coating weights, it is hoped that such differences will be small and that they will more or less "average out." In other words, it will be assumed that whatever differences there may be among the means of the four samples can be attributed to no other causes but systematic differences in measuring techniques and chance variability. This would make it possible to determine whether the results produced by the laboratories are consistent by comparing the variability of the four sample means with an appropriate measure of chance variation.

Now there remains the problem of deciding how many discs are to be sent to each laboratory and how the discs are actually to be selected. The question of sample size can be answered in many different ways, one of which is to use the formula on page 166 for the standard deviation of the sampling distribution of the difference between two means. Substituting known values of σ_1 and σ_2, and specifying what differences between the true means of any two of the laboratories should be detected with a probability of at least 0.95 (or 0.98, or 0.99), it is possible to determine $n_1 = n_2 = n$ (see Exercise 10 on page 273). Suppose that this method and, perhaps, also considerations of cost and availability of the necessary specimens lead to the decision to send a sample of 12 discs to each laboratory.

The problem of selecting the required 48 discs and allocating 12 to each laboratory is not as straightforward as it may seem at first. To begin with, suppose that a sheet of tin plate, sufficiently long and sufficiently wide, is selected and that the 48 discs are cut as shown in Figure 13.1. The twelve discs cut from strip 1 are sent to the first laboratory, the twelve discs from strip 2 are sent to the second laboratory, and so forth. If the four mean coating weights subsequently obtained were then found to differ significantly, would this allow us to conclude that these differences can be attributed to lack of consistency in the measuring techniques? Suppose, for instance, that additional investigation shows that the amount of tin deposited electrolytically on a long sheet of steel has a distinct and repeated pattern of variation perpendicular to the direction in which it is rolled. (Such a pattern might be caused by the placement of electrodes, "edge effects," and so forth.) Thus, even if all four laboratories measured the amount of tin consistently and without error, there could be cause for differences in the tin-coating weight determinations. The allocation of an entire strip of discs to each laboratory is such that inconsistencies among the laboratories' measuring techniques are inseparable from (or *confounded* with) whatever differences there may be in the actual amount of tin deposited perpendicular to the direction in which the sheet of steel is rolled.

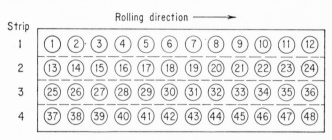

FIG. 13.1 Numbering of tin-plate samples

One way to avoid this kind of confounding is to number the discs and allocate them to the four laboratories *at random*, such as in the following arrangement, which was obtained with the aid of a table of random numbers:

Laboratory A: 3, 38, 17, 32, 24, 30, 48, 19, 11, 31, 22, 41
Laboratory B: 44, 20, 15, 25, 45, 4, 14, 5, 39, 7, 40, 34
Laboratory C: 12, 21, 42, 8, 27, 16, 47, 46, 18, 43, 35, 26
Laboratory D: 9, 2, 28, 23, 37, 1, 10, 6, 29, 36, 33, 13

If there were any actual pattern of tin-coating thickness on the sheet of tin plate, it would be "broken up" by the *randomization*.

Although we have identified and counteracted one possible systematic pattern of variation, there is no assurance that there can be no others. For instance, there may be systematic differences in the areas of the discs caused by progressive wear of the cutting instrument, or there may be scratches or other imperfections on one part of the sheet which could affect the measurements. Thus, there is always the possibility that differences in means attributed to inconsistencies among the laboratories are actually caused by some other uncontrolled variable, and it is the purpose of randomization to avoid confounding the variable under investigation with such other variables.

By distributing the 48 discs among the four laboratories entirely at random, we have no choice but to include whatever variation may be attributable to extraneous causes under the heading of "chance variation." This may give us an excessively large estimate of chance variation which, in turn, may make it difficult to detect differences between the true laboratory means. In order to avoid this, we could, perhaps, use only discs cut from the same strip (or from an otherwise homogeneous region). Unfortunately, this kind of controlled experimentation presents us with new complications. Of what use would it be, for example, to perform an experiment which allows us to conclude that the laboratories are consistent (or inconsistent), *if such a conclusion is limited to measurements made at a fixed distance from one edge of a sheet?* To consider a more poignant example, suppose that a manufacturer of plumbing materials wishes to compare the performance of several kinds of material to be used in underground water pipes. If such conditions as soil acidity, depth of pipe, and mineral content of water were all held fixed, any conclusions as to which material is best would be valid only for the given set of conditions. What the manufacturer really wants to know is which material is best over a fairly wide variety of conditions, and in designing a suitable experiment it would be advisable (indeed, necessary) to specify that pipe of each material be buried at each of several depths in each of several kinds of soil, and in locations where the water varies in hardness.

The foregoing serves to illustrate that it is seldom desirable to hold all or most extraneous factors fixed throughout an experiment in order to obtain an estimate of chance variation that is not "inflated" by variations due to other causes. (In fact, it is rarely, if ever, possible to exercise such strict control, that is, to hold *all* extraneous variables fixed.) In actual practice, experiments should be planned so that known sources of variability are deliberately varied over as wide a range as necessary; furthermore, they should be varied in such a way that their variability can be eliminated from the estimate of chance variation. One way to accomplish this is to repeat the experiment in several *blocks*, where known sources of variability (that is, extraneous variables) are held fixed in each block, but vary from block to block.

Returning to the tin-plating example, we might thus account for variations across the sheet of steel by randomly allocating three discs from each strip to each of the laboratories as in the following arrangement:

	Strip 1	*Strip 2*	*Strip 3*	*Strip 4*
Laboratory A:	8, 4, 10	23, 24, 19	26, 29, 35	37, 44, 48
Laboratory B:	2, 6, 12	21, 15, 22	34, 33, 32	45, 43, 46
Laboratory C:	1, 5, 11	16, 20, 13	36, 29, 30	41, 38, 47
Laboratory D:	7, 3, 9	17, 18, 14	28, 31, 25	39, 40, 42

In this experimental layout, the strips form the blocks, and if we base our estimate of chance variation on the variability *within* each of the sixteen sets of three discs, this estimate will not be inflated by the extraneous variable, that is, differences among the strips. (Note also that, with this arrangement, differences among the means obtained for the four laboratories cannot be attributed to differences among the strips. This cannot be said for the arrangement on page 263.)

The analysis of experiments in which blocking is used to eliminate one source of variability will be discussed in Section 13.3. The analysis of experiments in which two or three sources of variability are thus eliminated will be found in Section 13.5.

13.2 One-way Classifications

In this section we shall consider the statistical analysis of the completely randomized design, or *one-way classification*. We shall suppose that the experimenter has available the results of k independent random samples, each of size n, from k different populations (that is, data concerning k treatments, k groups, k methods of production, etc.); and he is concerned with testing the hypothesis that the means of these k populations are all equal. An example of such an experiment, with $k = 4$, is given by the layout on page 263. If we denote the jth observation in the ith sample by y_{ij}, the general schema for a one-way classification is as follows:

$$
\begin{array}{ll}
& \textit{Means} \\
\textit{Sample 1:} \quad y_{11}, y_{12}, \ldots, y_{1j}, \ldots, y_{1n} & \bar{y}_1 \\
\textit{Sample 2:} \quad y_{21}, y_{22}, \ldots, y_{2j}, \ldots, y_{2n} & \bar{y}_2 \\
\quad\quad\quad \cdot \quad\quad \cdot \quad\quad\quad \cdot \quad\quad\quad \cdot & \cdot \\
\textit{Sample i:} \quad y_{i1}, y_{i2}, \ldots, y_{ij}, \ldots, y_{in} & \bar{y}_i \\
\quad\quad\quad \cdot \quad\quad \cdot \quad\quad\quad \cdot \quad\quad\quad \cdot & \cdot \\
\textit{Sample k:} \quad y_{k1}, y_{k2}, \ldots, y_{kj}, \ldots, y_{kn} & \bar{y}_k \\
& \overline{\phantom{\bar{y}_k}} \\
& \bar{y}.
\end{array}
$$

With reference to the experimental layout on page 263, y_{ij} ($i = 1, 2, 3, 4$; $j = 1, 2, \ldots, 12$) is the jth tin-coating weight measured by the ith laboratory, $\bar{y}_i$ is the mean of the measurements obtained by the ith laboratory, and $\bar{y}.$ is the over-all mean (or *grand mean*) of all 48 observations.

To be able to test the hypothesis that the samples were obtained from k populations with equal means, we shall make several assumptions. Specifically, it will be assumed that we are dealing with *normal populations having equal variances.* There exist methods for testing the reasonableness of this last assumption (see the book by A. M. Mood and F. A. Graybill mentioned in the Bibliography), but the methods we shall develop in this chapter are fairly *robust;* that is, they are relatively insensitive to violations of the assumption of normality as well as the assumption of equal variances.

If μ_i denotes the mean of the ith population and σ^2 denotes the common variance of the k populations, we can express each observation y_{ij} as μ_i plus the value of a random component; that is, we can write

$$y_{ij} = \mu_i + \epsilon_{ij} \qquad \text{for } i = 1, 2, \ldots, k; j = 1, 2, \ldots, n$$

In accordance with the above assumptions, the ϵ_{ij} are values of independent, normally distributed random variables with zero means and the common variance σ^2. [Note that this equation, or *model*, can be regarded as a multiple regression equation; introducing the variables x_{il} which equal 0 or 1 depending on whether the two subscripts are unequal or equal, we can write

$$y_{ij} = \mu_1 x_{i1} + \mu_2 x_{i2} + \ldots + \mu_k x_{ik} + \epsilon_{ij}$$

The parameters μ_i can now be interpreted as regression coefficients, and they can be estimated by the least-squares methods of Chapter 12.]

To attain uniformity with corresponding equations for more complicated kinds of designs, it is customary to replace μ_i by $\mu + \alpha_i$, where μ is the mean of the μ_i and, hence, $\sum\limits_{i=1}^{k} \alpha_i = 0$ (see Exercise 11 on page 273). Using these new parameters, we can write the model equation for the one-way classification as

♦ $\qquad y_{ij} = \mu + \alpha_i + \epsilon_{ij} \qquad \text{for } i = 1, 2, \ldots, k; j = 1, 2, \ldots, n$ ♦

and the null hypothesis that the k population means are all equal can be replaced by the null hypothesis that $\alpha_1 = \alpha_2 = \ldots = \alpha_k = 0$. The alternative hypothesis that at least two of the population means are unequal is equivalent to the alternative hypothesis that $\alpha_i \neq 0$ for some i.

To test the null hypothesis that the k population means are all equal, we shall compare two estimates of σ^2—one based on the variation among the sample means, and one based on the variation within the samples. Since, by assumption, each sample comes from a population having the variance σ^2, this variance can be estimated by any one of the sample variances

$$s_i^2 = \sum_{j=1}^{n} (y_{ij} - \bar{y}_i)^2/(n - 1)$$

and, hence, also by their mean

$$\hat{\sigma}_W^2 = \sum_{i=1}^{k} s_i^2/k = \sum_{i=1}^{k} \sum_{j=1}^{n} (y_{ij} - \bar{y}_i)^2/k(n - 1)$$

Note that each of the sample variances s_i^2 is based on $n - 1$ degrees of freedom ($n - 1$ independent deviations from $\bar{y}_i$) and, hence, $\hat{\sigma}_W^2$ is based on $k(n - 1)$ degrees of freedom. Now, the variance of the k sample means is given by

$$s_{\bar{x}}^2 = \sum_{i=1}^{k} (\bar{y}_i - \bar{y}.)^2/(k - 1)$$

and *if the null hypothesis is true* it estimates σ^2/n. Thus, an estimate of σ^2 based on the differences among the sample means is given by

$$\hat{\sigma}_B^2 = n \cdot s_{\bar{x}}^2 = n \cdot \sum_{i=1}^{k} (\bar{y}_i - \bar{y}.)^2/(k-1)$$

and it is based on $k - 1$ degrees of freedom.

If the null hypothesis is true, it can be shown that σ_W^2 and σ_B^2 are independent estimates of σ^2, and it follows that

$$F = \frac{\hat{\sigma}_B^2}{\hat{\sigma}_W^2}$$

is a value of a random variable having the F distribution with $k - 1$ and $k(n-1)$ degrees of freedom. Since the *between sample variance*, σ_B^2, can be expected to exceed the *within sample variance*, σ_W^2, when the null hypothesis is *false*, the null hypothesis will be rejected if F exceeds F_α, where F_α is obtained from Table VI with $k - 1$ and $k(n-1)$ degrees of freedom.

The preceding argument has shown how the test of the equality of k means can be based on the comparison of two variance estimates. More remarkable, perhaps, is the fact that the two estimates in question [except for the divisors $k - 1$ and $k(n-1)$] can be obtained by "breaking up" or analyzing the total variance of all nk observations into two parts. The sample variance of all nk observations is given by

$$s^2 = \sum_{i=1}^{k} \sum_{j=1}^{n} (y_{ij} - \bar{y}.)^2/(nk-1)$$

and with reference to its numerator, called the *total sum of squares*, we shall now prove the following theorem.

THEOREM 13.1

$$\sum_{i=1}^{k} \sum_{j=1}^{n} (y_{ij} - \bar{y}.)^2 = \sum_{i=1}^{k} \sum_{j=1}^{n} (y_{ij} - \bar{y}_i)^2 + n \cdot \sum_{i=1}^{k} (\bar{y}_i - \bar{y}.)^2$$

The proof of this theorem is based on the identity

$$y_{ij} - \bar{y}. = (y_{ij} - \bar{y}_i) + (\bar{y}_i - \bar{y}.)$$

Squaring both sides and summing on i and j, we obtain

$$\sum_{i=1}^{k} \sum_{j=1}^{n} (y_{ij} - \bar{y}.)^2 = \sum_{i=1}^{k} \sum_{j=1}^{n} (y_{ij} - \bar{y}_i)^2 + \sum_{i=1}^{k} \sum_{j=1}^{n} (\bar{y}_i - \bar{y}.)^2$$
$$+ 2 \sum_{i=1}^{k} \sum_{j=1}^{n} (y_{ij} - \bar{y}_i)(\bar{y}_i - \bar{y}.)$$

Next, we observe that

$$\sum_{i=1}^{k} \sum_{j=1}^{n} (y_{ij} - \bar{y}_i)(\bar{y}_i - \bar{y}.) = \sum_{i=1}^{k} (\bar{y}_i - \bar{y}.) \sum_{j=1}^{n} (y_{ij} - \bar{y}_i) = 0$$

since $\bar{y}_i$ is the mean of the ith sample and, hence, $\sum\limits_{j=1}^{n} (y_{ij} - \bar{y}_i) = 0$ for all i. To complete the proof of Theorem 13.1, we have only to observe that the summand of the second sum on the right-hand side of the original identity does not involve the subscript j and that, consequently,

$$\sum_{i=1}^{k} \sum_{j=1}^{n} (\bar{y}_i - \bar{y}.)^2 = n \cdot \sum_{i=1}^{k} (\bar{y}_i - \bar{y}.)^2$$

It is customary to denote the *total sum of squares*, the left-hand member of the identity of Theorem 13.1, by SST. The first term on the right-hand side is $\hat{\sigma}_W^2$ times its degrees of freedom, and we refer to this sum as the *error sum of squares*, SSE. The term "error sum of squares" expresses the idea that the quantity estimates *random (or chance) error*. The second term on the right-hand side of the identity of Theorem 13.1 is σ_B^2 times its degrees of freedom, and we refer to it as the *between-samples sum of squares* or the *treatment sum of squares*, $SS(Tr)$. (Most of the early applications of this kind of analysis were in the field of agriculture, where the k populations represented different treatments, such as fertilizers, applied to agricultural plots.) Note that in this notation the F ratio on page 267 can be written

$$\blacklozenge \qquad F = \frac{SS(Tr)/(k-1)}{SSE/k(n-1)} \qquad \blacklozenge$$

The sums of squares required for substitution into this last formula are usually obtained by means of the following short-cut formulas, which the reader will be asked to verify in Exercise 12 on page 273. We first calculate SST and $SS(Tr)$ by means of the formulas

$$SST = \sum_{i=1}^{k} \sum_{j=1}^{n} y_{ij}^2 - C$$

$$\blacklozenge \qquad SS(Tr) = \frac{\sum\limits_{i=1}^{k} T_i^2}{n} - C \qquad \blacklozenge$$

where C, called the *correction term*, is given by

$$\blacklozenge \qquad C = \frac{T_.^2}{kn} \qquad \blacklozenge$$

and where T_i is the total of the n observations in the ith sample while $T_.^2$ is the grand total of all kn observations. The error sum of squares, SSE, is then obtained by subtraction; according to Theorem 13.1 we can write

$$\blacklozenge \qquad SSE = SST - SS(Tr) \qquad \blacklozenge$$

The results obtained in analyzing the total sum of squares into its components are conveniently summarized by means of the following kind of *analysis of variance table:*

Source of variation	Degrees of freedom	Sum of squares	Mean square	F
Treatments	$k - 1$	$SS(Tr)$	$MS(Tr)$ $= SS(Tr)/(k - 1)$	$\dfrac{MS(Tr)}{MSE}$
Error	$k(n - 1)$	SSE	MSE $= SSE/k(n - 1)$	
Total	$nk - 1$	SST		

(handwritten annotations in table: under $k-1$: "3"; near Error row: "4 · 3", "$4(11) = 44$")

Note that each *mean square* is obtained by dividing the corresponding sum of squares by its degrees of freedom.

To illustrate the analysis of variance (as this technique is appropriately called) for a one-way classification, suppose that in accordance with the layout on page 263 each laboratory measures the tin-coating weights of 12 discs and that the results are as follows:

(handwritten: $n = 12$)

Laboratory A: 0.25, 0.27, 0.22, 0.30, 0.27, 0.28, 0.32, 0.24, 0.31, 0.26, 0.21, 0.28   *= 3.21*
Laboratory B: 0.18, 0.28, 0.21, 0.23, 0.25, 0.20, 0.27, 0.19, 0.24, 0.22, 0.29, 0.16   *= 2.72*
Laboratory C: 0.19, 0.25, 0.27, 0.24, 0.18, 0.26, 0.28, 0.24, 0.25, 0.20, 0.21, 0.19   *= 2.76*
Laboratory D: 0.23, 0.30, 0.28, 0.28, 0.24, 0.34, 0.20, 0.18, 0.24, 0.28, 0.22, 0.21   *= 3.00*

(handwritten: $T = 11.69$)

The totals for the four samples are, respectively, 3.21, 2.72, 2.76, and 3.00, the grand total is 11.69, and the calculations required to obtain the necessary sums of squares are as follows:

$$C = (11.69)^2/48 = 2.8470$$

$$SST = (.25)^2 + (.27)^2 + \ldots + (.21)^2 - 2.8470 = 0.0809$$

$$SS(Tr) = \frac{(3.21)^2 + (2.72)^2 + (2.76)^2 + (3.00)^2}{n = 12} - 2.8470 = 0.0130$$

$$SSE = 0.0809 - 0.0130 = 0.0679$$

Thus, we get the following *analysis of variance table:*

Source of variation	Degrees of freedom	Sum of squares	Mean square	F
Laboratories	3	0.0130	0.0043	2.87
Error	44	0.0679	0.0015	
Total	47	0.0809		

(handwritten at right: $F = \dfrac{MS(Tr)}{MSE}$)

(handwritten at bottom:
$H_0 : M_1 = M_2 = M_3 = M_4$
$H_a :$ are different
Reject H_0 if $F > F_\alpha$

$F_\alpha \left[k-1, \; k(n-1) \right]$
$3, \; 44$ *)*

Since the value obtained for F exceeds 2.82, the value of $F_{.05}$ with 3 and 44 degrees of freedom, the null hypothesis can be rejected at the 0.05 level of significance; we conclude that the laboratories are *not* obtaining consistent results.

To estimate the parameters μ, α_1, α_2, α_3, and α_4 (or μ_1, μ_2, μ_3, and μ_4), we can use the method of least squares, minimizing

$$\sum_{i=1}^{4} \sum_{j=1}^{12} (y_{ij} - \mu - \alpha_i)^2$$

with respect to μ and the α_i, subject to the restriction that $\sum_{i=1}^{4} \alpha_i = 0$. This may be done by eliminating one of the α's or, better, by using the method of Lagrange multipliers, which is treated in most texts on advanced calculus. In either case we obtain the "intuitively obvious" estimates

$$\hat{\mu} = \bar{y}. \qquad = \qquad 0.244$$
$$\hat{\alpha}_1 = \bar{y}_1 - \bar{y}. = \qquad 0.024$$
$$\hat{\alpha}_2 = \bar{y}_2 - \bar{y}. = \quad -0.017$$
$$\hat{\alpha}_3 = \bar{y}_3 - \bar{y}. = \quad -0.014$$
$$\hat{\alpha}_4 = \bar{y}_4 - \bar{y}. = \qquad 0.006$$

and the corresponding estimates for the $\hat{\mu}_i$ are given by $\hat{\mu}_i = \bar{y}_i$.

The analysis of variance described in this section applies to one-way classifications where each sample has the same number of observations. If this is not the case and the sample sizes are $n_1, n_2, \ldots,$ and n_k, we have only to substitute $N = \sum_{i=1}^{k} n_i$ for nk throughout and write the computing formulas for SST and $SS(Tr)$ as

$$SST = \sum_{i=1}^{k} \sum_{j=1}^{n_i} y_{ij}^2 - C$$

$$SS(Tr) = \sum_{i=1}^{k} \frac{T_i^2}{n_i} - C$$

Otherwise, the procedure is the same as before. (See also Exercise 13 on page 274.)

EXERCISES

1. An experiment is performed to compare the cleansing action of two detergents, Detergent A and Detergent B. Twenty swatches of cloth are soiled with dirt and grease, each is washed with one of the detergents in an agitator-type machine, and then measured for "whiteness." Criticize the following aspects of the experiment:

(a) The entire experiment is performed with soft water.

(b) Fifteen of the swatches are washed with Detergent A and five with Detergent B.

(c) To accelerate the testing procedure, very hot water and 30-second washing times are used in the experiment.

(d) The "whiteness" readings of all swatches washed with Detergent A are taken first.

2. A certain *bon vivant*, wishing to ascertain the cause of his frequent hangovers, conducted the following experiment. On the first night, he drank nothing but whiskey and water; on the second night he drank vodka and water; on the third night he drank gin and water; and on the fourth night he drank rum and water. On each of the following mornings he had a hangover, and he concluded that it was the common factor, the water, that made him ill.

(a) This conclusion is obviously unwarranted, but can you state what principles of sound experimental design are violated?

(b) Give a less obvious example of an experiment having the same shortcomings.

(c) Suppose our friend had modified his experiment so each of the four alcoholic beverages was used both with and without water, so that the experiment lasted eight nights. Could the results of this enlarged experiment serve to support or refute the hypothesis that water was the cause of the hangovers? Explain.

3. Random samples of 4 brands of tires required the following braking distances while going at 30 miles per hour:

Brand A	Brand B	Brand C	Brand D
27	25	27	26
30	20	31	26
25	22	30	25
26	21	32	23

(a) Without using the short-cut formulas, calculate $\sum_{i=1}^{k} \sum_{j=1}^{n} (y_{ij} - \bar{y}.)^2$, $\sum_{i=1}^{k} \sum_{j=1}^{n} (y_{ij} - \bar{y}_i)^2$, and $n \cdot \sum_{i=1}^{k} (\bar{y}_i - \bar{y}.)^2$, and verify the identity of Theorem 13.1.

(b) Verify the results obtained for the three sums of squares by using the short-cut formulas on page 268.

4. To determine the effect on exit dust loading in a precipitator, the following measurements were made:

Total flow (cu ft/hr)	Exist dust loading (grains per cubic yard in flue gas)		
200	1.2	1.0	1.6
300	2.0	1.8	2.5
400	2.4	3.0	3.5
500	3.1	3.8	4.4

(a) Test whether the flow through the precipitator has an effect on the exit dust loading.

(b) Estimate the effects α_i corresponding to the different rates of flow.

5. Using the sums of squares obtained in Exercise 3, test at a level of signifi-cance of 0.05 whether the differences among the mean braking distances obtained for the four kinds of tires are significant.

6. Three specimens of each of five different metals were immersed in a highly corrosive solution, and their corrosion rates were measured with the following results:

Metal	Corrosion rates		
Aluminum	0.5	0.4	0.6
Stainless steel	0.6	0.7	0.6
Carbon steel	6.5	7.0	7.3
Enamel-coated steel	0.8	0.6	0.8
Nickel alloy	4.1	3.5	3.0

(a) Test the null hypothesis that the five metals have the same corrosion rate.

(b) Estimate the difference in corrosion rate between stainless steel and carbon steel, and give a 0.95 confidence interval for this difference.

7. In order to compare the effectiveness of three different types of phosphores-cent coatings of airplane instrument dials, 8 dials each are coated with the three types. Then the dials are illuminated by an ultraviolet light, and the following are the number of minutes each glowed after the light source was turned off:

Type A	Type B	Type C
46.3	48.7	62.3
48.2	53.6	64.7
42.0	49.3	56.2
41.8	47.3	60.2
48.9	51.4	53.6
51.0	53.9	55.5
49.7	43.6	61.8
50.1	48.8	54.5

(a) Calculate F and (assuming that the necessary conditions can be met) test at the 0.01 level whether the observed differences among the sample means can be attributed to chance.

(b) Estimate the parameters of the model used in the analysis of this experiment.

8. A manufacturer of electric irons, wishing to test the accuracy of thermostats from three different suppliers, tests the irons at the 500° F setting. The actual temperatures were measured by a thermocouple, with the following results:

> Supplier A: 494, 516, 487, 491
> Supplier B: 512, 528
> Supplier C: 480, 515, 510

Can it be concluded that there is a difference in accuracy of the thermostats furnished by the three suppliers?

9. Having 20 test plots available to compare the yield of three varieties of corn, an agricultural research worker plants 7 each with Varieties A and B, and 6 with Variety C. The following are the yields obtained in bushels per acre:

Variety A	Variety B	Variety C
81.6	73.5	89.6
66.7	77.3	86.1
72.9	57.5	72.4
86.7	69.0	78.4
73.5	62.4	85.2
63.8	77.7	70.5
69.2	71.5	

Estimate the true average yield for each variety, and test for significant differences among the sample means $\alpha = 0.05$.

10. Referring to the discussion on page 262, assume that the standard deviations of the tin-coating weights determined by any one of the three laboratories have the common value $\sigma = 0.012$, and that it is desired to be 95 per cent confident of detecting a difference in means between any two of the laboratories in excess of 0.01 pound per base box. Show that these assumptions lead to the decision to send a sample of 12 discs to each laboratory.

11. Show that if $\mu_i = \mu + \alpha_i$, and μ is the mean of the μ_i, it follows that $\sum_{i=1}^{k} \alpha_i = 0$.

12. Verify the short-cut formulas for computing SST and $SS(Tr)$ given on page 268.

13. State and prove a theorem analogous to Theorem 13.1 for the case where the size of the ith sample is n_i, that is, where the sample sizes are not necessarily equal.

13.3 Two-way Classifications

As we observed in Section 13.1, the estimate of chance variation (the experimental error) can often be reduced, that is, freed of variability due to extraneous causes, by dividing the observations in each classification into *blocks*. This is accomplished when known sources of variability (that is, extraneous variables) are held fixed in each block, but vary from block to block.

In this section we shall suppose that the experimenter has available measurements pertaining to a treatments distributed over b blocks. First, we shall consider the case where there is exactly one observation from each treatment in each block; with reference to the illustration on page 264, this case would arise if each laboratory tested one disc from each strip. Letting y_{ij} denote the observation pertaining to the ith treatment and the jth block, $\bar{y}_{i.}$ the mean of the b observations for the ith treatment, $\bar{y}_{.j}$ the mean of the a observations in the jth block, and $\bar{y}_{..}$ the grand mean of all the ab observations, we shall use the following layout for this kind of *two-way classification:*

$$Blocks$$

	$B_1 \quad B_2 \quad \ldots \quad B_j \quad \ldots \quad B_b$	$Means$
Treatment 1:	$y_{11}, y_{12}, \ldots, y_{1j}, \ldots, y_{1b}$	$\bar{y}_1.$
Treatment 2:	$y_{21}, y_{22}, \ldots, y_{2j}, \ldots, y_{2b}$	$\bar{y}_2.$
Treatment i:	$y_{i1}, y_{i2}, \ldots, y_{ij}, \ldots, y_{ib}$	$\bar{y}_i.$
Treatment a:	$y_{a1}, y_{a2}, \ldots, y_{aj}, \ldots, y_{ab}$	$\bar{y}_a.$
Means	$\bar{y}_{.1} \quad \bar{y}_{.2} \quad \ldots \quad \bar{y}_{.j} \quad \ldots \quad \bar{y}_{.b}$	$\bar{y}_{..}$

Note that when a dot is used in place of a subscript, this means that the mean is obtained by summing over that subscript.

The underlying model which we shall assume for the analysis of this kind of two-way classification with one observation per "cell" is given by

$$\blacklozenge \quad y_{ij} = \mu + \alpha_i + \beta_j + \epsilon_{ij} \quad \text{for } i = 1, 2, \ldots, a; j = 1, 2, \ldots, b \quad \blacklozenge$$

Here μ is the grand mean, α_i is the *effect* of the ith treatment, β_j is the *effect* of the jth block, and the ϵ_{ij} are values of *independent, normally distributed* random variables having *zero means* and the *common variance* σ^2. Analogous to the model for the one-way classification, we restrict the parameters by imposing the conditions that $\sum\limits_{i=1}^{a} \alpha_i = 0$ and $\sum\limits_{j=1}^{b} \beta_j = 0$ (see Exercise 10 on page 283).

In the analysis of a two-way classification where each treatment is represented once in each block, the major objective is to test for the significance of the difference among the $\bar{y}_{i.}$, that is, to test the null hypothesis

$$\alpha_1 = \alpha_2 = \ldots = \alpha_a = 0$$

In addition, it may also be desirable to test whether the blocking has been effective, that is, whether the null hypothesis

$$\beta_1 = \beta_2 = \ldots = \beta_b = 0$$

can be rejected. In either case, the alternative hypothesis is that at least one of the effects is different from zero.

As in the one-way analysis of variance, we shall base these significance tests on comparisons of estimates of σ^2—one based on the variation among treatments, one based on the variation among blocks, and one measuring the experimental error. Note that only the latter is an estimate of σ^2 when either (or both) of the null hypotheses do not hold. The required sums of squares are given by the three components into which the total sum of squares is "broken up" by means of the following theorem:

THEOREM 13.2

$$\sum_{i=1}^{a} \sum_{j=1}^{b} (y_{ij} - \bar{y}..)^2 = \sum_{i=1}^{a} \sum_{j=1}^{b} (y_{ij} - \bar{y}_{i.} - \bar{y}_{.j} + \bar{y}..)^2$$
$$+ b \sum_{i=1}^{a} (\bar{y}_{i.} - \bar{y}..)^2 + a \sum_{j=1}^{b} (\bar{y}_{.j} - \bar{y}..)^2$$

The left-hand side of this identity represents the total sum of squares, SST, and the terms on the right-hand side are, respectively, the error sum of squares, SSE, the treatment sum of squares, $SS(Tr)$, and the block sum of squares $SS(Bl)$. To prove this theorem, we make use of the identity

$$y_{ij} - \bar{y}.. = (y_{ij} - \bar{y}_{i.} - \bar{y}_{.j} + \bar{y}..) + (\bar{y}_{i.} - \bar{y}..) + (\bar{y}_{.j} - \bar{y}..)$$

and follow essentially the same argument as in the proof of Theorem 13.1.

In practice, we calculate the necessary sums of squares by means of short-cut formulas analogous to those on page 268, rather than by using the expressions which define these sums of squares in Theorem 13.2. In what follows, $T_{i.}$ is the sum of the b observations for the ith treatment, $T_{.j}$ is the sum of the a observations in the jth block, and $T_{..}$ is the grand total of all the observations. Using the *correction term*

$$C = \frac{T_{..}^2}{ab}$$

we have

$$SST = \sum_{i=1}^{a} \sum_{j=1}^{b} y_{ij}^2 - C$$

$$\blacklozenge \qquad SS(Tr) = \frac{\sum_{i=1}^{a} T_{i.}^2}{b} - C \qquad \blacklozenge$$

$$SS(Bl) = \frac{\sum_{j=1}^{b} T_{.j}^2}{a} - C$$

and
$$SSE = SST - SS(Tr) - SS(Bl)$$

Note that the divisors for $SS(Tr)$ and $SS(Bl)$ are the number of observations in the respective totals, $T_{i.}$ and $T_{.j}$. In Exercise 11 on page 283, the reader will be asked to verify that these computing formulas are, indeed, equivalent to the corresponding terms of the identity of Theorem 13.2.

Using these sums of squares, we can reject the null hypothesis that the α_i are all equal to zero at the level of significance α if

$$\blacklozenge \qquad F_{Tr} = \frac{MS(Tr)}{MSE} = \frac{SS(Tr)/(a-1)}{SSE/(a-1)(b-1)} \qquad \blacklozenge$$

exceeds F_α with $a - 1$ and $(a - 1)(b - 1)$ degrees of freedom. The null hypothesis that the β_j are all equal to zero can be rejected at the level of significance α if

$$\blacklozenge \qquad F_{Bl} = \frac{MS(Bl)}{MSE} = \frac{SS(Bl)/(b-1)}{SSE/(a-1)(b-1)} \qquad \blacklozenge$$

exceeds F_α with $b - 1$ and $(a - 1)(b - 1)$ degrees of freedom. Note that the mean squares, $MS(Tr)$, $MS(Bl)$, and MSE, are again defined as the corresponding sums of squares divided by their degrees of freedom.

The results obtained in this analysis are summarized in the following *analysis of variance table:*

Source of variation	Degrees of freedom	Sum of squares	Mean square	F
Treatments	$a - 1$	$SS(Tr)$	$MS(Tr)$ $= SS(Tr)/(a-1)$	$F_{Tr} = \dfrac{MS(Tr)}{MSE}$
Blocks	$b - 1$	$SS(Bl)$	$MS(Bl)$ $= SS(Bl)/(b-1)$	$F_{Bl} = \dfrac{MS(Bl)}{MSE}$
Error	$(a-1)(b-1)$	SSE	MSE $= SSE/(a-1)(b-1)$	
Total	$ab - 1$	SST		

Let us illustrate the analysis of a two-way classification with one observation for each treatment in each block, by considering an experiment designed to compare several hull designs of motorboats. Since conditions of wind and water could affect the top speed of a craft, perhaps to an even greater extent than differences in hull design, each of four hull designs was tested on three different days corresponding to calm, moderate, and choppy conditions. On each day, the four boats were run on a marked course in random sequence at top speed, and the times (in minutes) required to cover the course are as shown in the following table:

	Day 1	Day 2	Day 3	Totals
Design A	45	46	51	142
Design B	42	44	50	136
Design C	36	41	48	125
Design D	49	47	54	150
Totals	172	178	203	553

a *(handwritten above Day labels)*
b *(handwritten beside Design labels)*

$T_{i.}$ $\bar{y}_{i.} = \frac{142}{3}$

$\bar{y}_{i.} = \frac{T_{i.}}{a}$

$\bar{y}_{4.} = \frac{150}{3}$

$T_{.j}$ *(handwritten below Totals row)*

$\bar{y}_{.j} = \frac{T}{ab}$ *(handwritten, = T)*

Looking upon the designs as treatments and the days as blocks, we obtain the necessary sums of squares as follows:

$$C = \frac{(553)^2}{12} = 25{,}484$$

$$C = \frac{T^2}{ab} \text{ *(handwritten)*}$$

$$SST = (45)^2 + (46)^2 + \ldots + (54)^2 - 25{,}484 = 265$$

$$SS(Tr) = \frac{(142)^2 + (136)^2 + (125)^2 + (150)^2}{3} - 25{,}484 = 111$$

$$SS(Bl) = \frac{(172)^2 + (178)^2 + (203)^2}{4} - 25{,}484 = 135$$

(handwritten: SST − SS(Tr) − SS(Bl))

$$SSE = 265 - 111 - 135 = 19$$

Dividing the sums of squares by their respective degrees of freedom to obtain the appropriate mean squares, we get the results shown in the following analysis of variance table:

Source of variation	Degrees of freedom	Sums of squares	Mean square	F
Hull designs	3	111	37.0	11.6
Days	2	135	67.5	21.1
Error	6	19	3.2	
Total	11	265		

(handwritten annotations:) treatment → Hull designs; Blocks beside Days; $ab - 1$ below Total.

$F = \frac{37}{3.2}$

$F = \frac{67.5}{3.2}$

$F_{Tr}(3, 6)$ $F_{Bl} = (2, 6)$

Since $F_{Tr} = 11.6$ exceeds 9.78, the value of $F_{.01}$ with 3 and 6 degrees of freedom, we conclude that differences in hull design do affect the boats' top speed. Also, since $F_{Bl} = 21.1$ exceeds 10.9, the value of $F_{.01}$ with 2 and 6 degrees of freedom, we conclude that the differences in top speed due to weather conditions are significant, namely, that the blocking has been effective. (To make the effect of this blocking even more evident, the reader will be asked to verify in Exercise 6 on page 282 that the test for differences among hull designs would not yield significant results if we looked upon the data as a one-way classification.)

The effect α_i of the ith hull design can be estimated by means of the formula $\hat{\alpha}_i = \bar{y}_{i.} - \bar{y}_{..}$, which may be obtained by the method of least squares. The resulting estimates are

$$\hat{\alpha}_1 = 47.3 - 46.1 = \quad 1.2, \qquad \hat{\alpha}_2 = 45.3 - 46.1 = -0.8$$
$$\hat{\alpha}_3 = 41.7 - 46.1 = -4.4, \qquad \hat{\alpha}_4 = 50.0 - 46.1 = \quad 3.9$$

It should be observed that a two-way classification automatically allows for repetitions of the experimental conditions; for example, in the preceding experiment each hull design was tested three times. Further repetitions may be handled in several ways, and care must be taken that the model used appropriately describes the situation. One way to provide further repetition in a two-way classification is to include additional blocks—for example, to test each hull design on several additional days, randomizing the order of testing on each day. Note that the model remains essentially the same as before, the only change being an increase in b, and a corresponding increase in the degrees of freedom for blocks and for error. The latter is important, because an increase in the degrees of freedom for error makes the test of the null hypothesis $\alpha_i = 0$ for all i *more sensitive* to small differences among the treatment means. In fact, the real purpose of this kind of repetition is to increase the degrees of freedom for error, thereby increasing the sensitivity of the F tests (see Exercise 9 on page 283).

A second method is to repeat the entire experiment, using a new pattern of randomization to obtain $a \cdot b$ additional observations. This is possible only if the blocks are *identifiable*, that is, if the conditions defining each block can be repeated. For example, in the tin-coating weight experiment described in Section 13.1, the blocks are strips across the rolling direction of a sheet of tin plate, and, given a new sheet, it is possible to identify which is strip 1, which is strip 2, and so forth. In the example of this section, this kind of repetition (usually called *replication*) would be difficult because it would require that the weather conditions on the three days be exactly duplicated. This kind of repetition will be used in connection with Latin-square designs in Section 13.5. See also Exercises 7 and 8 on pages 282 and 283.

A third method of repetition is to include n observations for each treatment in each block. When an experiment is designed in this way, the n observations in each "cell" are regarded as *duplicates*, and it is to be expected that their variability will be somewhat less than experimental error. To illustrate this point, suppose that the tin-coating weights of three discs from adjacent positions in a strip are measured in sequence by one of the laboratories, using the same chemical solutions. The variability of these measurements will probably be considerably less than that of three discs from the same strip measured in that laboratory at different times, using different chemical solutions, and perhaps different technicians. The analysis of variance appropriate for this kind of repetition reduces essentially to a two-way analysis of variance applied to the *means* of the n duplicates in the $a \cdot b$ cells; thus, *there would be no gain in degrees of freedom for error*, and, consequently, *no gain in sensitivity of the F tests*.

13.4 Multiple Comparisons

The F tests used so far in this chapter showed whether differences among several means are significant, but they did not tell us whether a given mean (or group of means) differs significantly from another given mean (or group of means). In actual practice, the latter is the kind of information an investigator really wants; for instance, having determined on page 270 that the means of the tin-coating weights obtained by the four laboratories differ significantly, it may be important to find out which laboratory (or laboratories) differs from which others.

If an experimenter is confronted with k means, it may seem reasonable at first to test for significant differences between all possible pairs, that is, to perform $\binom{k}{2} = \dfrac{k(k-1)}{2}$ two-sample t tests as described on page 168. Aside from the fact that this would require a large number of tests even if k is relatively small, these tests would not be independent, and it would be virtually impossible to assign an over-all level of significance to this procedure.

Several *multiple-comparisons tests* have been proposed to overcome these difficulties, among them the Duncan *multiple-range test*, which we shall study in this section. (References to other multiple-comparisons tests are mentioned in the book by W. T. Federer listed in the Bibliography.) The assumptions underlying the Duncan multiple-range test are, essentially, those of the one-way analysis of variance for which the sample sizes are equal. The test compares the *range* of any set of p means with an appropriate *least significant range*, R_p, given by

$$R_p = s_{\bar{x}} \cdot r_p$$

$R_p = s_{\bar{x}} \cdot r_p$

Here $s_{\bar{x}}$ is an estimate of $\sigma_{\bar{x}} = \sigma/\sqrt{n}$, and it is computed by means of the formula

$$s_{\bar{x}} = \sqrt{\frac{MSE}{n}}$$

where MSE is the error mean square in the analysis of variance. The value of r_p depends on the desired level of significance and the number of degrees of freedom corresponding to MSE, and it may be obtained from Tables X(a) and (b) for $\alpha = 0.05$ and 0.01, for $p = 2, 3, \ldots, 10$, and for various degrees of freedom from 1 to 120.

To illustrate this multiple-comparisons procedure, let us refer to the data on page 269 and arrange the four sample means as follows in an increasing order of magnitude:

Laboratory	B	C	D	A
Mean	0.227	0.230	0.250	0.268

$p = 4$

Next, we compute $s_{\bar{x}}$, using the error mean square of 0.0015 in the analysis of variance on page 269, and we obtain

$$s_{\bar{x}} = \sqrt{\frac{0.0015}{12}} = 0.011$$

Then, we get (by linear interpolation) from Table X(a) the following values of r_p for $\alpha = 0.05$ and 44 degrees of freedom:

p = no. of means

p	2	3	4
r_p	2.85	3.00	3.09

Multiplying each value of r_p by $s_{\bar{x}} = 0.011$, we finally obtain

p	2	3	4
R_p	0.031	0.033	0.034

The range of *all four means* is $0.268 - 0.227 = 0.041$, which exceeds $R_4 = 0.034$, the least significant range. This result should have been expected, since the F test on page 270 showed that the differences among all four means are significant at $\alpha = 0.05$. To test for significant differences among *three adjacent means*, we obtain ranges of 0.038 and 0.023, respectively, for 0.230, 0.250, 0.268 and 0.227, 0.230, 0.250. Since the first of these values exceeds $R_3 = 0.033$, the differences observed in the first set are significant; since the second value does not exceed 0.033, the corresponding differences are not significant. Finally, for *adjacent pairs* of means we find that no adjacent pair has a range less than the least significant range $R_2 = 0.031$. All these results can be summarized by writing

$$0.227 \quad \underline{0.230 \quad 0.250 \quad 0.268}$$

where *a line is drawn under any set of adjacent means for which the range is less than the appropriate value of R_p, that is, under any set of adjacent means for which differences are not significant.* We thus conclude in our example that Laboratory A averages higher tin-coating weights than the other three laboratories.

If we apply this same method to the example of Section 13.3, where we compared the four hull designs, we obtain (see also Exercise 12 on page 283)

Hull design

C	B	A	D
41.7	45.3	47.3	50.0

In other words, among triplets of adjacent means both sets of differences are significant. So far as pairs of adjacent means are concerned, we find that only the difference between 41.7 and 45.3 is significant. Interpreting these results, we conclude that hull design *C* is significantly better than any of the others.

EXERCISES

1. To find the best arrangement of instruments on a control panel, four different displays were tested by simulating an emergency condition and observing the reaction time required to correct this condition. The reaction times (in tenths of a second) of three different subjects were as follows:

	Subject 1	Subject 2	Subject 3
Display A	8	14	10
Display B	11	15	11
Display C	5	11	6
Display D	12	18	15

Use the appropriate two-way analysis of variance to test whether there are significant differences among the displays.

2. Suppose that in the experiment described in Exercise 3 on page 271 the first measurement for each brand was obtained with a Chevrolet, the second with a Ford, the third with a Plymouth, and the fourth with a Rambler. Analyze the data as a two-way classification and test for differences among the tires at the 0.05 level of significance.

3. The following table gives the productivity (measured by the number of acceptable pieces per worker per hour) of three shifts in a given industrial plant, over a period of one week.

	Mon	*Tues*	*Wed*	*Thur*	*Fri*
First shift	5.6	6.1	5.9	6.5	5.8
Second shift	4.8	6.5	6.0	5.8	5.0
Third shift	3.9	5.8	4.2	5.9	5.1

Are there significant differences in productivity from shift to shift or from day to day?

4. The following are the number of defective pieces produced by four workmen operating, in turn, three different machines:

		\multicolumn{4}{c}{*Workman*}
		B_1	B_2	B_3	B_4
Machine	A_1	22	23	30	21
	A_2	14	15	22	15
	A_3	20	18	27	22

Looking upon the machines as "treatments" and the workmen as "blocks," analyze the data as a two-way classification. Also estimate how many defective pieces a workman might be expected to make while operating machine A_2.

5. Referring to Exercise 4 on page 271, suppose the data in each of the three columns were obtained from a different precipitator. Repeat the analysis of variance, treating the experiment as a two-way classification, and observe what change results in the error mean square.

6. To emphasize the importance of "blocking," reanalyze the data on page 277 pertaining to the hull designs as a one-way classification.

7. If, in a two-way classification, the entire experiment is repeated r times, the model becomes

$$y_{ijk} = \mu + \alpha_i + \beta_j + \rho_k + \epsilon_{ijk}$$

for $i = 1, 2, \ldots, a, j = 1, 2, \ldots, b$, and $k = 1, 2, \ldots, r$, where the sum of the α's, the sum of the β's, and the sum of the ρ's are equal to zero. The ϵ_{ijk} are again values of independent normally distributed random variables with zero means and the common variance σ^2.

(a) Write down (but do not prove) an identity analogous to the one of Theorem 13.2, which subdivides the total sum of squares into components attributable to treatments, blocks, replicates, and error.

(b) Generalize the computing formulas on page 276, so that they apply to a replicated randomized block design. Note that the divisor in each case equals the number of observations in the respective totals.

(c) If the number of degrees of freedom for the replicate sum of squares is $r - 1$, how many degrees of freedom are there for the error sum of squares?

8. Referring to Exercise 3, suppose that the productivity measurements were repeated for a second week with the following additional results:

			Second Week		
	Mon	Tues	Wed	Thur	Fri
First shift	5.4	6.5	5.9	7.1	6.2
Second shift	4.8	6.7	5.8	6.2	5.9
Third shift	4.3	6.4	4.6	5.9	5.3

Use the theory developed in Exercise 7 to analyze the combined results for the two weeks as a two-way classification with replication.

9. As was pointed out on page 278, two ways of increasing the size of a two-way classification experiment are (a) to double the number of blocks, and (b) to replicate the entire experiment. Discuss and compare the gain in degrees of freedom for the error sum of squares by the two methods.

10. Show that if $\mu_{ij} = \mu + \alpha_i + \beta_j$, the mean of the μ_{ij} (summed on j) is equal to $\mu + \alpha_i$, and the mean of the μ_{ij} summed on i and j is equal to μ, it follows that $\sum\limits_{i=1}^{a} \alpha_i = \sum\limits_{j=1}^{b} \beta_j = 0$.

11. Verify that the computing formulas for SST, $SS(Tr)$, $SS(Bl)$, and SSE, given on page 276, are equivalent to the corresponding terms of the identity of Theorem 13.2.

12. Verify the results of Duncan's test for the comparison of the four hull designs, given on page 281.

13. Use the Duncan test with $\alpha = 0.05$ to compare the effects of the phosphorescent coatings in Exercise 7 on page 272.

14. Use the Duncan multiple-range test and $\alpha = 0.05$ to analyze the means obtained for the four brands of tires in Exercise 3 on page 271.

15. Use Duncan's test with $\alpha = 0.01$ to compare the four instrument displays in Exercise 1. Which display or displays are best?

16. Use the Duncan multiple-range test and $\alpha = 0.01$ to analyze (a) the means obtained for the three machines, and (b) the means obtained for the ~~three~~ four workmen in Exercise 4.

13.5 Some Further Experimental Designs

The randomized-block design, or two-way classification, is appropriate when one extraneous source of variability is to be eliminated in comparing a set of sample means. An important feature of this kind of design is its *balance*, achieved by assigning the same number of observations for each treatment to each block. (In this connection, see also the comment on page 264, where we pointed out that differences due to blocks will not affect the means obtained for the different treatments.) The same kind of balance can be attained in more complicated kinds of designs, where it is desired to eliminate the effect of several extraneous sources of variability. In this section we shall introduce two further balanced designs, the Latin-square design and the Graeco-Latin-square design, which are used to eliminate the effects of two and three extraneous sources of variability, respectively.

To introduce the Latin-square design, suppose it is desired to compare three treatments, A, B, and C, in the presence of two other sources of variability. For example, the three treatments may be three methods for soldering copper electrical leads, and the two extraneous sources of variability may be (1) different operators doing the soldering, and (2) the use of different solder fluxes. If three operators and three fluxes are to be considered, the experiment might be arranged in the following pattern:

	Flux 1	Flux 2	Flux 3
Operator 1	A	B	C
Operator 2	C	A	B
Operator 3	B	C	A

Here each soldering method is applied once by each operator in conjunction with each flux, and if there are systematic effects due to differences among operators or differences among fluxes, these effects are present equally for each treatment, that is, for each method of soldering.

An experimental arrangement such as the one just described is called a *Latin square*. An $n \times n$ Latin square is a square array of n distinct letters, with each letter appearing once and only once in each row and in each column. Examples of Latin squares with $n = 4$ and $n = 5$ are shown in Figure 13.2, and larger ones may be obtained from the book by W. G. Cochran and G. M. Cox mentioned in the Bibliography. Note that in a Latin-square experiment involving n treatments, it is necessary to include n^2 observations, n for each treatment.

As we shall see on page 286, a Latin-square experiment without replication provides only $(n - 1)(n - 2)$ degrees of freedom for estimating the experimental error. Thus, such experiments are rarely run without *replication if n is small*, that is, without repeating the entire Latin-square pattern several times. If there is a total of r replicates, the analysis of the data presumes the following model, where $y_{ij(k)l}$ is the observation in the ith row and the jth column of the lth replicate, and the subscript k, in parentheses, indicates that it pertains to the kth treatment:

$$\blacklozenge \qquad y_{ij(k)l} = \mu + \alpha_i + \beta_j + \gamma_k + \rho_l + \epsilon_{ij(k)l} \qquad \blacklozenge$$

for $i, j, k = 1, 2, \ldots, n$, and $l = 1, 2, \ldots, r$, subject to the restrictions that $\sum_{i=1}^{n} \alpha_i = 0$, $\sum_{j=1}^{n} \beta_j = 0$, $\sum_{k=1}^{n} \gamma_k = 0$, and $\sum_{l=1}^{r} \rho_l = 0$. Here μ is the grand mean, α_i is the ith *row effect*, β_j is the jth *column effect*, γ_k is the kth *treatment effect*, ρ_l is the *effect* of the lth *replicate*, and the $\epsilon_{ij(k)l}$ are values of independent, normally distributed random variables with zero means and the common variance σ^2. Note that by "row effects" and "column effects"

5 × 5

4 × 4

A	B	C	D
B	C	D	A
C	D	A	B
D	A	B	C

A	B	C	D	E
B	A	E	C	D
C	D	A	E	B
D	E	B	A	C
E	C	D	B	A

FIG. 13.2 Latin squares

we mean the effects of the two extraneous variables, and that we are including replicate effects, since, as we shall see, replication can introduce a third extraneous variable. Note also that the subscript k is in parentheses in $y_{ij(k)l}$, because, for a given Latin-square design, k is automatically determined when i and j are known.

The main hypothesis we shall want to test is the null hypothesis $\gamma_k = 0$ for all k, namely, the null hypothesis that there is no difference in the effectiveness of the n treatments. However, we can also test whether the "cross blocking" of the Latin-square design has been effective; that is, we can test the two null hypotheses $\alpha_i = 0$ for all i and $\beta_j = 0$ for all j (against suitable alternatives) to see whether the two extraneous variables actually have an effect on the phenomenon under consideration. Furthermore, we can test the null hypothesis $\rho_l = 0$ for all l against the alternative that the ρ_l are not all equal to zero, and this test for *replicate effects* may be important if the parts of the experiment representing the individual Latin squares were performed on different days, by different technicians, at different temperatures, and so on.

The sums of squares required to perform these tests are usually obtained by means of the following short-cut formulas, where $T_{i..}$ is the total of the $r \cdot n$ observations in all of the ith rows, $T_{.j.}$ is the total of the $r \cdot n$ observations in all of the jth columns, $T_{..l}$ is the total of the n^2 observations in the lth replicate, $T_{(k)}$ is the total of all the $r \cdot n$ observations pertaining to the

kth treatment, and $T\ldots$ is the grand total of all the $r \cdot n^2$ observations:

$$C = \frac{(T\ldots)^2}{r \cdot n^2}$$

$$SS(Tr) = \frac{1}{r \cdot n} \sum_{k=1}^{n} T_{(k)}^2 - C$$

$$SSR = \frac{1}{r \cdot n} \sum_{i=1}^{n} T_{i..}^2 - C \qquad \text{(for row effects)}$$

$$SSC = \frac{1}{r \cdot n} \sum_{j=1}^{n} T_{.j.}^2 - C \qquad \text{(for column effects)}$$

$$SS(Rep) = \frac{1}{n^2} \sum_{l=1}^{r} T_{..l}^2 - C \qquad \text{(for replicates)}$$

$$SST = \sum_{i=1}^{n} \sum_{j=1}^{n} \sum_{l=1}^{r} y_{ij(k)l}^2 - C$$

$$SSE = SST - SS(Tr) - SSR - SSC - SS(Rep)$$

Note that again each divisor equals the number of observations in the corresponding squared totals. Finally, the results of the analysis are as shown in the following analysis of variance table:

Source of variation	Degrees of freedom	Sum of squares	Mean square	F
Treatments	$n - 1$	$SS(Tr)$	$MS(Tr) = \dfrac{SS(Tr)}{n - 1}$	$\dfrac{MS(Tr)}{MSE}$
Rows	$n - 1$	SSR	$MSR = \dfrac{SSR}{n - 1}$	$\dfrac{MSR}{MSE}$
Columns	$n - 1$	SSC	$MSC = \dfrac{SSC}{n - 1}$	$\dfrac{MSC}{MSE}$
Replicates	$r - 1$	$SS(Rep)$	$MS(Rep) = \dfrac{SS(Rep)}{r - 1}$	$\dfrac{MS(Rep)}{MSE}$
Error	$(n - 1)(rn + r - 3)$	SSE	$MSE = \dfrac{SSE}{(n - 1)(rn + r - 3)}$	
Total	$rn^2 - 1$	SST		

As before, the degrees of freedom for the total sum of squares equals the *sum* of the degrees of freedom for the individual components; thus, the degrees of freedom for error are usually found last, by subtraction.

To illustrate the analysis of a replicated Latin-square experiment, let us suppose that two replicates of the soldering experiment were run, using the following arrangement:

	Replicate I Flux			Replicate II Flux		
	1	*2*	*3*	*1*	*2*	*3*
Operator 1	A	B	C	C	B	A
Operator 2	C	A	B	A	C	B
Operator 3	B	C	A	B	A	C

The results, showing the number of pounds tensile force required to separate the soldered leads, were as follows:

Replicate I			Replicate II		
14.0	16.5	11.0	10.0	16.5	13.0
9.5	17.0	15.0	12.0	12.0	14.0
11.0	12.0	13.5	13.5	18.0	11.5

The total for the first treatment (Method A) is

$$14.0 + 17.0 + 13.5 + 13.0 + 12.0 + 18.0 = 87.5$$

while the totals for the other two treatments (Methods B and C) are

$$16.5 + 15.0 + 11.0 + 16.5 + 14.0 + 13.5 = 86.5$$

and $\quad\quad 11.0 + 9.5 + 12.0 + 10.0 + 12.0 + 11.5 = 66.0$

respectively. Also, the totals for the three rows are 81.0, 79.5, and 79.5, those for the three columns are 70.0, 92.0, and 78.0, the totals for the two replicates are 119.5 and 120.5, and the grand total is 240. We thus obtain

$$C = \frac{(240)^2}{18} = 3200.0$$

$$SS(Tr) = \frac{1}{6}\left[(87.5)^2 + (86.5)^2 + (66.0)^2\right] - 3200.0 = 49.1$$

$$SSR = \frac{1}{6}\left[(81.0)^2 + (79.5)^2 + (79.5)^2\right] - 3200.0 = 0.2$$

$$SSC = \frac{1}{6}\left[(70.0)^2 + (92.0)^2 + (78.0)^2\right] - 3200.0 = 41.3$$

$$SS(Rep) = \frac{1}{9}\left[(119.5)^2 + (120.5)^2\right] - 3200.0 = 0.1$$

$$SST = (14.0)^2 + (16.5)^2 + \ldots + (11.5)^2 - 3200.0 = 104.5$$

$$SSE = 104.5 - 49.1 - 41.3 - 0.2 - 0.1 = 13.8$$

and the results are as shown in the following analysis of variance table:

Source of variation	Degrees of freedom	Sum of squares	Mean square	F
Methods	2	49.1	24.6	17.6
Operators	2	0.2	0.1	0.1
Fluxes	2	41.3	20.6	14.7
Replicates	1	0.1	0.1	0.1
Error	10	13.8	1.4	
Total	17	104.5		

Since the F ratios for methods and fluxes both exceed 7.56, the value of $F_{.01}$ for 2 and 10 degrees of freedom, the differences due to methods as well as fluxes are significant. As can be seen by inspection, the differences due to the other two sources of variation (operators and replicates) are not significant. To go one step further, the Duncan multiple-range test of Section 13.4 gives the following *decision pattern* at the 0.01 level of significance:

	Method C	Method B	Method A
Mean	11.0	14.4	14.6

Thus, we conclude that Method C definitely yields weaker solder bonds than Methods A or B.

The elimination of three extraneous sources of variability can be accomplished by means of a design called a Graeco-Latin square. This design is a square array of n Latin letters and n Greek letters, with the Latin and Greek letters each forming a Latin square; furthermore, each Latin letter appears once and only once in conjunction with each Greek letter. The following is an example of a 4 × 4 Graeco-Latin square:

$A\alpha$	$B\beta$	$C\gamma$	$D\delta$
$B\delta$	$A\gamma$	$D\beta$	$C\alpha$
$C\beta$	$D\alpha$	$A\delta$	$B\gamma$
$D\gamma$	$C\delta$	$B\alpha$	$A\beta$

The construction of Graeco-Latin squares, also called *orthogonal* Latin squares, poses interesting mathematical problems, some of which are mentioned in the book by H. B. Mann listed in the Bibliography.

To give an example where the use of a Graeco-Latin square might be appropriate, suppose that in the soldering example an additional source of variability is the temperature of the solder. If three solder temperatures, denoted by α, β, and γ, are to be used together with the three methods, three operators (rows), and three solder fluxes (columns), a replicate of a suitable Graeco-Latin square experiment could be laid out as follows:

	Flux 1	*Flux 2*	*Flux 3*
Operator 1	$A\alpha$	$B\gamma$	$C\beta$
Operator 2	$C\gamma$	$A\beta$	$B\alpha$
Operator 3	$B\beta$	$C\alpha$	$A\gamma$

Thus, Method A would be used by operator 1 using solder flux 1 and temperature α, by operator 2 using solder flux 2 and temperature β, and by operator 3 using solder flux 3 and temperature γ. Similarly, Method B would be used by operator 1 using solder flux 2 and temperature γ, and so forth.

In a Graeco-Latin square each variable (represented by rows, columns, Latin letters, or Greek letters) is "distributed evenly" over the other variables. Thus, in comparing the means obtained for one variable, the effects of the other variables are all averaged out. The analysis of a Graeco-Latin square is similar to that of a Latin square, with the addition of an extra source of variability corresponding to the Greek letters.

There exists a wide variety of experimental designs other than the ones discussed in this chapter, that are suitable for many diverse purposes. Among the more widely used designs are the *incomplete block designs*, which are characterized by the feature that each treatment is not represented in each block. If the number of treatments under investigation in an experiment is large, it often happens that it is impossible to find homogeneous blocks such that all of the treatments can be accommodated in each block. For instance, if n paints are to be compared by applying each paint to a sheet of metal and then baking the sheets in an oven, it may be impossible to put all of the sheets in the oven at one time. Consequently, it would be necessary to use an experimental design in which $k < n$ treatments (paints) are included in each block (oven run). One way of doing this is to assign the treatments to each oven run in such a way that each treatment occurs together with each other treatment in the same number of blocks. This kind of design is called a *balanced incomplete-block design*, and for $n = 4$ and $k = 2$ we might use the following scheme:

Oven run	Paints
1	1 and 2
2	3 and 4
3	1 and 3
4	2 and 4
5	1 and 4
6	2 and 3

Balanced incomplete-block designs have the advantage that comparisons between any two treatments can be made with equal precision.

Since balanced incomplete-block designs may require too many blocks, many other schemes have been developed. Most of these experimental designs arose to meet the specific needs of experimenters, notably in the field of agriculture. As we have pointed out earlier, much of the language of experimental design, including such terms as "treatments," "blocks," "plots," etc., has been borrowed from agriculture. Only in recent years have the more sophisticated designs been applied to industrial and engineering experimentation, and, with more widespread application, it is to be expected that many new designs will be developed to meet the requirements in these fields.

EXERCISES

1. A Latin-square design with three replicates was used to compare three experimental fuels. The figures are the number of minutes engines E_1, E_2, and E_3, tuned up by mechanics M_1, M_2, and M_3, operated with 1 gallon of fuel A, B, or C. The replicates pertain to duplicates of the entire experiment performed (in randomized order) on three successive days.

	E_1		E_2		E_3	
M_1	A	16	B	21	C	14
M_2	B	25	C	18	A	23
M_3	C	16	A	21	B	26

	E_1		E_2		E_3	
M_1	A	17	B	23	C	13
M_2	B	28	C	19	A	21
M_3	C	12	A	20	B	25

	E_1		E_2		E_3	
M_1	A	15	B	20	C	14
M_2	B	26	C	16	A	24
M_3	C	19	A	24	B	28

Analyze these data and, if the null hypothesis concerning the effect of the fuels can be rejected, apply the Duncan multiple-range test to analyze the corresponding means.

2. Referring to the problem in which samples of tin plate are to be distributed among four laboratories (Section 13.1) suppose that we are concerned with systematic differences in tin-coating weight along the direction of rolling as well as across the rolling direction. To eliminate these two sources of variability, each of two sheets of tin plate is divided into 16 parts, representing four positions across and four positions along the rolling direction. Then, four samples from each sheet are sent to each of the laboratories A, B, C, and D, as shown, and the resulting tin-coating weights determined.

Replicate I

B .29	A .25	C .18	D .28
D .28	B .18	A .21	C .25
C .28	D .23	B .20	A .28
A .30	C .19	D .24	B .25

Rolling direction

Replicate II

C .20	A .24	D .20	B .27
B .28	C .19	A .22	D .28
D .34	B .23	C .21	A .28
A .32	D .22	B .16	C .27

Determine from these data whether the laboratories were obtaining consistent results. Also determine whether there are actual tin-coating weight differences across and along the rolling direction. (Use the 0.05 level of significance.)

3. The following are measurements of the breaking strength (in ounces) of linen threads A, B, C, D, and E, obtained by 5 different laboratory technicians on 5 different days:

Technicians

	T_1	T_2	T_3	T_4	T_5
D_1	A 30.2	B 24.3	C 19.6	D 21.5	E 17.3
D_2	B 21.4	C 27.1	D 23.4	E 24.5	A 31.0
D_3	C 20.7	D 26.5	E 25.2	A 29.1	B 20.6
D_4	D 20.7	E 24.7	A 32.3	B 25.2	C 22.2
D_5	E 20.6	A 35.8	B 23.9	C 23.6	D 21.5

Days labels the rows.

Analyze this Latin-square experiment and apply the Duncan multiple-range test with $\alpha = 0.01$ to the means of the breaking strengths of the five linen threads.

4. A clothing manufacturer wishes to determine which of four different needle designs is best for his sewing machines. The sources of variability which must be eliminated to make this comparison are the actual sewing machine used, the operator, and the type of thread. Using the Graeco-Latin-square design shown (the rows represent the operators, the columns represent the machines, the Latin letters represent the needles, and the Greek letters stand for the types of thread), the manufacturer recorded the number of rejected garments at the end of each of two days, with the following results:

First day

$C\alpha$ 42	$A\gamma$ 15	$B\delta$ 6	$D\beta$ 24
$D\delta$ 28	$B\beta$ 8	$A\alpha$ 24	$C\gamma$ 34
$B\gamma$ 5	$D\alpha$ 33	$C\beta$ 36	$A\delta$ 11
$A\beta$ 13	$C\delta$ 30	$D\gamma$ 21	$B\alpha$ 12

Second day

$D\gamma$ 18	$B\alpha$ 16	$A\beta$ 9	$C\delta$ 27
$C\beta$ 29	$A\delta$ 15	$B\gamma$ 7	$D\alpha$ 30
$A\alpha$ 21	$C\gamma$ 38	$D\delta$ 23	$B\beta$ 6
$B\delta$ 4	$D\beta$ 18	$C\alpha$ 37	$A\gamma$ 21

Using the 0.05 level of significance, determine whether there is a difference among the needles. Also, determine whether there are significant differences in the operators, the machines, and the types of thread.

5. To study the effectiveness of different kinds of packaging, a processor of breakfast foods performed the following Graeco-Latin square experiment, where A, B, C, D, and E represent different kinds of packaging, α, β, γ, δ, and ϵ represent (in increasing order of magnitude) the amount of money spent on newspaper ads for the product on the day before the experiment, and the rows represent different locations within identically disigned supermarkets, which are represented in turn by the five columns. The figures are the number of sales of the breakfast food from 9 A.M. to 11 A.M.

$A\alpha$	$B\beta$	$C\gamma$	$D\delta$	$E\epsilon$
50	51	53	55	56
$B\gamma$	$C\delta$	$D\epsilon$	$E\alpha$	$A\beta$
51	50	50	45	49
$C\epsilon$	$D\alpha$	$E\beta$	$A\gamma$	$B\delta$
45	37	39	40	41
$D\beta$	$E\gamma$	$A\delta$	$B\epsilon$	$C\alpha$
39	40	41	44	37
$E\delta$	$A\epsilon$	$B\alpha$	$C\beta$	$D\gamma$
43	47	41	42	42

Analyze this experiment.

6. The following is a simple way of constructing Graeco-Latin squares whose side is an odd prime p. We begin by constructing *two* Latin squares. In the first we put the number $i + j - 2$ into the cell belonging to the ith row and the jth column, subtracting p if an entry exceeds $p - 1$. Into the second square we put the number $2i + j - 3$ into the cell belonging to the ith row and the jth column, subtracting p or $2p$ so that each entry will not exceed $p - 1$. If we then substitute A, B, C, ... for 0, 1, ..., and $p - 1$ in the first square, and α, β, γ, ... for 0, 1, ..., and $p - 1$ in the second square, the superimposed squares will constitute a Graeco-Latin square.

(a) Verify that this method was used to construct the Graeco-Latin square of Exercise 5.

(b) Use this method to construct a 3×3 and a 7×7 Graeco-Latin square.

(c) Prove that this method will yield a Graeco-Latin square for any odd prime p. [*Hint:* First prove that each of the two squares is a Latin square, and then show that each pair of Roman and Greek letters occurs once and only once.]

FACTORIAL EXPERIMENTATION

14.1 Two-factor Experiments

In Chapter 13 we were interested mainly in the effects of one variable, whose values we referred to as "treatments." Extraneous variables were accommodated by means of blocks, replicates, or the rows and columns of Latin squares and more complicated kinds of designs. In this chapter we shall be concerned with the individual and joint effects of several variables, and combinations of the values, or *levels*, of these variables will now play the roles of the different treatments. Extraneous variables, if any, will be handled as before.

To consider a simple *two-factor* (two-variable) experiment, suppose it is desired to determine the effects of flue temperature and oven width on the time required to make coke. The experimental conditions used are

Oven width (inches)	Flue temperature (degrees F)
4	1600
4	1900
8	1600
8	1900
12	1600
12	1900

and if several blocks (or replicates) were run, each consisting of these six "treatments," it would be possible to analyze the data as a two-way classification and test for significant differences among the six treatment means. In this instance, however, the experimenter is interested in knowing far more than that—he wishes to know whether variations in oven width or in flue temperature affect the coking time, and perhaps also whether any changes in coking time attributable to variations in oven width are the same at different temperatures.

It is possible to answer questions of this kind if the experimental conditions, the treatments, consist of appropriate combinations of the *levels* (or values) of the various *factors*. The factors in this case are oven width and flue temperature; oven width has the *three levels* 4, 8, and 12 inches, while flue temperature has the *two levels* 1600 and 1900 degrees Fahrenheit. Note that the six treatments were chosen in such a way that each level of oven width is used once in conjunction with each level of flue temperature. In general, if two factors A and B are to be investigated at a levels and b levels, respectively, and if there are $a \cdot b$ experimental conditions (treatments) corresponding to all possible combinations of the levels of the two factors, the resulting experiment is referred to as a *complete $a \times b$ factorial experiment*. Note that if one or more of the $a \cdot b$ experimental conditions is omitted, the experiment can still be analyzed as a two-way classification, but it cannot readily be analyzed as a factorial experiment. It is customary to omit the word "complete," so that an *$a \times b$ factorial* experiment is understood to contain experimental conditions corresponding to all possible combinations of the levels of the two factors.

In order to obtain an estimate of the experimental error in a two-factor experiment it is necessary to replicate, that is, to repeat the entire set of $a \cdot b$ experimental conditions, say, a total of r times, randomizing the order of applying the conditions in each replicate. If y_{ijk} is the observation in the kth replicate, taken at the ith level of factor A and the jth level of factor B, the model assumed for the analysis of this kind of experiment is usually written as

$$\blacklozenge \qquad y_{ijk} = \mu + \alpha_i + \beta_j + (\alpha\beta)_{ij} + \rho_k + \epsilon_{ijk} \qquad \blacklozenge$$

for $i = 1, 2, \ldots, a$, $j = 1, 2, \ldots, b$, and $k = 1, 2, \ldots, r$. Here μ is the grand mean, α_i is the effect of the ith level of factor A, β_j is the effect of the jth level of factor B, $(\alpha\beta)_{ij}$ is the *interaction*, or joint effect, of the ith level of factor A and the jth level of factor B, and ρ_k is the effect of the kth replicate. As in the models used in Chapter 13, we shall assume that the ϵ_{ijk} are values of independent random variables having normal distributions with zero means and the common variance σ^2. Also, analogous to the restrictions imposed on the models on pages 266 and 275, we shall assume that

$$\sum_{i=1}^{a} \alpha_i = \sum_{j=1}^{b} \beta_j = \sum_{i=1}^{a} (\alpha\beta)_{ij} = \sum_{j=1}^{b} (\alpha\beta)_{ij} = \sum_{k=1}^{r} \rho_k = 0$$

It can be shown that these restrictions will assure unique estimates for the parameters μ, α_i, β_j, $(\alpha\beta)_{ij}$, and ρ_k.

To illustrate the model underlying a two-factor experiment, let us consider an experiment with two replicates in which factor A occurs at two levels, factor B occurs at two levels, and the replication effects are zero, that is, $\rho_1 = \rho_2 = 0$. In view of the restrictions on the parameters we also have

$$\alpha_2 = -\alpha_1, \quad \beta_2 = -\beta_1 \quad \text{and} \quad (\alpha\beta)_{21} = (\alpha\beta)_{12} = -(\alpha\beta)_{22} = -(\alpha\beta)_{11}$$

and the population means corresponding to the four experimental conditions defined by the two levels of factor A and the two levels of factor B can be written as

$$\mu_{111} = \mu_{112} = \mu + \alpha_1 + \beta_1 + (\alpha\beta)_{11}$$

$$\mu_{121} = \mu_{122} = \mu + \alpha_1 - \beta_1 - (\alpha\beta)_{11}$$

$$\mu_{211} = \mu_{212} = \mu - \alpha_1 + \beta_1 - (\alpha\beta)_{11}$$

$$\mu_{221} = \mu_{222} = \mu - \alpha_1 - \beta_1 + (\alpha\beta)_{11}$$

Substituting for $\mu_{ij1} = \mu_{ij2}$ the mean of all observations obtained for the ith level of factor A and the jth level of factor B, we get four simultaneous linear equations which can be solved for the parameters μ, α_1, β_1, and $(\alpha\beta)_{11}$ (see Exercise 7 on page 311).

To continue our illustration, let us now suppose that $\mu = 10$. If all of the other effects equalled zero, each of the μ_{ijk} would equal 10, and the response surface would be the horizontal plane shown in Figure 14.1(a). If we now add an effect of factor A, with $\alpha_1 = -4$, the response surface becomes the tilted plane shown in Figure 14.1(b), and if we add to this an effect of factor B, with $\beta_1 = 5$, we get the plane shown in Figure 14.1(c). Note that, so far, the effects of factors A and B are *additive*, that is, the change in the mean for either factor in going from level 1 to level 2 does not depend on the level of the other factor, and the response surface is a plane. If we now include an *interaction*, with $(\alpha\beta)_{11} = -2$, the plane becomes twisted as shown in Figure 14.1(d), the effects are no longer additive, and the response surface is no longer a plane. Note, also, that if the replication effects had not equalled zero, we would have obtained a different surface for each replicate; for each replicate the surface of Figure 14.1(d) would have been shifted an appropriate number of units up or down.

The analysis of an $a \times b$ *factorial experiment* is based on the following breakdown of the total sum of squares. First, we subdivide SST into

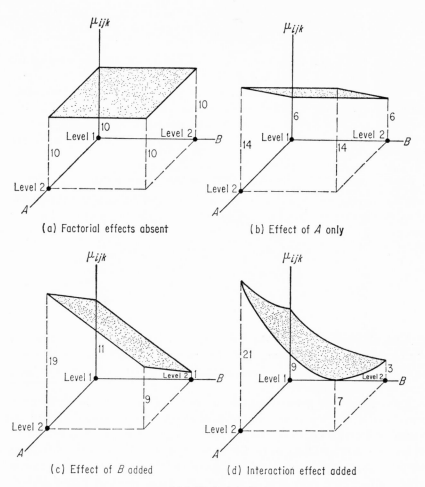

FIG. 14.1 Factorial effects

components attributed to treatments, replicates (or blocks), and error, by means of the identity

$$\sum_{i=1}^{a} \sum_{j=1}^{b} \sum_{k=1}^{r} (y_{ijk} - \bar{y}...)^2 = r \sum_{i=1}^{a} \sum_{j=1}^{b} (\bar{y}_{ij.} - \bar{y}...)^2$$

$$+ ab \sum_{k=1}^{r} (\bar{y}_{..k} - \bar{y}...)^2$$

$$+ \sum_{i=1}^{a} \sum_{j=1}^{b} \sum_{k=1}^{r} (y_{ijk} - \bar{y}_{ij.} - \bar{y}_{..k} + \bar{y}...)^2$$

Except for notation, this identity is equivalent to that of Theorem 13.2.

The total sum of squares, on the left-hand side of the identity, has $abr - 1$ degrees of freedom. The terms on the right are, respectively, the treatment sum of squares having $ab - 1$ degrees of freedom, the replicate (block) sum of squares having $r - 1$ degrees of freedom, and the error sum of squares having $(ab - 1)(r - 1)$ degrees of freedom. (Note that the various degrees of freedom are the same as those of the analysis of variance table on page 276 if we substitute ab for a and r for b.)

So far there is nothing new about the analysis of the data; it is the analysis of a two-way classification, *but the distinguishing feature of a factorial experiment is that the treatment sum of squares can be further subdivided into components corresponding to the various factorial effects*. Thus, for a two-factor experiment we have the following subdivision, or breakdown, of the treatment sum of squares:

$$r \sum_{i=1}^{a} \sum_{j=1}^{b} (\bar{y}_{ij.} - \bar{y}...)^2 = rb \sum_{i=1}^{a} (\bar{y}_{i..} - \bar{y}...)^2 + ra \sum_{j=1}^{b} (\bar{y}_{.j.} - \bar{y}...)^2$$

$$+ r \sum_{i=1}^{a} \sum_{j=1}^{b} (\bar{y}_{ij.} - \bar{y}_{i..} - \bar{y}_{.j.} + \bar{y}...)^2$$

The first term on the right measures the variability of the means corresponding to the different levels of factor A, and we refer to it as the *factor A sum of squares, SSA*. Similarly, the second term is the sum of squares for factor B, SSB, and the third term is the *interaction sum of squares* $SS(AB)$, which measures the variability of the means $\bar{y}_{ij.}$ that is not attributable to the individual (or separate) effects of factors A and B. The $ab - 1$ degrees of freedom for treatments are, accordingly, subdivided into $a - 1$ degrees of freedom for the effect of factor A, $b - 1$ for the effect of factor B, and

$$ab - 1 - (a - 1) - (b - 1) = (a - 1)(b - 1)$$

degrees of freedom for interaction.

To illustrate the analysis of a two-factor experiment, let us refer again to the coking experiment described on page 294, and let us suppose that three replicates yielded the following coking times (in hours):

a

Factor A Oven width	Factor B Flue temp.	Rep. 1	Rep. 2	Rep. 3	Total
4	1600	3.5	3.0	2.7	9.2
4	1900	2.2	2.3	2.4	6.9
8	1600	7.1	6.9	7.5	21.5
8	1900	5.2	4.6	6.8	16.6
12	1600	10.8	10.6	11.0	32.4
12	1900	7.6	7.1	7.3	22.0
	Total	36.4	34.5	37.7	108.6

Following the procedure used in analyzing a two-way classification, we first compute the correction term

$$C = \frac{(108.6)^2}{18} = 655.22$$

Then, the total sum of squares is given by

$$SST = (3.5)^2 + (2.2)^2 + \ldots + (7.3)^2 - 655.22 = 149.38$$

and the treatment and replicate (instead of blocks) sums of squares are given by

$$SS(Tr) = \frac{1}{3} [(9.2)^2 + (6.9)^2 + \ldots + (22.0)^2] - 655.22 = 146.05$$

$$SSR = \frac{1}{6} [(36.4)^2 + (34.5)^2 + (37.7)^2] - 655.22 = 0.86$$

Finally, by subtraction, we obtain

$$SSE = 149.38 - 146.05 - 0.86 = 2.47$$

Subdivision of the treatment sum of squares into components for factors A and B, and for interaction, can be facilitated by constructing the following kind of two-way table, where the entries are the totals in the right-hand column of the table giving the original data:

Factor B
Flue temperature

	1600	1900	
4	9.2	6.9	16.1
8	21.5	16.6	38.1
12	32.4	22.0	54.4
	63.1	45.5	108.6

Factor A
Oven width

Using formulas analogous to the ones with which we computed the sums of squares for various effects in Chapter 13, we now have for the two *main effects*

$$SSA = \frac{1}{b \cdot r} \sum_{i=1}^{a} T_{i..}^2 - C$$

$$= \frac{1}{6} [(16.1)^2 + (38.1)^2 + (54.4)^2] - 655.22 = 123.14$$

$$SSB = \frac{1}{a \cdot r} \sum_{j=1}^{b} T_{.j.}^2 - C$$

$$= \frac{1}{9} \left[(63.1)^2 + (45.5)^2 \right] - 655.22 = 17.21$$

and for the *interaction*

$$SS(AB) = SS(Tr) - SSA - SSB$$

$$= 146.05 - 123.14 - 17.21 = 5.70$$

Finally, dividing the various sums of squares by their degrees of freedom, and dividing the appropriate mean squares by the error mean square, we obtain the results shown in the following analysis of variance table:

Source of variation	Degrees of freedom	Sum of squares	Mean square	F
Replication	2	0.86	0.43	1.72
Main effects: A B	 2 1	 123.14 17.21	 61.57 17.21	 246 68.8
Interaction	2	5.70	2.85	11.4
Error	10	2.47	0.25	
Total	17	149.38		

The *F* test for replications is not significant at the 0.05 or 0.01 levels of significance, but the other three *F* tests are significant at the 0.01 level of significance. Hence, we reject the null hypothesis that the α_i are all equal to zero, the null hypothesis that the β_j are all equal to zero, and the null hypothesis that the $(\alpha\beta)_{ij}$ are all equal to zero. These results are illustrated in Figure 14.2, showing the trend of mean coking times for changing oven width at each of the flue temperatures. It is apparent from this figure that the increase in coking time for changing oven width is *greater* at the lower flue temperature. In view of this interaction, great care must be exercised in stating the results of this experiment. For instance, it would be very misleading to state merely that the effect of increasing flue temperature from 1600 to 1900 degrees Fahrenheit is to lower the coking time by

$\dfrac{63.1}{9} - \dfrac{45.5}{9} = 1.96$ hours. In fact, the coking time is lowered on the average by as little as 0.77 hours when the oven width is 4 inches, and by as much as 3.47 hours when the oven width is 12 inches.

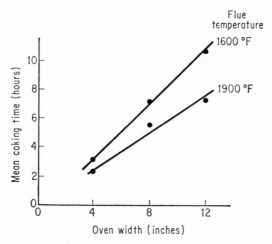

FIG. 14.2 Results of coking experiment

14.2 Multifactor Experiments

Much industrial research and experimentation is conducted to discover the individual and joint effects of several factors on variables which are most relevant to phenomena under investigation. The experimental designs most often used are of the simple randomized-block or two-way classification type, but the distinguishing feature of most of them is the factorial arrangement of the treatments, or experimental conditions. As we observed in the preceding section, r sets of data pertaining to $a \cdot b$ experimental conditions can be analyzed as a factorial experiment in r replicates if the experimental conditions represent all possible combinations of the levels of two factors A and B. In this section, we shall extend the discussion to factorial experiments involving more than two factors, that is, to experiments where the experimental conditions represent all possible combinations of the levels of three or more factors.

To illustrate the analysis of a multifactor experiment, let us consider the following situation. A warm sulfuric pickling bath is used to remove oxides from the surface of a metal prior to plating, and it is desired to determine what factors in addition to the concentration of the sulfuric acid might affect the electrical conductivity of the bath. As it is felt that the salt concentration as well as the bath temperature might also affect the electrical conductivity, an experiment is planned to determine the individual and joint effects of these three variables on the electrical conductivity of the bath. In order to cover the ranges of concentrations and temperatures normally encountered, it is decided to use the following levels of the three factors:

Factor	Level 1	Level 2	Level 3	Level 4
A. Acid concentration (per cent)	0	6	12	18
B. Salt concentration (per cent)	0	10	20	
C. Bath temperature (degrees F)	80	100		

The resulting factorial experiment requires $4 \cdot 3 \cdot 2 = 24$ experimental conditions in each replicate, where each experimental condition is a pickling bath made up according to specifications. The order in which these pickling baths are made up should be random. Let us suppose that two replicates of the experiment have actually been completed, that is, the electrical conductivities of the various pickling baths have been measured, and that the results are as shown in the table on page 303.

The model we shall assume for the analysis of this experiment (or any similar three-factor experiment) is an immediate extension of the one used in Section 14.1. If y_{ijkl} is the conductivity measurement obtained at the ith level of acid concentration, the jth level of salt concentration, the kth level of bath temperature, in the lth replicate, we write

$$y_{ijkl} = \mu + \alpha_i + \beta_j + \gamma_k + (\alpha\beta)_{ij} + (\alpha\gamma)_{ik} + (\beta\gamma)_{jk}$$

$$+ (\alpha\beta\gamma)_{ijk} + \rho_l + \epsilon_{ijkl}$$

for $i = 1, 2, \ldots, a, j = 1, 2, \ldots, b, k = 1, 2, \ldots, c,$ and $l = 1, 2, \ldots, r.$ We also assume that the sums of the main effects (α's, β's, and γ's) as well as the sum of the replication effects are equal to zero, that the sums of the two-way interaction effects summed on either subscript equal zero for any value of the other subscript, and that the sum of the three-way interaction effects summed on any one of the subscripts is zero for any values of the other two subscripts. As before, the ϵ_{ijkl} are assumed to be values of independent random variables having zero means and the common variance σ^2.

We begin the analysis of the data by treating the experiment as a two-

RESULTS OF ACID-BATH EXPERIMENT

| Level of factor | | | Conductivity (mhos/cm³) | | |
A	B	C	Rep. 1	Rep. 2	Total
1	1	1	0.99	0.93	1.92
1	1	2	1.15	0.99	2.14
1	2	1	0.97	0.91	1.88
1	2	2	0.87	0.86	1.73
1	3	1	0.95	0.86	1.81
1	3	2	0.91	0.85	1.76
2	1	1	1.00	1.17	2.17
2	1	2	1.12	1.13	2.25
2	2	1	0.99	1.04	2.03
2	2	2	0.96	0.98	1.94
2	3	1	0.97	0.95	1.92
2	3	2	0.94	0.99	1.93
3	1	1	1.24	1.22	2.46
3	1	2	1.12	1.15	2.27
3	2	1	1.15	0.95	2.10
3	2	2	1.11	0.95	2.06
3	3	1	1.03	1.01	2.04
3	3	2	1.12	0.96	2.08
4	1	1	1.24	1.20	2.44
4	1	2	1.32	1.24	2.56
4	2	1	1.14	1.10	2.24
4	2	2	1.20	1.19	2.39
4	3	1	1.02	1.01	2.03
4	3	2	1.02	1.00	2.02
		Total	25.53	24.64	50.17

way classification with $a \cdot b \cdot c$ treatments and r replicates (blocks), and using the short-cut formulas on page 276, we obtain

$$C = \frac{(50.17)^2}{48} = 52.4381$$

$$SST = (0.99)^2 + (1.15)^2 + \ldots + (1.00)^2 - 52.4381 = 0.6624$$

$$SS(Tr) = \frac{1}{2} [(1.92)^2 + (2.14)^2 + \ldots + (2.02)^2] - 52.4381 = 0.5712$$

$$SSR = \frac{1}{24} [(25.53)^2 + (24.64)^2] - 52.4381 = 0.0165$$

$$SSE = 0.6624 - 0.5712 - 0.0165 = 0.0747$$

The degrees of freedom for these sums of squares are, respectively, 47, 23, 1, and 23.

Next, we shall want to subdivide the treatment sum of squares into the three *main effect sums of squares SSA, SSB, SSC*, the three *two-way interaction sums of squares, SS(AB), SS(AC)*, and *SS(BC)*, and the *three-way interaction sum of squares SS(ABC)*. To facilitate the calculation of these sums of squares we first construct the following three tables analogous to the one on page 299:

		B 1	B 2	B 3	
	1	4.06	3.61	3.57	11.24
	2	4.42	3.97	3.85	12.24
A	3	4.73	4.16	4.12	13.01
	4	5.00	4.63	4.05	13.68
		18.21	16.37	15.59	50.17

		C 1	C 2	
	1	5.61	5.63	11.24
	2	6.12	6.12	12.24
A	3	6.60	6.41	13.01
	4	6.71	6.97	13.68
		25.04	25.13	50.17

		B 1	B 2	B 3	
	1	8.99	8.25	7.80	25.04
C	2	9.22	8.12	7.79	25.13
		18.21	16.37	15.59	50.17

The entries of these tables are the totals of all measurements obtained at the respective levels of the two variables. Note the self-checking feature of these tables; the same marginal totals appear several times, thus providing a rapid and effective check on the calculations.

To calculate SSA, SSB, and $SS(AB)$ we refer to the first of the above tables and an identity analogous to the one on page 298. As a matter of fact, the calculations parallel those for calculating SSA, SSB, and $SS(AB)$ in the two-factor experiment. To take the place of the treatment sum of squares we first calculate

$$rc \sum_{i=1}^{a} \sum_{j=1}^{b} (\bar{y}_{ij..} - \bar{y}....)^2 = \frac{1}{r \cdot c} \sum_{i=1}^{a} \sum_{j=1}^{b} T_{ij..}^2 - C$$

$$= \frac{1}{4} [(4.06)^2 + (4.42)^2 + \ldots + (4.05)^2] - 52.4381$$

$$= 0.5301$$

and we then obtain

$$SSA = \frac{1}{bcr} \sum_{i=1}^{a} T_{i...}^2 - C$$

$$= \frac{1}{12} [(11.24)^2 + \ldots + (13.68)^2] - 52.4381$$

$$= 0.2750$$

$$SSB = \frac{1}{acr} \sum_{j=1}^{b} T_{.j..}^2 - C$$

$$= \frac{1}{16} [(18.21)^2 + (16.37)^2 + (15.59)^2] - 52.4381$$

$$= 0.2262$$

and $$SS(AB) = 0.5301 - 0.2750 - 0.2262$$

$$= 0.0289$$

Performing the same calculations for the second of the three tables on page 304 we obtain, similarly,

$$SSC = 0.0002 \quad \text{and} \quad SS(AC) = 0.0085$$

and the analysis of the third table yields

$$SS(BC) = 0.0042$$

For the three-way interaction sum of squares we finally obtain by subtraction

$SS(ABC)$

$$= SS(Tr) - SSA - SSB - SSC - SS(AB) - SS(AC) - SS(BC)$$
$$= 0.5712 - 0.2750 - 0.2262 - 0.0002 - 0.0289 - 0.0085 - 0.0042$$
$$= 0.0282$$

Note that the degrees of freedom for each main effect is one less than the number of levels of the corresponding factor. The degrees of freedom for each interaction is the *product* of the degrees of freedom for those factors appearing in the interaction. Thus, the degrees of freedom for the three main effects are 3, 2, and 1 in this example, while the degrees of freedom for the two-way interactions are 6, 3, and 2, and the degrees of freedom for the three-way interaction is 6.

The following table shows the complete analysis of variance for the acid-bath experiment:

Source of variation	Degrees of freedom	Sum of squares	Mean square	F
Replicates	1	0.0165	0.0165	5.16
Main effects:				
A	3	0.2750	0.0917	28.66
B	2	0.2262	0.1131	35.34
C	1	0.0002	0.0002	< 1
Two-factor interactions:				
AB	6	0.0289	0.0048	1.50
AC	3	0.0085	0.0028	< 1
BC	2	0.0042	0.0021	< 1
Three-factor interaction:				
ABC	6	0.0282	0.0047	1.47
Error	23	0.0747	0.0032	
Total	47	0.6624		

Obtaining the appropriate values of $F_{.05}$ and $F_{.01}$ from Table VI, we find that the test for replicates is significant at the 0.05 level (perhaps the two replicates were performed under different atmospheric conditions or the thermometer used to measure bath temperatures went out of calibration, etc.), the tests for the factor A and factor B main effects are significant at the 0.01 level, while none of the other F's are significant at either level.

We conclude from this analysis that variations in acid concentration and salt concentration affect the electrical conductivity, variations in bath temperature do not, and that there are no interactions. To go one step further, we might investigate the *magnitudes* of the effects by studying graphs of means like those shown in Figures 14.3 and 14.4. Here we find

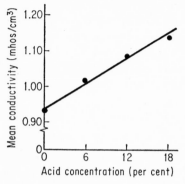

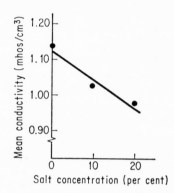

FIG. 14.3 Effect of acid concentration   FIG. 14.4 Effect of salt concentration

that the conductivity increases as acid is added and decreases as salt is added; using the methods of Chapter 12 we might even fit lines, curves, or surfaces to describe the response surface relating conductivity to the variables under consideration.

The general computational procedure for a multifactor experiment is similar to the method illustrated here for a $4 \times 3 \times 2$ factorial experiment. We first analyze the data as a two-way classification (or whatever other design is being used) and then we analyze the treatment sum of squares into the components attributed to the various main effects and interactions. In general, the sum of squares for each main effect is found by adding the squares of the totals corresponding to the different levels of that factor, dividing by the number of observations comprising each of these totals, and then subtracting the correction term. The sum of squares for any interaction is found by adding the squares of all totals obtained by summing over those subscripts pertaining to factors not involved in the interaction, dividing by the number of observations comprising each of these totals, and then subtracting the correction term *and* all sums of squares corresponding to main effects and fewer-factor interactions involving the factors contained in that interaction.

EXERCISES

1. The following data are the lifetimes (in hours) of four different designs of an airplane wing subjected to three different kinds of continuous vibrations (at

constant frequency, sweeping back and forth at a constant rate over a given band width, and generated by a random-noise generator). The experiment is a 3 × 4 factorial with 2 replications, with the first figure in each cell referring to the first replicate and the second figure to the second replicate.

	Design 1	Design 2	Design 3	Design 4
Vibration 1	876, 913	1156, 1219	1234, 1181	825, 797
Vibration 2	1412, 1290	1876, 1710	1591, 1649	1083, 1161
Vibration 3	1291, 1412	2115, 1963	1650, 1712	1148, 1262

(a) Analyze the data first as a two-way classification with 12 treatments and 2 blocks (replicates).

(b) Calculate the sums of squares corresponding to the main effects and interaction, and present the results in an analysis of variance table.

(c) Interpret the results of the experiment.

2. To determine optimum conditions for a plating bath, the effects of sulfone concentration and bath temperature on the reflectivity of the plated metal are studied in a 2 × 5 factorial experiment. The results of three replicates are as follows:

Concentration (grams/liter)	Temperature (degrees F)	Reflectivity Rep. 1	Rep. 2	Rep. 3
4	80	33	37	34
4	100	30	36	35
4	120	31	32	34
4	140	29	21	24
4	160	17	16	20
8	80	37	45	40
8	100	36	44	39
8	120	37	31	36
8	140	34	46	39
8	160	31	39	32

Analyze these results and determine the bath condition or conditions that produce the highest reflectivity. Also construct a 0.95 confidence interval for the reflectivity of the plating bath corresponding to these optimum conditions.

3. Suppose that in the experiment described on page 277 it is desired to determine also whether there is an interaction between the hull designs and the weather conditions, that is, whether one hull design might perform better under calm conditions, another might perform better under choppy conditions, and so forth. Combining the data on page 277 with the replicate of

the experiment given below, test for a significant interaction and discuss the results.

	Day 1	Day 2	Day 3
Design A	39	42	58
Design B	44	46	48
Design C	34	47	45
Design D	47	45	57

4. The following tables give the weights (in grams) of food ingested by two different strains of rats after having been deprived of food for the stated number of hours and then having been given the stated dosage of a certain drug:

| | | Replicate 1 | | Replicate 2 | |
		Strain A	Strain B	Strain A	Strain B
Dosage 0.1 mg/kg	1 hour	9.07	6.02	8.77	7.59
	5 hours	9.16	7.05	11.82	9.21
	9 hours	16.08	12.01	14.65	15.35
Dosage 0.3 mg/kg	1 hour	5.63	5.87	8.76	6.13
	5 hours	11.57	9.56	11.53	8.30
	9 hours	10.30	10.13	14.46	9.26
Dosage 0.5 mg/kg	1 hour	4.42	4.35	3.01	3.81
	5 hours	5.22	8.01	9.21	10.10
	9 hours	7.27	8.17	6.10	11.16

Perform an appropriate analysis of variance and interpret the results.

5. To study the performance of three detergents at different washing times and at different temperatures, a laboratory technician performed a $2 \times 2 \times 3$ factorial experiment with 3 replicates. The results are shown below; the entries are "whiteness" readings obtained with specially designed equipment

Detergent	Washing time (minutes)	Water temperature	Rep. 1	Whiteness Rep. 2	Rep. 3
A	10	hot	76	72	73
A	10	warm	51	48	50
A	20	hot	77	74	79
A	20	warm	61	62	62
B	10	hot	63	62	60
B	10	warm	45	48	43
B	20	hot	63	64	59
B	20	warm	55	53	58
C	10	hot	64	60	63
C	10	warm	47	42	49
C	20	hot	65	66	62
C	20	warm	56	54	54

(a) Analyze this experiment first as a two-way classification with 12 treatments and 3 replicates (blocks).

(b) Complete the analysis by computing the sums of squares corresponding to the various main effects and interactions.

(c) Present the results in an analysis of variance table and interpret the experiment.

6. To study the effects of ingot location (A), slab position (B), specimen preparation (C), and twisting temperature (D) on the number of turns required to break a steel specimen by twisting, the following observations were recorded:

A	B	C	D	No. of turns Rep. 1	Rep. 2
top	1	turn	2100° F	24	22
top	1	turn	2200	25	28
top	1	turn	2300	41	39
top	1	grind	2100	18	18
top	1	grind	2200	33	27
top	1	grind	2300	35	41
top	2	turn	2100	22	19
top	2	turn	2200	26	31
top	2	turn	2300	37	43
top	2	grind	2100	23	7
top	2	grind	2200	30	26
top	2	grind	2300	34	30
mid	1	turn	2100	26	19
mid	1	turn	2200	30	31
mid	1	turn	2300	39	42
mid	1	grind	2100	19	19
mid	1	grind	2200	31	31
mid	1	grind	2300	26	35
mid	2	turn	2100	30	26
mid	2	turn	2200	31	34

				No. of turns	
				Rep.	Rep.
A	B	C	D	1	2
mid	2	turn	2300° F	39	42
mid	2	grind	2100	22	20
mid	2	grind	2200	32	26
mid	2	grind	2300	38	22
bot	1	turn	2100	18	21
bot	1	turn	2200	35	32
bot	1	turn	2300	34	37
bot	1	grind	2100	21	19
bot	1	grind	2200	20	29
bot	1	grind	2300	44	31
bot	2	turn	2100	23	22
bot	2	turn	2200	31	26
bot	2	turn	2300	38	41
bot	2	grind	2100	18	19
bot	2	grind	2200	31	24
bot	2	grind	2300	35	41

Analyze this experiment.

7. Solve the four equations on page 296 for μ, α_1, β_1, and $(\alpha\beta)_{11}$ in terms of the population means μ_{ij1} corresponding to the four experimental conditions in the first replicate. Note that these equations serve as a guide for estimating the parameters in terms of the *sample means* corresponding to the various experimental conditions.

14.3 2^n Factorial Experiments

There are several reasons why factorial experiments are often performed with each factor taken at only two levels. Primarily, the number of experimental conditions in a factorial experiment increases multiplicatively with the number of levels of each factor; thus, if many factors are to be investigated simultaneously, it may be economically impossible to include more than two levels of each factor. Another important reason for treating 2^n factorial experiments separately is that there exist computational short-cuts which apply only to this case. In fact, the remainder of this section will be devoted to these computational short-cuts, while other advantages, such as the ease of confounding higher-order interactions and the adaptability of 2^n factorials to experiments involving fractional replication, will be discussed in succeeding sections.

Before we introduce some of the special notation used in connection with 2^n factorial experiments, let us point out that such experiments do have some drawbacks. Since each factor is measured only at two levels, it is impossible to judge whether the effects produced by variations in a factor are linear or, perhaps, parabolic or exponential. For this reason 2^n factorial experiments are often used in "screening experiments," which are followed up by experiments involving fewer factors (ordinarily those found to be "significant" individually or jointly in the screening experiment) taken at more than two levels.

In the analysis of a 2^n factorial experiment it is convenient to denote the two levels of each factor by 0 and 1 (instead of 1 and 2). Thus, the models used for the analysis of this kind of experiment differ from those of Section 14.2 only inasmuch as we now have $i = 0$, 1 instead of $i = 1$, 2, . . . , a, $j = 0$, 1 instead of $j = 1$, 2, . . . , b, and so forth. For instance, for a 2^3 factorial experiment the model on page 302 becomes

$$y_{ijkl} = \mu + \alpha_i + \beta_j + \gamma_k + (\alpha\beta)_{ij} + (\alpha\gamma)_{ik} + (\beta\gamma)_{jk}$$
$$+ (\alpha\beta\gamma)_{ijk} + \rho_l + \epsilon_{ijkl}$$

for $i = 0$, 1, $j = 0$, 1, $k = 0$, 1, and $l = 1$, 2, . . . , r. The ϵ_{ijkl} are defined as before, and the parameters are now subject to the restrictions $\alpha_1 = -\alpha_0$, $\beta_1 = -\beta_0$, $\gamma_1 = -\gamma_0$, $(\alpha\beta)_{10} = (\alpha\beta)_{01} = -(\alpha\beta)_{11} = -(\alpha\beta)_{00}$, . . . , and $\sum_{l=1}^{r} \rho_l = 0$. Note that besides the parameters for replicates we need only *one parameter of each kind:* that is, besides the parameters for replicates, we can express the entire model in terms of the parameters μ, α_0, β_0, γ_0, $(\alpha\beta)_{00}$, $(\alpha\gamma)_{00}$, $(\beta\gamma)_{00}$, and $(\alpha\beta\gamma)_{000}$.

A 2^n factorial experiment requires 2^n experimental conditions; since their number can be fairly large, it will be convenient to represent the experimental conditions by means of a special notation and list them in a so-called standard order. The notation consists of representing each experimental condition by the product of lower-case letters corresponding to the factors which are taken at level 1, called the "higher level." If a lower-case letter corresponding to a factor is missing, this means that the factor is taken at level 0, called the "lower level." Thus, in a three-factor experiment, ac represents the experimental condition where factors A and C are taken at the higher level and factor B is taken at the lower level, c represents the experimental condition where factor C is taken at the higher level and factors A and B are taken at the lower level, and so forth. The symbol "1" is used to denote the experimental condition in which all factors are taken at the lower level.

Although the experimental conditions are applied in a random order during the experiment itself, for the purpose of analyzing the results it is convenient to arrange them in a so-called *standard order*. For $n = 2$, this order is 1, a, b, ab, and for $n = 3$ it is the order shown in the following table:

Experimental condition	Level of factor A	B	C
1	0	0	0
a	1	0	0
b	0	1	0
ab	1	1	0
c	0	0	1
ac	1	0	1
bc	0	1	1
abc	1	1	1

Note that the symbols for the first four experimental conditions are like those for a two-factor experiment, and that the second four are obtained by multiplying each of the first four symbols by c. Similarly, the arrangement for $n = 4$ on page 315 is obtained by first listing the eight symbols for a three-factor experiment and then repeating the set with each symbol multiplied by d.

Throughout this and the preceding chapter we referred to the total of all observations corresponding to a given experimental condition as a treatment total, and we represented these totals by means of symbols such as $T_{i.}$, $T_{ij..}$, and so forth. Having introduced a special notation for the experimental conditions in a 2^n factorial experiment, we extend this notation by letting (1), (a), (b), (ab), (c), $\ldots$, be the treatment totals corresponding to experimental conditions 1, a, b, ab, c, $\ldots$. Thus, in a three-factor experiment

$$(1) = \sum_{\ell=1}^{r} y_{000\ell} \qquad\qquad (a) = \sum_{\ell=1}^{r} y_{100\ell}$$

$$(bc) = \sum_{\ell=1}^{r} y_{011\ell} \qquad\qquad (abc) = \sum_{\ell=1}^{r} y_{111\ell}$$

. . . .

The computational short-cuts referred to on page 311 consist, essentially, of expressing estimates of the various main effects and interactions, as well as the corresponding sums of squares, in terms of *linear combinations* of the treatment totals. To illustrate what we mean, let us consider the quantity.

$$-(1) + (a) - (b) + (ab) - (c) + (ac) - (bc) + (abc)$$

which is a linear combination, with coefficients $+1$ and -1, of the treatment totals corresponding to the eight experimental conditions. Referring to the model equation on page 312 and making use of the relationships among the parameters (but leaving all details to the reader in Exercises 5, 6, and 7 on page 321) it can be shown that

$$-(1) + (a) - (b) + (ab) - (c) + (ac) - (bc) + (abc) = -8r\alpha_0 + \epsilon_A$$

where ϵ_A is a corresponding linear combination of sums of the ϵ_{ijkl}. From Theorem 8.1 on page 166 it follows that ϵ_A is a value of a random variable whose distribution has zero mean; as a matter of fact, it can be shown that ϵ_A is a value of a random variable having a normal distribution with zero mean and the variance $8r\sigma^2$. Referring to the above linear combination as the *effect total* $[A]$ for factor A, we find that $-[A]/8r$ provides an estimate of α_0, the main effect for factor A, and it can be shown that $[A]^2/8r$ actually equals SSA, the sum of squares for the main effect of factor A.

Similarly analyzing the linear combination

$$(1) + (a) - (b) - (ab) - (c) - (ac) + (bc) + (abc)$$

the reader will be asked to show in Exercise 7 on page 321 that it equals $8r(\beta\gamma)_{00} + \epsilon_{BC}$, where ϵ_{BC} is a corresponding linear combination of sums of the ϵ_{ijkl}. Referring to this linear combination of treatment totals as the *effect total* $[BC]$ for the two-way interaction of factors B and C, we find that $[BC]/8r$ provides an estimate of $(\beta\gamma)_{00}$, the effect of the BC interaction, and it can also be shown that $[BC]^2/8r$ equals $SS(BC)$, the sum of squares for the BC interaction. Proceeding in this fashion, we can present linear combinations of the treatment totals which yield estimates of the various other main effects and interactions, and whose squares, divided by $8r$, yield the corresponding sums of squares. These linear combinations, or *effect totals*, can easily be obtained with the use of the following *table of signs:*

(1)	(a)	(b)	(ab)	(c)	(ac)	(bc)	(abc)	Effect totals
1	1	1	1	1	1	1	1	$[I]$
−1	1	−1	1	−1	1	−1	1	$[A]$
−1	−1	1	1	−1	−1	1	1	$[B]$
1	−1	−1	1	1	−1	−1	1	$[AB]$
−1	−1	−1	−1	1	1	1	1	$[C]$
1	−1	1	−1	−1	1	−1	1	$[AC]$
1	1	−1	−1	−1	−1	1	1	$[BC]$
−1	1	1	−1	1	−1	−1	1	$[ABC]$

The entries of this table are the coefficients of the linear combinations of the treatment totals for the various main effects and interactions. As an aid for constructing similar tables for $n = 4$, $n = 5$, etc., note that for each main effect there is a "$+1$" when the factor is at the higher level and a "-1" when the factor is at the lower level. The signs for an interaction effect are obtained by multiplying the corresponding coefficients of *all* factors contained in the interaction. Thus, for $[AB]$ we multiply each sign for $[A]$ by the corresponding sign for $[B]$, getting

$(-1)(-1)$ $(1)(-1)$ $(-1)(1)$ $(1)(1)$ $(-1)(-1)$ $(1)(-1)$ $(-1)(1)$ $(1)(1)$

or   1 -1 -1 1   1 -1 -1 1

Note also that in the above table $[I]$ stands for the grand total of all the observations, so that $[I]^2/8r$ gives the correction term for calculating SST, SSE, SSR, and $SS(Tr)$.

Although we have illustrated the above short-cut method for obtaining the various main-effect and interaction sums of squares with reference to a 2^3 factorial experiment, the only difference in a 2^n factorial experiment with $n > 3$ is that we require a more extensive table of signs and that the respective sums of squares are obtained by dividing the squares of the effect totals by $r \cdot 2^n$. To illustrate this technique and introduce a further simplification, let us consider the following 2^4 factorial experiment, designed to determine the effects of certain variables on the reliability of a rotary stepping switch. The factors studied were as follows:

Factor	Low level	High level
A. Lubrication	dry	lubricated
B. Dust protection	unprotected	enclosed in dust cover
C. Spark suppression	no	yes
D. Current	0	0.5 amp.

Each switch was operated continuously until a malfunction occurred, and the number of hours of operation was recorded. The whole experiment was performed twice, with the following results:

Experimental condition	Hours of operation Rep. 1	Rep. 2	Total
1	828	797	1625
a	997	948	1945
b	735	776	1511
ab	807	1003	1810
c	994	949	1943
ac	1069	1094	2163
bc	989	1215	2204
abc	889	1010	1899
d	593	813	1406
ad	773	1026	1799
bd	740	922	1662
abd	936	1138	2074
cd	748	970	1718
acd	1202	1182	2384
bcd	1103	966	2069
$abcd$	985	1154	2139
Totals	14,388	15,963	30,351

Analyzing these data first as a two-way classification with 16 treatments and 2 replications (blocks), we obtain

$$C = \frac{(30,351)^2}{32} = 28,786,975$$

$$SST = (828)^2 + (997)^2 + \ldots + (1154)^2 - 28,786,975$$
$$= 744,876$$

$$SS(Tr) = \frac{1}{2}\left[(1625)^2 + (1945)^2 + \ldots + (2139)^2\right] - 28,786,975$$
$$= 547,288$$

$$SSR = \frac{1}{16}\left[(14,388)^2 + (15,963)^2\right] - 28,786,975$$
$$= 77,520$$

$$SSE = 744,876 - 547,288 - 77,520 = 120,068$$

In order to subdivide the treatment sum of squares into SSA, SSB, $\ldots$, and $SS(ABCD)$, we could construct a table of signs like the one on page 314, calculate the effect totals, and then divide the squares of the effect totals by $r \cdot 2^n = 2 \cdot 2^4 = 32$. For the A factor main effect we would thus obtain

$$[A] = -1625 + 1945 - 1511 + 1810 - 1943 + 2163 - 2204 + 1899$$
$$-1406 + 1799 - 1662 + 2074 - 1718 + 2384 - 2069 + 2139$$
$$= 2075$$

and
$$SSA = \frac{(2075)^2}{32} = 134,551$$

These calculations are quite tedious, but they can be simplified considerably by using a further short-cut, called the *method of Yates*. This method of calculating the effect totals is illustrated in the table on page 317. The experimental conditions and the corresponding totals are listed in *standard order*. In the column marked (1), the upper half is obtained by adding successive pairs of treatment totals, and the lower half is obtained by subtracting successive pairs. Thus, in column (1) we obtained

$$1625 + 1945 = 3570$$
$$1511 + 1810 = 3321$$
$$\cdot \ \cdot \ \cdot \ \cdot \ \cdot \ \cdot \ \cdot \ \cdot \ \cdot$$
$$\overline{2069 + 2139 = 4208}$$
$$\overline{1945 - 1625 = \quad 320}$$

$$1810 - 1511 = 299$$
$$\cdot \quad \cdot \quad \cdot \quad \cdot \quad \cdot \quad \cdot \quad \cdot \quad \cdot \quad \cdot$$
$$2139 - 2069 = 70$$

Experi-mental condition	Treat-ment totals	(1)	(2)	(3)	(4)	Identifi-cation	Sum of squares
1	1,625	3,570	6,891	15,100	30,351	[I]	28,786,975
a	1,945	3,321	8,209	15,251	2,075	[A]	134,551
b	1,511	4,106	6,941	534	385	[B]	4,632
ab	1,810	4,103	8,310	1,541	−1,123	[AB]	39,410
c	1,943	3,205	619	−252	2,687	[C]	225,624
ac	2,163	3,736	−85	637	−773	[AC]	18,673
bc	2,204	4,102	805	−546	−179	[BC]	1,001
abc	1,899	4,208	736	−577	−1,119	[ABC]	39,130
d	1,406	320	−249	1,318	151	[D]	713
ad	1,799	299	−3	1,369	1,007	[AD]	31,689
bd	1,662	220	531	−704	889	[BD]	24,698
abd	2,074	−305	106	−69	−31	[ABD]	30
cd	1,718	393	−21	246	51	[CD]	81
acd	2,384	412	−525	−425	635	[ACD]	12,601
bcd	2,069	666	19	−504	−671	[BCD]	14,070
abcd	2,139	70	−596	−615	−111	[ABCD]	385

Note that the first total in each pair is subtracted from the second. Column (2) is then obtained by performing the identical operations on the entries of column (1), and columns (3) and (4) are obtained in the same manner from the entries in columns (2) and (3), respectively. Column (4), and in general column (n), gives the effect totals in standard order, as shown. Each sum of squares is then obtained as before, by squaring the corresponding effect total and then dividing the result by $r \cdot 2^n = 2 \cdot 2^4 = 32$.

Dividing the sums of squares by their degrees of freedom to obtain the mean squares, and dividing the various mean squares by the error mean square, we get the following analysis of variance table for the 2^4 factorial experiment:

Source of variation	Degrees of freedom	Sum of squares	Mean square	F
Replicates	1	77,520	77,520	9.68
Main effects:				
A	1	134,551	134,551	16.81
B	1	4,632	4,632	< 1
C	1	225,624	225,624	28.19
D	1	713	713	< 1
Two-factor interactions:				
AB	1	39,410	39,410	4.92
AC	1	18,673	18,673	2.33
AD	1	31,689	31,689	3.96
BC	1	1,001	1,001	< 1
BD	1	24,698	24,698	3.09
CD	1	81	81	< 1
Three-factor interactions:				
ABC	1	39,130	39,130	4.89
ABD	1	30	30	< 1
ACD	1	12,601	12,601	1.57
BCD	1	14,070	14,070	1.76
Four-factor interactions:				
ABCD	1	385	385	< 1
Error	15	120,068	8,005	
Total	31	744,876		

Since $F_{.05} = 4.54$ and $F_{.01} = 8.68$ for 1 and 15 degrees of freedom, we find that the replication effects as well as the effects of lubrication and spark suppression are significant at the 0.01 level, and that there are significant interactions at the 0.05 level between lubrication, dust protection, and spark suppression. The reader will be asked to interpret these results and estimate the magnitude of some of the effects in Exercise 8 on page 321.

EXERCISES

1. A taste-testing experiment was performed to discover what, if any, effect the physical properties of a certain food have on its taste. The results, expressed as ratings by a judge on a scale from 1 to 10, are given in the following table:

A Color	B Consistency	C Texture	Ratings Rep. 1	Rep. 2
light	light	fine	8	6
light	light	coarse	7	8
light	heavy	fine	9	9
light	heavy	coarse	2	1
dark	light	fine	7	6
dark	light	coarse	8	6
dark	heavy	fine	8	9
dark	heavy	coarse	3	2

(a) Analyze the results first as a two-way classification with 7 degrees of freedom for treatments and 1 degree of freedom for blocks (replicates).

(b) Use an appropriate table of signs to calculate the effect totals $[A]$, $[B]$, $[C]$, $[AB]$, $[AC]$, $[BC]$, $[ABC]$.

(c) Using the results obtained in (b) find the sums of squares corresponding to the main effects and interactions, and check their total against the treatment sum of squares obtained in (a).

(d) Arrange the data with treatment combinations in standard order, and use the Yates method to find the effect totals. Compare with the results obtained in (b).

(e) Construct an analysis of variance table and analyze the experiment.

2. An experiment was conducted to determine the effects of certain alloying elements on the ductility of a metal, and the following results were obtained:

Carbon	Manganese	Nickel	Breaking strength (ft-lb) Rep. 1	Rep. 2	Rep. 3
0.2%	0.5%	0.0%	34.6	37.5	36.1
0.2	0.5	3.0	46.4	42.4	44.8
0.2	1.0	0.0	41.8	38.0	37.2
0.2	1.0	3.0	40.0	44.7	45.3
0.5	0.5	0.0	37.8	32.7	31.6
0.5	0.5	3.0	33.2	36.2	35.5
0.5	1.0	0.0	38.2	40.4	36.8
0.5	1.0	3.0	46.2	43.5	49.2

Perform an appropriate analysis of variance and interpret the results.

3. An experiment was conducted to determine the effects of the following factors on the gain of a semiconductor device:

Factor	Level 0	Level 1
A. Location of assembly	Laboratory	Production line
B. Partial pressure of controlling material	10^{-15}	10^{-4}
C. Relative humidity	1%	30%
D. Aging time	72 hours	144 hours

The results were as follows:

Experimental condition	Gain Rep. 1	Gain Rep. 2
1	39.0	43.2
a	31.8	43.7
b	47.0	51.4
ab	40.9	40.3
c	43.8	40.5
ac	29.3	52.9
bc	34.8	48.2
abc	45.6	58.2
d	40.1	41.9
ad	42.0	40.5
bd	54.9	53.0
abd	39.9	40.2
cd	43.1	40.2
acd	30.1	39.9
bcd	35.6	53.7
abcd	41.4	49.5

Perform an appropriate analysis of variance and interpret the results.

4. A screening experiment was conducted to determine what factors are influential in controlling the final phosphorus content of steel produced in a converter. The levels of the factors studied and the experimental results are contained in the following table:

E Pouring temp. (°F)	D Lime ratio	C Oxygen	B Original phosphorus	A Original manganese	Final phosphorus Rep. 1	Final phosphorus Rep. 2
2400	3	5%	0.15%	1%	0.003%	0.001%
2400	3	5	0.15	3	0.004	0.009
2400	3	5	0.30	1	0.002	0.008
2400	3	5	0.30	3	0.015	0.007
2400	3	15	0.15	1	0.002	0.005
2400	3	15	0.15	3	0.011	0.006
2400	3	15	0.30	1	0.004	0.001
2400	3	15	0.30	3	0.002	0.004
2400	4	5	0.15	1	0.000	0.003
2400	4	5	0.15	3	0.008	0.002
2400	4	5	0.30	1	0.003	0.007
2400	4	5	0.30	3	0.005	0.012
2400	4	15	0.15	1	0.010	0.006
2400	4	15	0.15	3	0.006	0.001
2400	4	15	0.30	1	0.006	0.014
2400	4	15	0.30	3	0.011	0.015
2600	3	5	0.15	1	0.003	0.007
2600	3	5	0.15	3	0.007	0.004
2600	3	5	0.30	1	0.011	0.005

E Pouring temp. (°F)	D Lime ratio	C Oxygen	B Original phosphorus	A Original manganese	Final phosphorus Rep. 1	Rep. 2
2600	3	5	0.30	3	0.010	0.017
2600	3	15	0.15	1	0.004	0.008
2600	3	15	0.15	3	0.019	0.013
2600	3	15	0.30	1	0.004	0.008
2600	3	15	0.30	3	0.017	0.023
2600	4	5	0.15	1	0.007	0.004
2600	4	5	0.15	3	0.015	0.009
2600	4	5	0.30	1	0.004	0.011
2600	4	5	0.30	3	0.010	0.006
2600	4	15	0.15	1	0.017	0.011
2600	4	15	0.15	3	0.005	0.010
2600	4	15	0.30	1	0.014	0.009
2600	4	15	0.30	3	0.016	0.011

Analyze the results of this experiment.

5. Writing the treatment total (a) as the sum of the corresponding observations y_{100l} and substituting for these observations the expressions given by the model equation on page 312, it can be shown that

$$(a) = r[\mu + \alpha_1 + \beta_0 + \gamma_0 + (\alpha\beta)_{10} + (\alpha\gamma)_{10} + (\beta\gamma)_{00} + (\alpha\beta\gamma)_{100}] + \sum_{l=1}^{r} \epsilon_{100l}$$

Making use of the restrictions imposed on the parameters, rewrite this expression for (a) in terms of the parameters μ, α_0, β_0, γ_0, $(\alpha\beta)_{00}$, $(\alpha\gamma)_{00}$, $(\beta\gamma)_{00}$, and $(\alpha\beta\gamma)_{000}$.

6. Duplicating the work of Exercise 5, express (1), (b), (ab), (c), (ac), (bc), and (abc) in terms of the parameters μ, α_0, β_0, γ_0, $(\alpha\beta)_{00}$, $(\alpha\gamma)_{00}$, $(\beta\gamma)_{00}$, and $(\alpha\beta\gamma)_{000}$.

7. Using the results of Exercises 5 and 6, verify the expressions for $[A]$ and $[BC]$ obtained on page 314. Also express ϵ_A in terms of the quantities ϵ_{ijkl}.

8. Interpret the results of the analysis of variance given by the table on page 318, and estimate the magnitude of the significant effects.

9. A computational check on the sums of squares obtained for the various main effects and interactions is that their *sum* must equal the treatment sum of squares obtained by analyzing the data first as a two-way classification. Perform this check on the sums of squares given in the table on page 318.

10. If it is desired to find an expression for an effect total without constructing a complete table of signs, one can use the following method, illustrated by finding $[ABC]$ for a 2^4 factorial experiment. We take the expression $(a \pm 1)(b \pm 1)(c \pm 1)(d \pm 1)$ with a "+" if the corresponding letter does *not* appear in the symbol for the main effect or interaction for which we want

to calculate an effect total, and a "$-$" if the corresponding letter does appear. Thus, for finding $[ABC]$ we write

$$(a - 1)(b - 1)(c - 1)(d + 1) = abcd + abc - abd - acd - bcd - ab$$
$$- ac + ad - bc + bd + cd + a + b$$
$$+ c - d - 1$$

and after arranging the terms in standard order and adding parentheses we finally obtain

$$[ABC] = -(1) + (a) + (b) - (ab) + (c) - (ac) - (bc) + (abc) - (d)$$
$$+ (ad) + (bd) - (abd) + (cd) - (acd) - (bcd) + (abcd)$$

(i) Use this method to express $[B]$, $[AC]$, and $[ABC]$ in terms of the treatment totals in a 2^3 factorial experiment.

(ii) Use this method to express $[AC]$ and $[BCD]$ in terms of the treatment totals in a 2^4 factorial experiment.

14.4 Confounding in a 2^n Factorial Experiment

In some experiments it is impossible to run all the required experimental conditions in one block. For example, if a 2^3 factorial experiment involves eight combinations of paint pigments that are to be applied to a surface and baked in an oven which can accommodate only four specimens, it becomes necessary to divide the eight treatments into two blocks (oven runs) in each replicate. As we have pointed out earlier, if the block size is too small to accommodate all treatments, this requires special, so-called *incomplete block* designs.

When the experimental conditions are distributed over several blocks, one or more of the effects may become confounded (inseparable) with possible block effects, that is, between-block differences. For example, if in the 2^3 factorial experiment referred to in the preceding paragraph, experimental conditions a, ab, ac, and abc are included in one oven run (Block 1) and experimental conditions 1, b, c, and bc are included in a second oven run (Block 2), then the "block effect," the difference between the two block totals, is given by

$$[(a) + (ab) + (ac) + (abc)] - [(1) + (b) + (c) + (bc)]$$

Referring to the table of signs on page 314, we observe that this quantity is, in fact, the effect total $[A]$, so that the estimate of the main effect of factor A is *confounded with blocks*. Note that all other factorial effects remain unconfounded; for each other effect total there are two $+1$ coefficients and two -1 coefficients in each block, so that the block effects cancel out. This kind of argument can also be used to decide what experimental conditions to put into each block to confound a given main effect or interaction. For instance, had we wanted to confound the ABC interaction with blocks in the above example, we could have put experimental conditions a, b, c, and abc, whose totals have $+1$ coefficients in $[ABC]$, into one block, and experimental conditions 1, *ab*, *ac*, and *bc*, whose totals have −1 coefficients, into another.

In general, confounding in a 2^n factorial experiment can be much more complicated than in the example just given. To avoid serious difficulties, we shall require that the number of blocks used is a power of 2, say 2^p. It turns out that the price paid for running 2^n factorial experiment in 2^p blocks is that a total of $2^p - 1$ effects are confounded with blocks. To make it clear just which effects are confounded, and to indicate a method that can be used to confound only certain effects and no others, it is helpful to define the term "generalized interaction" as follows: the *generalized interaction* of two effects is the "product" of these effects, with like letters cancelled. Thus, the generalized interaction of AB and CD is $ABCD$, and the generalized interaction of ABC and BCD is $A\cancel{B}\cancel{C}\cancel{B}\cancel{C}D$, or AD. To confound a 2^n factorial experiment in 2^p blocks, the following method can be used: one selects any p effects for confounding, making sure that none is the generalized interaction of any of the others selected. Then, it can be shown that a further $2^p - (p + 1)$ effects are automatically confounded with blocks; together with the p effects originally chosen, this gives a total of $2^p - 1$ confounded effects in the experiment. The additional confounded effects are, in fact, the generalized interactions of the p effects originally chosen.

To illustrate the construction of a confounded design, let us divide a 2^4 factorial experiment into four blocks so that desired effects are confounded with blocks. In actual practice one ordinarily confounds only the higher-order interactions (in the hope that they are nonexistent anyhow). Since we have decided upon four blocks, we have $2^p = 4$ and $p = 2$, and we shall arbitrarily select two higher-order interactions for confounding. If we were to select $ABCD$ and BCD, then their generalized interaction, A, would also be confounded. Thus, to avoid confounding any main effects, and to confound as few two-factor interactions as possible, we shall select ABD and ACD, noting that the BC is also confounded. (Observe that it is impossible to avoid confounding at least one main effect or two-factor interaction in this experiment.)

In order to assign the 16 experimental conditions to four blocks, we first distribute them into two blocks, so that the ABD interaction is confounded with blocks. Referring to an appropriate table of signs, we put all treatments whose totals have a "$+1$" in the row for $[ABD]$ into one block, all those whose totals have a "-1" into a second block, and we get the following blocks:

> *First block:*   *a*   *b*   *ac*   *bc*   *d*   *abd*   *cd*   *abcd*
> *Second block:*   1   *ab*   *c*   *abc*   *ad*   *bd*   *acd*   *bcd*

Note that each experimental condition in the first block has an *odd number* of letters in common with ABD, while each experimental condition in the second block has an *even number* of letters in common with ABD. This odd-even rule provides an alternate way of distributing experimental conditions among two blocks to confound a given effect, and it has the advantage that it does not require the construction of a complete table of signs.

So far, we have confounded the ABD interaction by dividing the 16 experimental conditions into two blocks; now we shall confound the ACD interaction by dividing each of these blocks into two blocks of four conditions each. Using the odd-even rule just described (or a table of signs), we obtain the following four blocks:

Block 1:	*a*	*bc*	*d*	*abcd*
Block 2:	*b*	*ac*	*abd*	*cd*
Block 3:	*ab*	*c*	*bd*	*acd*
Block 4:	*1*	*abc*	*ad*	*bcd*

By comparing these blocks with a table of signs, or, equivalently, by applying the odd-even rule, the reader will be asked to verify in Exercise 8 on page 332 that the BC interaction is also confounded with blocks, while all other effects are left unconfounded.

The analysis of a confounded 2^n factorial experiment is similar to that of an unconfounded experiment, with the exception that the sums of squares for the confounded effects are not computed, and we compute a block sum of squares as if the experiment consisted of br blocks rather than b blocks in each of r replicates. Referring to our example of a 2^4 factorial experiment with the ABD, ACD, and BC interactions confounded, and using two replicates, we have the following *dummy* analysis of variance table.

Source of variation	Degrees of freedom
Blocks	7
Main effects	4
Unconfounded two-factor interactions	5
Unconfounded three-factor interactions	2
Four-factor interaction	1
Intrablock error	12
Total	31

The sum of squares for blocks is obtained, as usual, by adding the squares of the eight block totals, dividing the result by 4 (the number of observations in each block), and subtracting the correction term. The total sum of squares and the sums of squares for the unconfounded factorial effects are obtained in the usual way, and the sum of squares for the *intrablock error*, a measure of the variability *within blocks*, is obtained by subtraction.

To illustrate the analysis of a confounded 2^n factorial experiment, let us suppose that each replicate of the stepping-switch experiment described in the preceding section was actually run in four blocks, because only four mountings were available for the 16 switches. (The order of running the blocks is assumed to have been randomized within each replicate, and the assignment of switches is assumed to have been randomized within each block.) Assuming also that the *ABD*, *ACD*, and *BC* interactions were confounded with the blocks as shown on page 324, we obtain the following block totals from the data on page 315:

	Block 1	Block 2	Block 3	Block 4
Replicate 1	3564	3488	3743	3593
Replicate 2	4130	3978	4056	3799

Thus, the sum of squares for blocks is given by

$$SS(Bl) = \frac{(3564)^2 + (3488)^2 + \ldots + (3799)^2}{4} - 28{,}786{,}975$$

$$= 101{,}240$$

where the correction factor is the same as in the analysis on page 316.

Copying the total sum of squares and the sums of squares for the various unconfounded effects from the table on page 318, we obtain the analysis of variance table for the confounded factorial experiment shown on the top of page 326. In this analysis, the A and C main effects are again significant at the 0.01 level, but none of the other main effects or interactions is significant.

If there is replication, some of the lost information about the confounded effects can be recovered by a further breakdown of the above blocks sum of squares. This analysis consists of dividing the sum of squares for blocks into a component for each of the confounded effects, a component for replications, and a residual component called the "interblock error," which is a measure of the variability *between blocks*. Copying the sum of squares for replicates as well as those for the *BC*, *ABD*, and *ACD* interactions from the analysis of variance table on page 318, and copying the

Source of variation	Degrees of freedom	Sum of squares	Mean square	F
Blocks	7	101,240	14,463	1.58
Main effects:				
A	1	134,551	134,551	14.68
B	1	4,632	4,632	< 1
C	1	225,624	225,624	24.62
D	1	713	713	< 1
Unconfounded two-factor interactions:				
AB	1	39,410	39,410	4.30
AC	1	18,673	18,673	2.04
AD	1	31,689	31,689	3.46
BD	1	24,698	24,698	2.69
CD	1	81	81	< 1
Unconfounded three-factor interactions:				
ABC	1	39,130	39,130	4.27
BCD	1	14,070	14,070	1.54
Four-factor interaction:				
ABCD	1	385	385	< 1
Intrablock error	12	109,980	9,165	
Total	31	744,876		

blocks sum of squares from the *intrablock* analysis of variance table above we obtain the following *interblock* analysis of variance:

Source of variation	Degrees of freedom	Sum of squares	Mean square	F
Replicates	1	77,520	77,520	23.05
Confounded effects:				
BC	1	1,001	1,001	< 1
ABD	1	30	30	< 1
ACD	1	12,601	12,601	3.75
Interblock error	3	10,088	3,363	
Total (blocks)	7	101,240		

Note that the interblock error is obtained by subtraction and that the F ratios are obtained by dividing the mean squares for the confounded effects and the mean square for replicates by the mean square for the interblock error. Only the F test for replicates is significant (at the 0.05 level). The small number of degrees of freedom for the interblock error implies that the sensitivity of these significance tests is *very poor;* in fact, it rarely pays to make this kind of interblock analysis unless the number of replications is relatively large.

14.5 Fractional Replication

In studies involving complex production lines, chemical processes such as may be encountered in the petroleum, plastics, or metals industries, physical-chemical processes such as may be encountered in the electronics or space-technology industries, and in many other engineering studies, the experimenter is often faced with a large and bewildering array of interrelated variables. The principles of factorial experimentation treated so far in this chapter help him to "sort out" these variables, to discover which of them have the greatest influence on the process under consideration, and what important interrelationships may exist.

There are, however, some serious limitations to the simultaneous study of a large number of factors. Even if each factor is assigned only two levels, one replicate of a six-factor experiment requires 64 observations; there are 128 observations in one replicate of a seven-factor experiment, and 1024 observations in one replicate of a ten-factor experiment. The economic and practical limitations of these large numbers make it necessary to seek out ways in which the size of factorial experiments can be kept within manageable bounds. Of course, it must be emphasized that there is no substitute for careful preliminary planning which, coupled with engineering insight, can result in the elimination of many needless factors.

In spite of the most careful preliminary planning, however, it is often difficult to avoid having to include as many as six or ten (or more) factors in a single experiment. One way to reduce the size of such an experiment would be to break it up into several parts, each part involving the deliberate variation of one factor while all others are held fixed. This would have the undesirable consequence that we could not study any of the interactions. Even if we were to include half the factors in one part and the other half in another, such as replacing a ten-factor experiment (requiring 1024 observations) by two five-factor experiments (each requiring 32 observations), any interaction between factors in the first part and factors in the second part would be irretrievably lost. It is possible to overcome some of these difficulties by observing that most of the time we are not interested in *all* the interactions. For instance, it is possible to perform only a fraction of a 2^n factorial and yet obtain most of the desired information, say, about the main effects and two-factor interactions (but not the higher interactions).

The principles involved in *fractional replication*, that is, in performing only a fraction of a complete 2^n factorial experiment, are similar to those used in confounding. To obtain a *half-replicate* one selects only one of the two blocks into which the experimental conditions have been divided by confounding one effect; to obtain a *quarter-replicate* one selects only one of the four blocks into which the experimental conditions have been divided by confounding two effects, and so forth. In contrast to a confounded experiment as discussed in Section 14.4, we find that in a fractional replicate *the effects are confounded, not with blocks, but with each other.* To illustrate, suppose that only the experimental conditions a, b, c, and abc are included in a half-replicate of a 2^3 factorial experiment. (This is one block of a 2^3 factorial experiment with the ABC interaction confounded.) Considering the table of signs on page 314 with all columns except those corresponding to a, b, c, and abc crossed out, we find that the effect total for factor A is now given by

$$[A] = (a) - (b) - (c) + (abc)$$

If we write $(a) = \sum_{l=1}^{r} y_{100l}$, $(b) = \sum_{l=1}^{r} y_{010l}$, $\ldots$, and substitute for the y_{ijkl} the expressions given by the model equation on page 312, we obtain

$$[A] = -4r[\alpha_0 - (\beta\gamma)_{00}] + \epsilon$$

where ϵ is the value of a random variable having zero mean (see Exercise 16 on page 334). We thus find that $[A]$ measures the main effect of factor A as well as the BC interaction, so that these two effects have become inseparable, or confounded. Note also that in the reduced table of signs (having columns only corresponding to a, b, c, and abc) the signs for $[A]$ and $[BC]$ are identical, and hence $[A] = [BC]$. In Exercise 17 on page 334, the reader will be asked to show that for the given fractional replicate the main effect for factor B is, similarly, confounded, or *aliased*, with the AC interaction, while the main effect for factor C is confounded, or aliased, with the AB interaction. The ABC interaction cannot be estimated.

With careful design, it is generally possible to confound all main effects and two-factor interactions *only* with interactions of higher order. This is illustrated in the following example, where we shall construct a half-replicate of a 2^5 factorial. First, we select an effect (usually a higher-order interaction) to split the experiment into two blocks, as in confounding. The effect chosen is called the *defining contrast*, and it cannot be estimated at all by the fractional replicate. Every other effect is aliased with another effect, namely, its generalized interaction (see page 323) with the defining contrast. Thus, if the defining contrast is $ABCDE$, the main effect for factor A has the four-factor interaction $BCDE$ as its alias, BC and ADE are an alias pair, and so forth. As we have seen, only the combined effect (the sum or difference of the aliased effects) can be estimated in the experiment. However, if it can be assumed that there are no higher-order interactions, one can attribute the effect of the alias pair BC and ADE entirely to the two-factor interaction BC, one can attribute the effect of the alias pair A and $BCDE$ entirely to the main effect of factor A, and so forth. A complete listing of the aliases in a half-replicate of a 2^5 factorial experiment having the defining contrast $ABCDE$ is as follows:

$$A \text{ and } BCDE, \quad B \text{ and } ACDE, \quad C \text{ and } ABDE, \quad D \text{ and } ABCE$$
$$E \text{ and } ABCD, \quad AB \text{ and } CDE, \quad AC \text{ and } BDE, \quad AD \text{ and } BCE$$
$$AE \text{ and } BCD, \quad BC \text{ and } ADE, \quad BD \text{ and } ACE, \quad BE \text{ and } ACD$$
$$CD \text{ and } ABE, \quad CE \text{ and } ABD, \quad DE \text{ and } ABC$$

Note that no main effect or two-factor interaction is aliased with another main effect or two-factor interaction.

The sixteen experimental conditions to be included in the half-replicate are given by those in either of the two blocks obtained by confounding the defining contrast. Choosing "evens" in the odd-even rule, namely, those conditions which have an even number of letters in common with the defining contrast $ABCDE$, we obtain the following half-replicate:

$$
\begin{array}{llll}
1 & ad & ae & de \\
ab & bd & be & abde \\
ac & cd & ce & acde \\
bc & abcd & abce & bcde
\end{array}
$$

To go one step further, let us illustrate how to construct a quarter-replicate of the given 2^5 factorial. We shall do this by dividing the above half-replicate in half, confounding the three-factor interaction ABC. Again using "evens," we get the following eight experimental conditions:

$$
\begin{array}{llll}
1 & de & ab & abde \\
ac & acde & bc & bcde
\end{array}
$$

Since DE, the generalized interaction of the two confounded effects, is also confounded, we now have the three defining contrasts $ABCDE$, ABC, and DE. None of these effects can be estimated in the quarter-replicate, and each other effect is aliased with its three generalized interactions with the three defining contrasts. The complete aliasing is as follows:

Alias sets

A,	BCDE,	BC,	ADE
B,	ACDE,	AC,	BDE
C,	ABDE,	AB,	CDE
D,	ABCE,	ABCD,	E
AD,	BCE,	BCD,	AE
BD,	ACE,	ACD,	BE
CD,	ABE,	ABD,	CE

We have given this quarter-replicate merely as an illustration; it would hardly seem useful in actual practice because of the hopeless aliasing of main effects and two-factor interactions. Nevertheless, quarter-replicates of six- and seven-factor experiments (and even eighth-replicates of seven- and eight-factor experiments) can often provide much useful information.

The analysis of a fractional factorial is practically the same as that of a fully replicated factorial experiment. Given the fraction $1/2^p$ of a 2^n factorial, there are 2^{n-p} experimental conditions, and the method of Yates can be used as if the experiment were a 2^{n-p} factorial. Some care must be exercised to arrange the experimental conditions in a modified "standard order" as indicated in Exercise 14 on page 333.

When dealing with fractional factorials, there is the problem of obtaining an estimate of the experimental error. For example, in the half-replicate of a 2^5 factorial described on page 328, the breakdown of the total sum of squares having 15 degrees of freedom yields sums of squares for main effects (5 degrees of freedom), sums of squares for two-factor interactions (10 degrees of freedom), but no component (0 degrees of freedom) for the experimental error. In a situation like this, and in all other cases where the number of degrees of freedom for error is small, it is best to include a limited amount of replication. This may be accomplished by randomly selecting several experimental conditions, and making additional observations corresponding to these conditions. Furthermore, if it can be assumed that there are no higher-order interactions, the total of the sums of squares corresponding to higher-order interactions *which are not aliased with main effects or lower-order interactions* can be attributed to "error," and used in the denominator of the F test (see Exercise 15 below). In this way, use can be made of the "hidden replication" inherent in most large factorial experiments.

To summarize, fractional replication is useful whenever the number of factors to be included in an experiment is large and it is not economically feasible to include all possible experimental conditions. The reduction in size (and, therefore, in cost) of a fractionally replicated experiment is partially offset by the loss of information caused by aliasing, and by the difficulties inherent in estimating the experimental error. A more detailed discussion of fractional replication, including fractional replicates of 3^n experiments and a variety of other designs, can be found in the book by W. G. Cochran and G. M. Cox listed in the Bibliography.

EXERCISES

1. List the experimental conditions included in each block, if a 2^4 factorial experiment is to be confounded

   (a) in 2 blocks on $ABCD$,

   (b) in 4 blocks on $ABCD$ and AB.

   What other interaction is confounded in part (b)?

2. A 2^5 factorial experiment, having the factors A, B, C, D, and E, is to be run in several blocks. Show which treatments are assigned to each block if

   (a) there are to be two blocks, with the $ABCD$ interaction confounded;

   (b) there are to be four blocks, with the $ABDE$ and CDE interactions confounded. What other factorial effect or effects are also confounded?

3. List the experimental conditions included in each block if a 2^6 factorial experiment is to be confounded in 8 blocks on $ABDE$, $BCDF$, and ABC. What other factorial effects are confounded?

4. What is the largest number of blocks in which one can perform a 2^6 factorial experiment without confounding any main effects?

5. Suppose that in Exercise 1 on page 318 the judge rates the foods in sets of four, with a rest period in between, and that the experiment was actually performed so that each replicate consisted of two blocks with ABC confounded. Perform an intrablock analysis of the data.

6. Four new drugs are to be investigated to determine their effectiveness as tranquilizers, individually and in combination with each other. Each patient was given regular doses of one of the sixteen tranquilizers formed from these drugs (including a placebo corresponding to the 0 level for each drug) and, after a two-week period, the effect of these tranquilizers on the emotional stability of each patient was judged (on a scale from 1 to 5) by five psychiatrists. To keep the staff work load within reasonable bounds, two hospitals were used in this experiment, and eight patients were selected by the staff of each hospital for each trial (replicate); thus, the experiment involved two replicates of two blocks each, with the $ABCD$ interaction confounded. The results of the two 2-week trials were as follows:

| FIRST HOSPITAL | | | SECOND HOSPITAL | | |
Treatment combination	Mean rating Trial 1	Trial 2	Treatment combination	Mean rating Trial 1	Trial 2
1	2.0	2.6	a	2.8	2.6
ab	3.8	3.4	b	3.6	2.0
ac	4.2	4.8	c	2.4	1.8
bc	4.8	4.0	abc	4.0	3.8
ad	1.8	2.4	d	1.8	2.2
bd	3.4	3.8	abd	1.6	2.0
cd	4.6	2.8	acd	3.6	2.4
abcd	4.2	4.6	bcd	3.4	3.8

If a high rating indicates satisfactory progress, which drug combination (or combinations) seems to be the most promising? Perform an intrablock analysis of variance to test for significant effects.

7. Suppose that in Exercise 4 on page 320 only 8 specimens could be tested in any one shift, and that the experiment was actually performed so that each replicate consists of four blocks with ABC, ADE, and $BCDE$ confounded.

   (a) If for each factor levels 0 and 1 are, respectively, the lower and higher values, construct a table showing which experimental conditions go into each of the four blocks.

   (b) Perform an intrablock analysis of the experiment.

8. Verify that in the example on page 324 all treatment totals having $+1$ as a coefficient in $[BC]$ are in Blocks 1 and 4, that all treatment totals having -1 as a coefficient in $[BC]$ are in Blocks 2 and 3, and, hence, that the BC interaction is confounded with blocks.

9. Show that the "odd-even" rule for assigning treatments to blocks, given on page 324, is equivalent to the method described in Exercise 10 on page 321.

10. Referring to Exercise 2, suppose that in each case the block containing treatment combination 1 was chosen as a fractional replicate of a 2^5 factorial.

    (a) Show the alias pairs in the resulting half-replicate.

    (b) Show the alias sets in the resulting quarter-replicate.

    (In practice, random selection should be used to choose the block to be included in a fractional replicate.)

11. Referring to Exercise 1, list the alias sets if an experiment consists of

    (a) a 1/2 replicate of a 2^4 factorial experiment with $ABCD$ confounded,

    (b) a 1/4 replicate of a 2^4 factorial experiment with $ABCD$ and AB confounded.

12. Construct a half-replicate of a 2^6 factorial having the defining contrast $ABCDEF$. List the 32 treatments in the block containing experimental condition 1, and show the alias pairs.

13. Design an experiment consisting of a 1/4 replicate of a 2^7 factorial with *ABCDE*, *ABCFG*, and *DEFG* confounded, if the experimental condition with each factor at the 0 level is to be included. Also exhibit all alias sets.

14. Referring to Exercise 12, we can define a *modified standard order* for the 32 treatment combinations in the half-replicate as follows. First, we list the 32 treatment combinations corresponding to the five factors *A*, *B*, *C*, *D*, and *E* in standard order. Then we append the letter *f* to 16 of these treatment combinations, so that the list contains the same ones as the block chosen for the half-replicate.

   (a) Use this method to list the treatment combinations obtained in Exercise 12 in modified standard order.

   (b) Generalize the above rule for arranging the treatment combinations in modified standard order so that it applies to a half-replicate of a 2^n factorial experiment. (For a $1/2^p$ fractional replicate of a 2^n factorial, a modified standard order can be obtained by noting that any block chosen contains a subset of $n - p$ letters which form a complete replicate of a 2^{n-p} factorial. The modified standard order is then obtained by using these letters only and later appending the remaining p letters to get the required treatment combinations.)

15. The following factors are to be studied in a half-replicate of a 2^6 factorial experiment (defining contrast *ABCDEF*), designed to evaluate several chemicals as insecticides.

Factor	Level 0	Level 1
A. BMC	0%	5%
B. Malathion	3%	6%
C. Tedion	1%	2%
D. Chlordane	2%	5%
E. Lindane	1%	4%
F. Pyrethrum	2%	4%

Each experimental unit consists of 10 insects, and the average lifetimes (in seconds) after application of the respective insecticides are as follows, in the random order in which they are obtained:

ce	181	acdf	162	bd	135	abdf	131
ae	172	1	182	df	171	ab	136
abef	140	bf	171	acef	159	bcde	105
bcdf	165	cf	176	bc	179	abcdef	109
acde	139	be	187	ac	165	af	176
ef	186	abce	131	bcef	181	ad	150
de	164	abcf	125	cdef	163	abde	115
abcd	112	adef	158	bdef	128	cd	166

   (a) Write down the alias pairs.

(b) Arrange the results in modified standard order (see Exercise 14) and use the method of Yates to find the effect totals.

(c) Identify the effect totals as follows. In the last column of the Yates table, write down the 32 combinations $[I]$, $[A]$, $[B]$, $[AB]$, ..., $[ABCDE]$ in standard order. Each of these is aliased with another one; identify the alias pairs by using the main effect or lower-order interaction. (For example, $ABCDE$ is aliased with F—identify the effect total $[ABCDE]$ as that of the main effect F.) Note that ten of the alias pairs are three-factor interactions aliased with three-factor interactions—label these "error."

(d) Obtain the mean squares and complete the analysis of variance. Note that the error mean square, having 10 degrees of freedom, is the average of the mean squares of the ten effects labeled "error."

16. Verify the expression obtained for $[A]$ on page 328.

17. Duplicating the steps indicated on page 328, show that in the given design the main effect for factor B is confounded with the AC interaction. [*Hint:* Express $[B]$ and $[AC]$ in terms of the parameters of the model.]

15 | APPLICATIONS TO QUALITY ASSURANCE

15.1 Quality Assurance

Although there is the tendency to think of the subject of quality assurance as a recent development, there is nothing new about the basic idea of making a quality product characterized by a high degree of uniformity. For centuries skilled artisans have striven to make products distinctive through superior quality, and once a standard of quality was achieved, to eliminate insofar as possible all variability between products that were nominally alike.

The idea that statistics might be instrumental in assuring the quality of manufactured products goes back no farther than the advent of mass production, and the widespread use of statistical methods in problems of quality assurance is even more recent than that. Many problems in the manufacture of a product are amenable to statistical treatment, and we have already studied some of them in earlier parts of this book. When we speak of (statistical) quality assurance, we are referring essentially to the three special techniques to which we shall devote the remainder of this chapter: *quality control, acceptance sampling,* and *the establishment of tol-*

erance limits. Note that the word "quality," when used technically as in this discussion, refers to some *measurable* or *countable* property of a product, such as the outside diameter of a ball bearing, the breaking strength of a yarn, the number of imperfections in a piece of cloth, the potency of a drug, and so forth.

15.2 Quality Control

It may surprise some persons to learn that two apparently identical parts made under carefully controlled conditions, from the same batch of raw material, and only seconds apart by the same machine, can nevertheless be different in many respects. Indeed, any manufacturing process, however good, is characterized by a certain amount of variability which is of a random nature, and which cannot be completely eliminated.

When the variability present in a production process is confined to *chance variation*, the process is said to be in a state of *statistical control*. Such a state is usually attained by finding and eliminating trouble of the sort causing another kind of variation, called *assignable variation*, which may be due to poorly trained operators, poor-quality raw materials, faulty machine settings, worn parts, and the like. Since manufacturing processes are rarely free from trouble of this kind, it is important to have some systematic method of detecting serious deviations from a state of statistical control when, or if possible *before*, they actually occur. It is to this end that *control charts* are principally used.

In what follows, we shall differentiate between *control charts for measurements* and *control charts for attributes*, depending on whether the observations with which we are concerned are measurements or count data (say, the number of defectives in a sample of a given size). In either case, a control chart consists of a *central line* (see Figure 15.1) corresponding to the *average* quality at which the process is to perform, and lines corresponding to the *upper and lower control limits*. These limits are chosen so that values falling between them can be attributed to chance, while values falling beyond them are interpreted as indicating a lack of control. By plotting the results obtained from samples taken periodically at frequent intervals, it is possible to check by means of such a chart whether the process is under control, or whether trouble of the sort indicated above has entered the process. When a sample point falls beyond the control limits, one looks for trouble, but even if the points fall between the control limits, a trend or some other systematic pattern may serve notice that action should be taken to avoid serious trouble.

The ability to "read" control charts and to determine from them just what corrective action should be taken is a matter of experience and highly developed judgment. A quality-control engineer must not only understand the statistical foundation of his subject, but he must also be thoroughly acquainted with the processes themselves. The engineering and managerial aspects of quality control (and quality assurance in general), which nowa-

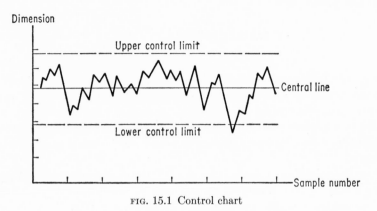

FIG. 15.1 Control chart

days includes incoming raw materials, outgoing products, and in-process control, constitute an extensive subject in themselves. In this chapter we shall present only the statistical aspects of the subject; more complete discussions of other aspects can be found in the book by D. J. Cowden listed in the Bibliography.

15.3 Control Charts for Measurements

When dealing with measurements, it is customary to exercise control over the average quality of a process as well as its variability. The first goal is accomplished by plotting the means of periodic samples on a so-called *control chart for means*, or more succinctly, an $\bar{x}$ *chart*. Variability is controlled by plotting the sample ranges or standard deviations, respectively, on an R *chart* or a σ *chart*, depending on which statistic is used to estimate the population standard deviation.

If the process mean and standard deviation, μ and σ, are known, and it is reasonable to treat the measurements as samples from a normal population, we can assert with a probability of $1 - \alpha$ that the mean of a random sample of size n will fall between $\bar{x} - z_{\alpha/2} \dfrac{\sigma}{\sqrt{n}}$ and $\bar{x} + z_{\alpha/2} \dfrac{\sigma}{\sqrt{n}}$. These two limits on $\bar{x}$ provide upper and lower control limits, and, under the given assumptions, they enable the quality-control engineer to determine whether or not to make an adjustment in the process.

In actual practice, μ and σ are usually unknown and it is necessary to estimate their values from a large sample (or samples) taken while the process is "in control." For this reason and because there may be no assurance that the measurements can be treated as samples from a normal population, the confidence level $1 - \alpha$ associated with the control limits is only approximate, and such "probability limits" are seldom used in practice. Instead, it is common industrial practice to use "three-sigma limits" obtained by substituting 3 for $z_{\alpha/2}$. With three-sigma limits one usually is highly confident that the process will not be declared out of control when, in fact, it is actually in control.

If there exists a long history of a process in good control, μ and σ can be estimated from past data practically without error. Thus, the *central line* of an $\bar{x}$ chart is given by μ and the *upper and lower three-sigma control limits* are given by $\mu \pm A\sigma$, where $A = 3/\sqrt{n}$ and n is the size of each sample.* For convenience, values of A for $n = 2, 3, \ldots$, and 15 are given in Table XI. The use of a constant sample size n simplifies the maintenance and interpretation of an $\bar{x}$ chart, but as the reader will observe in Exercise 4 on page 346, this restriction is not absolutely necessary.

In the more common case where the population parameters are *unknown*, it is necessary to estimate these parameters on the basis of preliminary samples. For this purpose, it is usually desirable to obtain the results of 20 or 25 consecutive samples taken when the process is in control. If k samples are used, each of size n, we shall denote the mean of the ith sample by $\bar{x}_i$, and the grand mean of the k sample means by $\bar{\bar{x}}$, that is,

$$\blacklozenge \qquad \bar{\bar{x}} = \frac{1}{k} \sum_{i=1}^{k} \bar{x}_i \qquad \blacklozenge$$

The process variability σ can be estimated either from the standard deviations or the ranges of the k samples. Since the sample size commonly used in connection with control charts for measurements is small, there is usually very little loss of efficiency in estimating σ from the sample ranges. (For an example where sample standard deviations are used in this connection, see Exercise 5 on page 347.) Denoting the range of the ith sample by R_i, we shall thus make use of the statistic

$$\blacklozenge \qquad \bar{R} = \frac{1}{k} \sum_{i=1}^{k} R_i \qquad \blacklozenge$$

Since $\bar{\bar{x}}$ provides an unbiased estimate of the population mean μ, the central line for the $\bar{x}$ chart is given by $\bar{\bar{x}}$. The statistic $\bar{R}$ does not provide

---

* Throughout this chapter we shall depart somewhat from the customary quality-control notation, in order to be consistent with the more widely accepted statistical notation used elsewhere in this book. (For instance, in quality control it is customary to denote the sample mean and standard deviation by $\bar{x}$ and σ, and the corresponding population parameters by $\bar{x}'$ and σ'.)

an unbiased estimate of σ, but multiplying $\overline{R}$ by the constant A_2, we obtain an unbiased estimate of $3\sigma/\sqrt{n}$. The constant multiplier A_2, tabulated in Table XI for various values of n, depends on the assumption that the measurements constitute a sample from a normal population. Thus, the central line and the upper and lower three-sigma control limits, UCL and LCL, for an $\bar{x}$ chart (*with μ and σ estimated from past data*) are given by

$$\text{central line} = \bar{\bar{x}}$$

$$UCL = \bar{\bar{x}} + A_2\overline{R}$$

$$LCL = \bar{\bar{x}} - A_2\overline{R}$$

An example of this kind of control chart for the mean is shown in Figure 15.2.

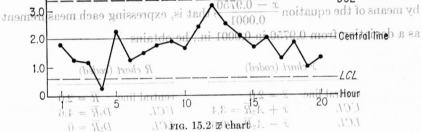

FIG. 15.2 $\bar{x}$ chart.

In controlling a process, it may not be enough to monitor the population mean. Although an increase in process variability may become apparent from increased fluctuations of the $\bar{x}$'s, a more sensitive test of shifts in process variability is provided by a separate control chart, an R chart based on the sample ranges or a so-called σ chart based on the sample standard deviations. An example of the latter may be found in Exercise 5 on page 347.

The central line and control limits of an R chart are based on the distribution of the range of samples of size n from a normal population. As we observed on page 176, the mean and the standard deviation of this sampling distribution are given by $d_2\sigma$ and $d_3\sigma$, respectively, when σ is known. Thus, three-sigma control limits for the range are given by $d_2\sigma \pm 3d_3\sigma$, and the complete set of control-chart values for an R chart (*with σ known*) is given by

$$\text{central line} = d_2\sigma$$

$$UCL = D_2\sigma$$

$$LCL = D_1\sigma$$

Here $D_1 = d_2 - 3d_3$ and $D_2 = d_2 + 3d_3$, and values of these constants can be found in Table XI for various values of n.

If σ is unknown, it is estimated from past data as previously described, and the control-chart values for an R chart (*with σ unknown*) are as follows:

$$\text{central line} = \overline{R}$$

♦
$$UCL = D_4\overline{R}$$
♦

$$LCL = D_3\overline{R}$$

Here $D_3 = D_1/d_2$ and $D_4 = D_2/d_2$, and values of these constants can also be found in Table XI for various values of n.

To illustrate the construction of an $\overline{x}$ chart and an R chart, let us consider the following example. A manufacturer of a certain bearing knows from a preliminary record of 20 hourly samples of size 4 that for the diameters of these bearings $\overline{\overline{x}} = 0.9752$ and $\overline{R} = 0.0002$. Coding his data by means of the equation $\dfrac{x - 0.9750}{0.0001}$, that is, expressing each measurement as a deviation from 0.9750 in 0.0001 in., he obtains

$\overline{x}$ chart (coded)		R chart (coded)	
central line	$\overline{\overline{x}} = 2.0$	central line	$\overline{R} = 2.0$
UCL	$\overline{\overline{x}} + A_2\overline{R} = 3.4$	UCL	$D_4\overline{R} = 4.6$
LCL	$\overline{\overline{x}} - A_2\overline{R} = 0.6$	LCL	$D_3\overline{R} = 0$

The values of $A_2 = 0.729$, $D_3 = 0$, and $D_4 = 2.282$ for samples of size 4 were obtained from Table XI. Graphically, these control charts are shown

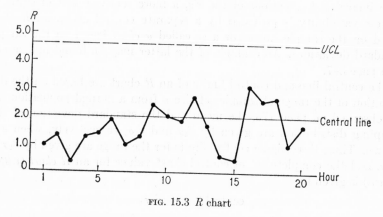

FIG. 15.3 R chart

in Figures 15.2 and 15.3, where we have also indicated the results subsequently obtained in the following 20 samples:

Hour		Coded sample values			$\bar{x}$	R
1	1.7	2.2	1.9	1.2	1.75	1.0
2	0.8	1.5	2.1	0.9	1.32	1.3
3	1.0	1.4	1.0	1.3	1.18	0.4
4	0.4	−0.6	0.7	0.2	0.18	1.3
5	1.4	2.3	2.8	2.7	2.30	1.4
6	1.8	2.0	1.1	0.1	1.25	1.9
7	1.6	1.0	1.5	2.0	1.52	1.0
8	2.5	1.6	1.8	1.2	1.78	1.3
9	2.9	2.0	0.5	2.2	1.90	2.4
10	1.1	1.1	3.1	1.6	1.72	2.0
11	1.7	3.6	2.5	1.8	2.40	1.9
12	4.6	2.8	3.5	1.9	3.20	2.7
13	2.6	2.8	3.2	1.5	2.52	1.7
14	2.3	2.1	2.1	1.7	2.05	0.6
15	1.9	1.6	1.8	1.4	1.68	0.5
16	1.3	2.0	3.9	0.8	2.00	3.1
17	2.8	1.5	0.6	0.2	1.28	2.6
18	1.7	3.6	0.9	1.5	1.92	2.7
19	1.6	0.6	1.0	0.8	1.00	1.0
20	1.7	1.0	0.5	2.2	1.35	1.7

Inspection of Figure 15.2 shows that only one of the points falls outside of the control limits, but it also shows that there may nevertheless have been a downward shift in the process average. Figure 15.3 shows a definite downward shift in the process variability; note especially that most of the sample ranges fall below the central line of the R chart.

The reader may have observed the close connection between the use of control charts and the testing of hypotheses. A point on an $\bar{x}$ chart that is out of control corresponds to a sample for which the null hypothesis that $\mu = \mu_0$ is rejected. To be more precise, we should say that control-chart techniques provide sequential, *temporally ordered* sets of tests. We are interested not only in the positions of individual points, but also in possible trends or other patterns exhibited by the points representing successive samples. We might, thus, use the sign test (see page 213) to check whether there has been a shift in the product average in the above example, or a run test (see page 219) to determine whether there is a significant trend.

15.4 Control Charts for Attributes

Although more complete information can usually be gained from measurements made on a finished product, it is often quicker and cheaper to check the product against specifications on an "attribute" or "go, no-go" basis. For example, in checking the diameter and eccentricity of a ball bearing it is far simpler to determine whether it will pass through circular holes cut in a template than to make several measurements of the diameter with a micrometer. In this section we shall discuss two fundamental kinds of control charts used in connection with attribute sampling, the *fraction-defective chart*, also called a *"p* chart," and the *number-of-defects chart*, also called a *"c* chart." To clarify the distinction between "number defective" and "number of defects," note that a unit tested can have several defects, while, on the other hand, it is either defective or it is not. In many applications, a unit is referred to as defective if it has at least one defect.

Control limits for a fraction-defective chart are based on the sampling theory for proportions introduced in Section 10.1, namely, on the normal curve approximation to the binomial distribution. Thus, if a standard is given, that is, if the fraction defective should take on some preassigned value p, the cental line is p and three-sigma control limits for the fraction defective in random samples of size n are given by $p \pm 3 \sqrt{\dfrac{p(1-p)}{n}}$. If no standard is given, which is more frequently the case in actual practice, p will have to be estimated from past data. If k samples are available, d_i is the number of defectives in the ith sample, and n_i is the number of observations in the ith sample, it is customary to estimate p as the proportion of defectives in the combined sample, namely, as

$$\bar{p} = \frac{d_1 + d_2 + \ldots + d_k}{n_1 + n_2 + \ldots + n_k}$$

Substituting $\bar{p}$ for p in the above formulas, we obtain the following control-chart values for a *fraction-defective chart based on the analysis of past data:*

$$\text{central line} = \bar{p}$$

$$UCL = \bar{p} + 3 \sqrt{\frac{\bar{p}(1-\bar{p})}{n}}$$

$$LCL = \bar{p} - 3 \sqrt{\frac{\bar{p}(1-\bar{p})}{n}}$$

Note that if p is small, as is often the case in practice, substitution in the formula for the lower control limit might yield a negative number. When this occurs, it is customary to regard the lower control limit as if it were zero and, in effect, to use only the upper control limit. Another complication that can arise if p is small is that the binomial distribution may not be adequately approximated by the normal distribution. Generally speaking, the use of the above control limits for p charts is unrealistic whenever n and p are such that the underlying binomial (or hypergeometric) distribution cannot be approximated by a normal curve (see page 73). In such cases it is best to use an upper control limit obtained directly from a table of binomial probabilities or, perhaps, use the Poisson approximation to the binomial distribution.

Equivalent to the p chart for the fraction defective is the control chart for the *number of defectives*. Instead of plotting the fraction defective in a sample of size n, one plots the number of defectives, and the control-chart values for this kind of chart are obtained by multiplying the above values for the central line and the control limits by n. Thus, if p is estimated by $\bar{p}$, the control-chart values for a *number-of-defectives* chart are as follows:

$$\text{central line} = n\bar{p}$$

$$UCL = n\bar{p} + 3\sqrt{n\bar{p}(1-\bar{p})}$$

$$LCL = n\bar{p} - 3\sqrt{n\bar{p}(1-\bar{p})}$$

As an illustration of a p chart, suppose it is desired to control the output of a certain transistor production line to maintain a "yield" of 60 per cent, that is, a proportion defective of 40 per cent. To this end, daily samples of 100 units are checked to electrical specifications, with the following results:

Date	Number of defectives	Date	Number of defectives	Date	Number of defectives
3-12	24	3-26	44	4- 9	23
3-13	38	3-27	52	4-10	31
3-16	62	3-30	45	4-13	26
3-17	34	3-31	30	4-14	32
3-18	26	4- 1	34	4-15	35
3-19	36	4- 2	33	4-16	15
3-20	38	4- 3	22	4-17	24
3-23	52	4- 6	34	4-20	38
3-24	33	4- 7	43	4-21	21
3-25	44	4- 8	28	4-22	16

Since the standard is given as $p = 0.40$, the control-chart values are

$$\text{central line} = 0.40$$

$$UCL = 0.40 + 3\sqrt{\frac{(0.40)(0.60)}{100}} = 0.55$$

$$LCL = 0.40 - 3\sqrt{\frac{(0.40)(0.60)}{100}} = 0.25$$

The corresponding control chart with points for the 30 sample fractions defective is shown in Figure 15.4, and it exhibits some interesting characteristics. Note that there is only one point out of control on the high side, but there are seven points out of control on the low side. Most of these seven "low points" occurred after April 1, and there appears to be a general downward trend. In fact, there is an unbroken run of eleven points below the central line after April 7. It would appear from this chart that the yield is not yet stabilized, and that the process is potentially capable of maintaining a yield well above the nominal 60 per cent value.

There are situations where it is necessary to control the number of *defects* in a unit of product, rather than the fraction defective. For example, in the production of carpeting it is important to control the number of defects per hundred yards; in the production of newsprint one may wish to control the number of defects per roll. These situations are similar to the one described in Section 4.4, which led to the Poisson distribution. Thus, if c is the number of defects per manufactured unit, c is taken to be a value of a random variable having the Poisson distribution.

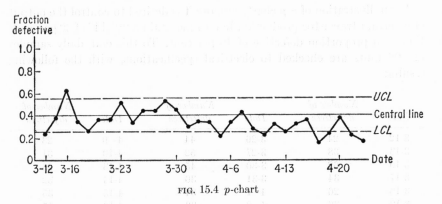

FIG. 15.4 p-chart

It follows that the center line for a *number of defects chart* is the parameter λ of the corresponding Poisson distribution, and that three-sigma control limits can be based on the fact that the standard deviation of this distribution is $\sqrt{\lambda}$. If λ is unknown, that is, if no standard is given, its value is usually estimated from at least 20 values of c observed from past data. If k is the number of units of product available for estimating λ, and if c_i is the number of defects in the ith unit, then λ is estimated by

$$\bar{c} = \frac{1}{k} \sum_{i=1}^{k} c_i$$

and the control-chart values for the *c-chart* are

$$\text{central line} = \bar{c}$$

$$UCL = \bar{c} + 3\sqrt{\bar{c}}$$

$$LCL = \bar{c} - 3\sqrt{\bar{c}}$$

To illustrate this kind of control chart, suppose that it is known from past experience that on the average an aircraft assembly made by a certain company has $\bar{c} = 4$ missing rivets. The corresponding control chart for

the number of missing rivets is shown in Figure 15.5, on which we have
also plotted the results of inspection which revealed 4, 6, 5, 1, 2, 3, 5, 7,

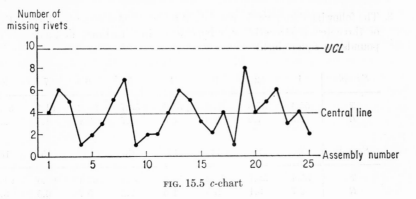

FIG. 15.5 *c*-chart

1, 2, 2, 4, 6, 5, 3, 2, 4, 1, 8, 4, 5, 6, 3, 4, and 2 missing rivets in 25
assemblies.

EXERCISES

1. A company is initiating a process for the mass-manufacture of compression
   springs. The specifications require that the free lengths of the springs have
   $\mu = 1.500$ in. and $\sigma = 0.010$ in.

   (a) Use the specifications to calculate a central line and three-sigma control
       limits for an $\bar{x}$ chart with $n = 5$.

   (b) Use the specifications to calculate a central line and three-sigma control
       limits for an R chart with $n = 5$.

   (c) Plot the following means and ranges, obtained in 20 successive random
       samples of size 5, on charts based on the control-chart constants ob-
       tained in parts (a) and (b), and discuss the process.

Sample	$\bar{x}$	R	Sample	$\bar{x}$	R
1	1.515	0.036	11	1.492	0.025
2	1.465	0.058	12	1.534	0.041
3	1.528	0.037	13	1.502	0.047
4	1.532	0.022	14	1.520	0.015
5	1.510	0.026	15	1.490	0.030
6	1.477	0.026	16	1.475	0.026
7	1.490	0.056	17	1.538	0.039
8	1.444	0.019	18	1.521	0.047
9	1.489	0.035	19	1.509	0.027
10	1.523	0.054	20	1.489	0.040

2. Calculate $\bar{x}$ and $\bar{R}$ for the data of part (c) of Exercise 1, and use these values to construct the central lines and three-sigma control limits for new $\bar{x}$ and R charts to be used in the control of the free lengths of the compression springs.

3. The following data give the means and ranges of 25 samples, each consisting of three tensile-strength measurements of iron castings, in thousands of pounds per square inch:

Sample	1	2	3	4	5	6	7	8
$\bar{x}$	55.1	57.6	52.8	51.4	53.7	59.2	61.1	52.8
R	2.5	1.0	3.9	5.6	2.7	3.1	1.5	2.2

Sample	9	10	11	12	13	14	15	16
$\bar{x}$	55.4	58.1	56.2	55.7	51.9	59.4	62.6	64.5
R	2.7	3.1	5.0	1.6	2.2	5.7	6.5	3.6

Sample	17	18	19	20	21	22	23	24	25
$\bar{x}$	61.1	62.4	57.9	58.6	63.3	59.7	58.2	61.6	62.3
R	1.4	4.3	2.2	2.7	3.0	1.1	2.1	1.6	2.4

(a) Use these data to find the central line and control limits for an $\bar{x}$ chart.

(b) Use these data to find the central line and control limits for an R chart.

(c) Plot the given data on $\bar{x}$ and R charts based on the control-chart constants computed in parts (a) and (b), and interpret the results.

(d) Using runs above and below the central line (similar to runs above and below the median discussed on page 221), test at a level of significance of 0.05 whether there is a trend in the $\bar{x}$ values.

(e) Would it be reasonable to use the control limits found in this exercise in connection with subsequent tensile-strength measurements from the same process? Why?

4. Reverse-current readings (in nanoamps) are made on a sample of ten transistors every half hour. Since some of the units may prove to be "shorts" or "opens," it is not always possible to obtain ten readings. The following table shows the number of readings made at the end of each half-hour interval during an eight-hour shift, and the mean reverse currents obtained.

Sample	1	2	3	4	5	6	7	8
n	9	7	10	8	8	9	6	10
$\bar{x}$	12.5	15.6	11.1	9.7	10.2	12.3	11.6	21.9

Sample	9	10	11	12	13	14	15	16
n	10	9	8	7	9	10	8	7
$\bar{x}$	16.7	14.2	9.8	13.1	11.6	9.5	17.2	10.1

(a) Find the central line for an $\bar{x}$ chart by taking the weighted mean of the sixteen $\bar{x}$'s, weighting each value with the size of the corresponding sample.

(b) Construct a table showing the central line found in part (a) and three-sigma control limits corresponding to $n = 6, 7, 8, 9,$ and 10. Use $R = 4.0$, a value based on prior data.

(c) Plot the data on a control chart like the one of Figure 15.6, and interpret the results.

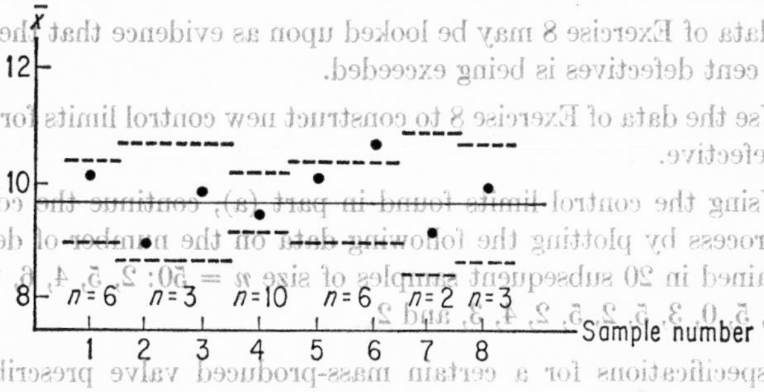

FIG. 15.6 Exercise 4

5. If the sample standard deviations instead of the sample ranges are used to estimate σ, the control limits for the resulting $\bar{x}$ chart are given by $\bar{\bar{x}} \pm A_1\bar{s}$, where $\bar{s}$ is the mean of the sample standard deviations obtained from given data, and A_1 can be found in Table XI. Note that in connection with problems of quality control the sample standard deviation is defined using the divisor n instead of $n - 1$. The corresponding R chart is replaced by a σ chart, having the central line $c_2\bar{s}$ and the upper and lower control limits $B_3\bar{s}$ and $B_4\bar{s}$, where B_3 and B_4 can be obtained from Table XI.

(a) Construct an $\bar{x}$ chart and a σ chart for 20 samples of size 4 which had $\bar{x}$ equal to 23.3, 23.4, 22.5, 20.3, 19.5, 21.8, 24.1, 24.9, 23.9, 24.4, 22.1, 21.6, 21.1, 20.3, 19.0, 20.4, 20.4, 20.4, 19.4, 21.2, and s equal to 3.1, 0.3, 1.2, 4.3, 2.9, 1.3, 0.8, 1.5, 1.0, 1.5, 1.0, 0.8, 2.0, 1.3, 0.3, 1.0, 0.9, 1.1, 0.8, 2.0.

(b) Would it be reasonable to use these control limits for subsequent data? Why?

6. In order to establish control charts for a process making shafts, thirty samples of 4 measurements of the outside diameters are taken, and the results are $\bar{\bar{x}} = 2.426''$ and $\bar{s} = 0.003''$. Using the method of Exercise 5 construct

an $\bar{x}$ chart for $n = 4$, and on it plot the following means obtained in 25 successive samples: 2.428, 2.430, 2.421, 2.425, 2.432, 2.440, 2.427, 2.421, 2.424, 2.425, 2.429, 2.426, 2.430, 2.424, 2.428, 2.422, 2.426, 2.427, 2.429, 2.425, 2.424, 2.429, 2.430, 2.421, and 2.429. Discuss the results.

7. Suppose that in the example of Exercise 6 it is desired to establish control also over the variability of the process. Using the method of Exercise 5 and the values of $\bar{x}$ and $\bar{s}$ given in Exercise 6, calculate the central line and control limits for a σ chart with $n = 4$.

8. Thirty successive samples of 50 gear covers each, taken from a production line, contained, respectively, 3, 2, 3, 0, 5, 10, 3, 3, 5, 6, 2, 3, 3, 2, 6, 3, 5, 5, 0, 6, 5, 3, 9, 3, 1, 2, 2, 5, 4, and 5 defectives. If the fraction defective is to be maintained at 0.05, construct a p chart for these data and state whether or not this standard is being met.

9. The data of Exercise 8 may be looked upon as evidence that the standard of 5 per cent defectives is being exceeded.

(a) Use the data of Exercise 8 to construct new control limits for the fraction defective.

(b) Using the control limits found in part (a), continue the control of the process by plotting the following data on the number of defectives obtained in 20 subsequent samples of size $n = 50$: 2, 5, 4, 6, 2, 4, 4, 5, 7, 8, 5, 0, 3, 5, 2, 5, 2, 4, 3, and 2.

10. The specifications for a certain mass-produced valve prescribe a testing procedure according to which each valve can be classified as satisfactory or unsatisfactory (defective). Past experience has shown that the process can perform so that $\bar{p} = 0.03$. Construct a three-sigma control chart for the *number* of defectives obtained in samples of size 100, and on it plot the following numbers of defectives obtained in such samples randomly selected from 30 successive half-days' production: 3, 1, 4, 2, 2, 0, 1, 4, 5, 3, 2, 1, 1, 0, 2, 2, 3, 4, 1, 0, 3, 1, 2, 5, 2, 7, 2, 3, 1, and 2.

11. The standard for a process producing paper in continuous rolls is 4 defects per hundred yards of paper. Based on the following set of 25 observations, giving the number of defects for hundred yards, can it be concluded that the process is in control to this standard?

Inspection no.	1	2	3	4	5	6	7	8	9	10	11	12
No. of defects	2	5	1	3	1	0	3	6	3	4	3	4

Inspection no.	13	14	15	16	17	18	19	20	21	22	23	24	25
No. of defects	3	4	5	10	5	5	8	5	4	7	1	1	5

12. A process for the manufacture of large sheets of glass has performed in the past with an average of 3.8 imperfections per sheet. Construct a c chart to

be used in the inspection of the glass and discuss the control if 25 successive pieces inspected contained, respectively, 5, 3, 2, 4, 1, 8, 4, 5, 6, 3, 4, 2, 6, 4, 5, 1, 2, 3, 5, 7, 1, 2, 2, 4, and 5 imperfections.

15.5 Tolerance Limits

Inherent in every phase of industrial quality control is the problem of comparing some quality characteristic or measurement of a finished product against given specifications. Sometimes the specifications, or *tolerance limits*, are so stated by the customer or by the design engineer that any appreciable departure will make the product unusable. There remains, however, the problem of producing the part so that an acceptably high proportion of units will fall within tolerance limits specified for the given quality characteristic. Also, if a product is made without prior specifications, or if modifications are made, it is desirable to know within what limits the process can hold a quality characteristic a reasonably high percentage of the time. We, thus, speak of "natural" tolerance limits, that is, we let the process establish its own limits which, according to experience, can be met in actual practice.

If reliable information is available about the distribution underlying the measurement in question, it is a relatively simple matter to find natural tolerance limits. For instance, if long experience with a product enables us to assume that a certain dimension is normally distributed with the mean μ and the standard deviation σ, it is easy to construct limits between which we can expect to find any given proportion P of the population. For $P = 0.90$ we have the tolerance limits $\mu \pm 1.645\sigma$, and for $P = 0.95$ we have $\mu \pm 1.96\sigma$, as can easily be verified from a table of normal curve areas.

In most practical situations the true values of μ and σ are not known, and tolerance limits must be based on the mean $\bar{x}$ and the standard deviation s of a random sample. Whereas $\mu \pm 1.96\sigma$ are limits including 95 per cent of a normal population, the same cannot be said for the limits $\bar{x} \pm 1.96s$. These limits are values of random variables and they may or may not include a given proportion of the population. Nevertheless, it is possible to determine a constant K so that *one can assert with a degree of confidence* $1 - \alpha$ *that the proportion of the population contained between* $\bar{x} - Ks$ *and* $\bar{x} + Ks$ *is at least* P. Such values of K for random samples from normal populations are given in Table XII for $P = 0.90$, 0.95, and 0.99, degrees of confidence of 0.95 and 0.99, and selected values of n from 2 to 1000.

To illustrate this technique, suppose that a manufacturer takes a sample of size $n = 100$ from a very large lot of mass-produced compression springs and that he obtains $\bar{x} = 1.507$ and $s = 0.004$ in. for the free lengths of the springs. Choosing a level of confidence of 0.99 and a minimum proportion of $P = 0.95$, he obtains the tolerance limits $1.507 \pm (2.355)(0.004)$; in other words, the manufacturer can assert with a degree of confidence of 0.99 that at least 95 per cent of the springs in the entire lot have free lengths from 1.497 to 1.517 inches. Note that in problems like these the minimum proportion P as well as the degree of confidence $1 - \alpha$ must be specified; also note that the lower tolerance limit is rounded *down* and the upper tolerance limit is rounded *up*.

To avoid confusion, let us also point out that there is an essential difference between confidence limits and tolerance limits. Whereas confidence limits are used to estimate a parameter of a population, tolerance limits are used to indicate between what limits one can find a certain proportion of a population. This distinction is emphasized by the fact that when n becomes large the length of a confidence interval approaches zero, while the tolerance limits will approach the corresponding values for the population. Thus, for large n, K approaches 1.96 in the columns for $P = 0.95$ in Table XII.

EXERCISES

1. In a study designed to determine the time required to assemble a given piece of machinery, 50 workers averaged 42.5 minutes with a standard deviation of 3.8 minutes. Establish tolerance limits for which one can assert with a degree of confidence 0.95 that *at least 90 per cent* of the workers (in the population of workers from which the sample was selected) can assemble the piece of machinery within these limits.

2. To check the diameter of a large incoming shipment of "O gauge" wire, the diameters of a random sample of 16 pieces of wire were measured, yielding a mean and a standard deviation of 0.338 and 0.012 in., respectively. Establish tolerance limits with $\alpha = 0.01$ and $P = 0.99$, and express *in words* what these tolerance limits mean.

3. In a random sample of 50 piston rings chosen from a production line, the mean edge width was 0.1284 in., and the standard deviation was 0.0005 in.

   (a) Between what limits can it be said with 95 per cent confidence that at least 90 per cent of the edge widths of piston rings produced by this production line will lie?

   (b) Find 95 per cent confidence limits for the true mean edge width, and explain the difference between these limits and the tolerance limits found in part (a).

4. *Nonparametric tolerance limits* can be based on the extreme values in a random sample of size n taken from any continuous population. The following equation relates the quantities n, P, and α, where P is the minimum propor-

tion of the population contained between the smallest and largest observations with confidence $1 - \alpha$:

$$n P^{n-1} - (n-1) P^n = \alpha$$

An approximate solution for n is given by

$$n \approx \frac{1}{2} + \frac{1+P}{1-P} \cdot \frac{\chi_\alpha^2}{4}$$

where χ_α^2 is the value of chi-square for 4 degrees of freedom that corresponds to a right-hand tail of area α.

(a) How large a sample is required to be 95 per cent certain that at least 90 per cent of the population will be included between the extreme values of the sample?

(b) At least what proportion of the population can be expected to be included between the extreme values of a sample of size 100 with 95 per cent confidence?

15.6 Acceptance Sampling

Manufactured goods are shipped to the purchaser in lots ranging in size from only a few to many thousands of individual items. Ideally, each lot should not contain any defectives, but practically speaking it is rarely possible to meet this goal. Recognizing the fact that some defective goods are bound to be delivered, even if each lot were to be inspected 100 per cent, most consumers require that evidence, based on careful inspection, be given that the proportion of defectives in each lot is not excessive.

A frequently used and highly effective method for providing such evidence is that of sampling inspection, where items are selected from each lot prior to shipment (or prior to acceptance by the consumer), and a decision is made on the basis of this sample whether to accept or reject the lot. Acceptance of a lot ordinarily implies that it can be shipped (or be accepted by the consumer), even though it may contain some defective items. Arrangements between the producer and the consumer may allow for some form of credit to be given for defectives subsequently discovered by the consumer. Rejection of a lot need not mean that it is to be scrapped; a rejected lot may be subjected to closer inspection with the aim of eliminating all defective items.

Since the cost of inspection is rarely negligible (sometimes it is nearly as high as or higher than the cost of production), it is seldom desirable to inspect each item in a lot. Thus, acceptance inspection usually involves sampling; more specifically, a random sample is selected from each lot and the lot is accepted if the number of defectives found in the sample does not exceed a given *acceptance number*. This procedure is equivalent to a test of the null hypothesis that the proportion defective p in the lot equals some specified value p_0 against the alternative that it equals p_1, where $p_1 > p_0$. In acceptance sampling the value p_0 is called the *acceptable quality level* or *AQL*, and p_1 is called the *lot tolerance per cent defective* or *LTPD*. The probability of a Type I error, α, can be interpreted as an upper limit to the proportion of "good" lots (lots with $p \leq p_0$) that will be rejected, and in this context it is called the *producer's risk*. The probability of a Type II error, β, gives an upper bound to the proportion of "bad" lots (lots with $p \geq p_1$) that will be accepted, and it is called the *consumer's risk*.

A *single-sampling plan* is simply a specification of the sample size and the acceptance number to be used, and its choice is usually based on a specified *AQL* and (or) *LTPD* in association with given producer's and (or) consumer's risks. A given sampling plan is best described by its operating-characteristic or *OC* curve, which gives the probability of acceptance for each value that can be assumed by the lot proportion defective p. Thus, the *OC* curve describes the degree of protection offered by the sampling plan against incoming lots of various qualities. If a sample of size n is taken from a lot containing N units, and if the acceptance number is c, the probability of accepting a lot containing the proportion of defectives p (the lot contains Np defectives) can be calculated by using the hypergeometric distribution, as follows:

$$\blacklozenge \qquad L(p) = \sum_{x=0}^{c} h(x; n, Np, N) \qquad \blacklozenge$$

For example, if the lot size is $N = 100$, the sample size is $n = 10$, and the acceptance number is $c = 1$, we have

$$L(p) = \frac{\binom{100p}{0}\binom{100(1-p)}{10} + \binom{100p}{1}\binom{100(1-p)}{9}}{\binom{100}{10}}$$

Since calculations involving the hypergeometric distribution are fairly tedious, especially when n and N are large, it is customary in acceptance sampling to approximate the hypergeometric distribution with the binomial distribution, as on page 48. For instance, for $p = 0.10$ the exact value is $L(0.10) = 0.739$, as the reader will be asked to verify in Exercise 5 on page 360, while Table I with $n = 10$ and $p = 0.10$ yields the binomial approximation

$$L(0.10) \simeq B(1; 10, 0.10) = 0.736$$

A sketch of the *OC* curve for the sampling plan $n = 10$, $c = 1$ can be made rapidly with the aid of Table I, and the result is shown in Figure 15.7. From this curve it can be seen that the producer's risk is approximately 0.05 when the *AQL* is 0.04, and the consumer's risk is approximately 0.10 when the *LTPD* is 0.34.

A sampling plan can also be described by means of its *average outgoing quality* or *AOQ* curve. This curve describes the degree of protection offered by the sampling plan by showing the average quality of outgoing lots corresponding to each quality level of incoming lots (that is, lots prior to inspection). If incoming lots are of good quality, that is, if their proportion defective is smaller than the *AQL*, very few lots will be rejected and the average outgoing quality or *AOQ* will be good. If the incoming lots

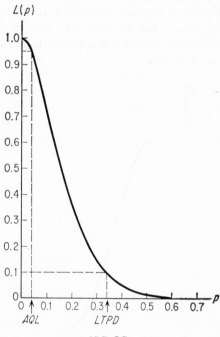

FIG. 15.7 *OC* curve

are of poor quality, that is, if their proportion defective is larger than the *LTPD*, most of them will be rejected. If all rejected lots are inspected 100 per cent and all defective units are replaced by good units prior to acceptance of the lot, then the average outgoing quality will be good even though the average incoming quality is poor. It is when the average incoming quality lies between the *AQL* and the *LTPD* that the poorest quality of lots will be shipped. In general, there will be a maximum *AOQ* over all values of incoming quality p, and this value is called the *average outgoing quality limit*, or *AOQL*.

It is not difficult to derive a formula for finding the *AOQ* corresponding to a given incoming quality p under the assumption that all defectives in rejected lots are replaced by acceptable items prior to their final acceptance. If the incoming quality is p, the probability that a lot will be accepted is $L(p)$, and each such lot contains the proportion p of defectives. The proportion $1 - L(p)$ of lots which are eventually rejected contain no defectives, and it follows that the AOQ is given by $p \cdot L(p) + 0 \cdot [1 - L(p)]$, or

$$AOQ = p \cdot L(p)$$

More common practice is to remove or replace defectives found in accepted as well as rejected lots, but the modification thus required in the AOQ is usually minor and it is customary to use the above formula regardless of the inspection procedure. The AOQ curve for the sampling plan $n = 10$, $c = 1$ is shown in Figure 15.8, and it is apparent from this figure that the $AOQL$ is approximately 0.081.

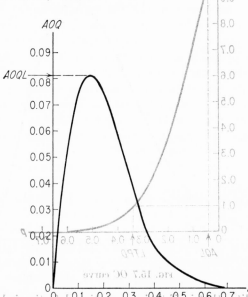

FIG. 15.8 AOQ curve

Sometimes, smaller samples (and hence, reductions in cost) can be achieved without sacrifice in the degree of protection by the use of so-called *double* or *multiple sampling*. A *double sampling plan* involves the selection of a random sample of size n_1 from a lot; if the sample contains c_1 or fewer defectives, the lot is accepted; if it contains c_1' or more defectives ($c_1' > c_1$) the lot is rejected; otherwise, a second sample of size n_2 is taken from the lot, and the lot is accepted unless the total number of defectives in the combined sample of size $n_1 + n_2$ exceeds c_2. A *multiple sampling plan* is similar in nature to a double sampling plan, but it involves more than two stages. An example of such a plan is shown in the following table:

| Sample | Sample size | Combined samples | | |
		Size	Acceptance number	Rejection number
First	20	20	—	3
Second	20	40	1	4
Third	20	60	(3)	5
Fourth	20	80	3	6
Fifth	20	100	5	7
Sixth	20	120	6	8
Seventh	20	140	7	8

In the first step, the lot is rejected if there are 3 or more defectives, otherwise sampling continues; in the second step, the lot is accepted if the combined sample contains at most 1 defective, it is rejected if there are 4 or more defectives, otherwise sampling continues. This goes on, if necessary, until in the final step the lot is accepted if there are at most 7 defectives in the combined sample of size 140, and otherwise it is rejected.

By an appropriate choice of the sample sizes and the acceptance and rejection numbers it is possible to match the *OC* curve of a double or multiple sampling plan closely to that of an equivalent single sampling plan. Thus, the degree of protection offered by a double or multiple sampling plan can be made essentially the same as that offered by an equivalent single sampling plan.

The advantage of double or multiple sampling is that there is a high probability that a very good lot will be accepted or a very poor lot will be rejected on the basis of the first sample (or, at least, an early sample), thus reducing the required amount of inspection. On the other hand, if the lot quality is "intermediate," the total sample size required may actually be larger than that of the equivalent single sampling plan. To illustrate, consider the following double sampling plan:

| Sample | Sample size | Combined samples | | |
		Size	Acceptance number	Rejection number
First	15	15	1	5
Second	30	45	5	6

If the incoming lot quality is $p = 0.05$, the probability that a second sample will be required is the same as the probability that there are 2, 3, or 4 defectives in a sample of size 15. According to Table I, this probability is equal to

$$B(4; 15, 0.05) - B(1; 15, 0.05) = 0.170$$

Thus, on the average, it will require a sample of size $15 + (0.170)(30) = 20.1$ to decide whether to accept or reject an incoming lot of quality $p = 0.05$. Similar calculations enable us to find the average sample size required to inspect a lot having any given incoming quality p. A graph showing the relation between the average sample size (also called the *average sample number*) and the incoming lot quality is called an *ASN* curve; the *ASN* curve for the double sampling plan described above is shown in Figure 15.9.

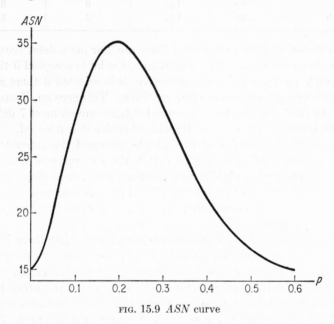

FIG. 15.9 *ASN* curve

Several standard sampling plans have been published to facilitate the use of acceptance sampling (see the book by I. W. Burr listed in the Bibliography). Among the most widely used standard plans are those contained in the *Military Standard 105D Tables* (see Bibliography). These plans stress the maintenance of a specified *AQL*, and they are designed to encourage the producer to offer only good products to the consumer. To accomplish this there are three general levels of inspection corresponding to different consumer's risks. (Inspection level II is normally chosen; level I uses smaller sample sizes and level III uses larger sample sizes than level II.) There are also three types of inspection: normal, tightened, and reduced. The type of inspection depends on whether the average proportion defectives for prior samples has been above or below the *AQL*, and it may be changed during the course of inspection. Under tightened inspection the producer's risk is increased and the consumer's risk is (slightly) decreased; under reduced inspection the consumer's risk is increased and the producer's risk is (slightly) decreased. Tables are available for single, double, and multiple sampling, and a brief portion of these tables is included in this book in Tables XIII and XIV.

The procedure in using MIL-STD-105D for single sampling is first to find the sample size code letter corresponding to the lot size and the desired inspection level and type. Then, using the sample size code letter thus obtained and the appropriate AQL, one finds the sample size and the acceptance number from the master table. A portion of the table for finding sample size code letters is given in Table XIII, and a portion of the master table for normal inspection is included in Table XIV.

To illustrate the use of MIL-STD-105D, suppose that incoming lots contain 2000 items, and inspection level II is to be used in conjunction with normal inspection and an AQL of 0.025, or 2.5 per cent. From Table XIII we find that the sample size code letter is K. Then, entering Table XIV in the row labeled K, we find that the sample size to be used is 125. Using the column labeled 2.5, we find that the acceptance number is 7 and the rejection number is 8. Thus, if a single sample of size 125, selected at random from a lot of 2000 items, contains 7 or fewer defectives the lot is to be accepted; if the sample contains 8 or more defectives the lot is to be rejected.

The concept of multiple sampling is carried to its extreme in so-called *sequential sampling*. A sampling procedure is said to be *sequential* if, after each observation, one of the following decisions is made: accept whatever hypothesis is being tested, reject the hypothesis, or take another observation. Although sequential procedures are used also in connection with other kinds of problems, we shall discuss this kind of sampling only in connection with acceptance sampling, where we shall thus decide after the inspection of each successive item whether to accept a lot, reject it, or continue sampling.

The construction of a sequential sampling plan consists of finding two sequences of numbers a_n and r_n, where n is the number of observations, so that the lot is accepted as soon as the number of defectives is less than or equal to a_n for some n, the lot is rejected as soon as the number of defectives is greater than or equal to r_n for some n, and sampling continues so long as the number of defectives in a sample of size n falls between a_n and r_n. If an acceptance plan is to have p_0 and p_1 as its AQL and $LTPD$, the producer's risk α, and the consumer's risk β, it can be shown (see the book by A. Wald in the Bibliography) that the required values of a_n and r_n can be computed by means of the formulas

$$a_n = \frac{\log\dfrac{\beta}{1-\alpha} + n \cdot \log\dfrac{1-p_0}{1-p_1}}{\log\dfrac{p_1}{p_0} - \log\dfrac{1-p_1}{1-p_0}}$$

$$r_n = \frac{\log\dfrac{1-\beta}{\alpha} + n \cdot \log\dfrac{1-p_0}{1-p_1}}{\log\dfrac{p_1}{p_0} - \log\dfrac{1-p_1}{1-p_0}}$$

If a_n is not an integer, it is replaced by the largest integer less than a_n; if r_n is not an integer, it is replaced by the smallest integer greater than r_n. To illustrate this procedure, let $p_0 = 0.05$, $p_1 = 0.20$, $\alpha = 0.05$, and $\beta = 0.10$. Substituting these values into the above formulas for a_n and r_n, we obtain

$$a_n = -1.45 + 0.11n,$$
$$r_n = 1.86 + 0.11n$$

and, letting $n = 1, 2, 3, \ldots$, and 25, we get the acceptance and rejection numbers shown in the second and forth columns of the following table:

Number of items inspected n	Acceptance number a_n	Number of defectives d_n	Rejection number r_n
1	–	0	–
2	–	0	–
3	–	0	3
4	–	0	3
5	–	0	3
6	–	0	3
7	–	0	3
8	–	0	3
9	–	0	3
10	–	1	3
11	–	1	4
12	–	1	4
13	–	1	4
14	0	1	4
15	0	1	4
16	0	1	4
17	0	2	4
18	0	2	4
19	0	2	4
20	0	2	5
21	0	3	5
22	0	3	5
23	1	3	5
24	1	3	5
25	1	3	5

In the third column we have indicated the results obtained in an inspection where the 8th, 17th, 19th, 22nd, and 23rd items are defective, and where the inspection terminates with rejection of the lot after inspection of the 23rd item.

The tabular procedure illustrated can be replaced by an equivalent graphical procedure for carrying out sequential sampling inspection. Plotting the values of a_n and r_n obtained from the equations on page 358 (without rounding), we obtain two *straight lines* like those of Figure 15.10.

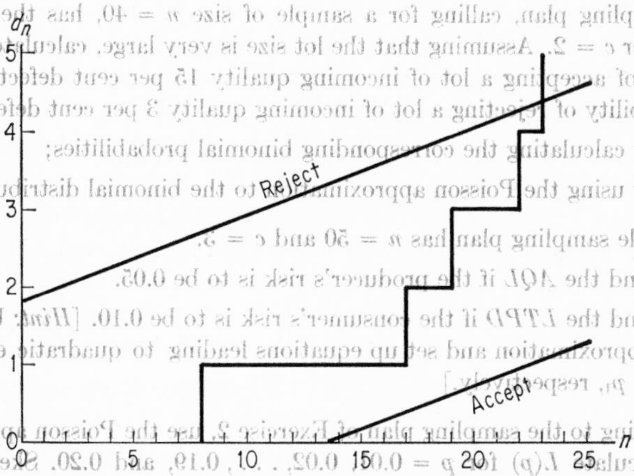

FIG. 15.10 Graphical procedure for sequential sampling

Sampling terminates with rejection or acceptance if the number of defectives observed falls above the line for r_n or below the line for a_n, respectively.

The main advantage of sequential sampling is that it can materially reduce the required amount of inspection. Studies have shown that the average decrease in sample size is often near 50 per cent when compared with the sample size of equivalent single sampling plans. The major disadvantage is that, in a sequential sampling plan, there is no upper limit to the number of items that might have to be inspected in order to reach a decision concerning the acceptance or rejection of a lot. In fact, the sample size is a random variable and its value will occasionally be very large. For this reason it is customary to *truncate* sequential sampling procedures by selecting a number N such that a decision must be made to accept or reject a lot prior to, or at $n = N$.

EXERCISES

1. A single sampling plan calls for a sample of size 200.

    (a) Use the normal approximation to find the acceptance number c if the AQL is to be 4 per cent and the producer's risk is to be $\alpha = 0.025$.

    (b) Using the acceptance number obtained in part (a), determine the consumer's risk if the $LTPD$ is to be 10 per cent.

2. A sampling plan, calling for a sample of size $n = 40$, has the acceptance number $c = 2$. Assuming that the lot size is very large, calculate the probability of accepting a lot of incoming quality 15 per cent defective and the probability of rejecting a lot of incoming quality 3 per cent defective,

    (a) by calculating the corresponding binomial probabilities;

    (b) by using the Poisson approximation to the binomial distribution.

3. A single sampling plan has $n = 50$ and $c = 3$.

    (a) Find the AQL if the producer's risk is to be 0.05.

    (b) Find the $LTPD$ if the consumer's risk is to be 0.10. [*Hint:* Use the normal approximation and set up equations leading to quadratic equations in p_0 and p_1, respectively.]

4. Referring to the sampling plan of Exercise 2, use the Poisson approximation to calculate $L(p)$ for $p = 0.01, 0.02, \ldots, 0.19$, and 0.20. Sketch the OC curve for this sampling plan and read off the consumer's and producer's risks corresponding to an AQL of 3.5 per cent and an $LTPD$ of 12.5 per cent.

5. With reference to the example on page 352, verify that

    (a) $L(0.10) = 0.739$, using the exact (hypergeometric) formula;

    (b) $L(0.10 \simeq 0.736$, using the approximate (binomial) formula;

    (c) the OC curve is as given in Figure 15.7;

    (d) the AOQ curve is as given in Figure 15.8.

6. Calculate $L(p)$ for selected values of p and sketch the OC curve for the single sampling plan $n = 80$, $c = 2$. [*Hint:* Assume a large lot size, and use the normal approximation to the binomial distribution.]

7. Sketch the AOQ curve for the sampling plan of Exercise 6, and estimate the $AOQL$.

8. Using the values of $L(p)$ obtained in Exercise 4, sketch the AOQ curve for the given sampling plan and estimate the $AOQL$.

9. Referring to the double sampling plan on page 355, use Table I and the normal approximation (when necessary) to calculate the producer's risk α when the AQL is $p_0 = 0.10$.

10. Calculate the average sample size required for selected values of p and sketch the ASN curve for the following double sampling plan:

| Sample | Sample size | Combined samples | | |
		Size	Accepiance number	Rejection number
First	12	12	1	4
Second	40	52	4	5

11. An incoming lot of 1000 items is to be inspected using MIL-STD-105D, with normal inspection at general inspection level II and an AQL of 1.5 per cent. What single sampling plan should be used?

12. A lot of 100 items is to be inspected at an AQL of 10 per cent. If MIL-STD-105D is to be used, with normal inspection at general inspection level II, what single sampling plan is required?

13. Find formulas for the acceptance and rejection numbers for the sequential sampling plan having an AQL of 0.10, an $LTPD$ of 0.30, a producer's risk of 0.05, and a consumer's risk of 0.10. If a sample should contain defectives on the third, fifth, seventh, and eighth trials, would this plan accept or reject the corresponding lot prior to the tenth trial? If so, on which trial?

14. A sequential sampling plan is to have $p_0 = 0.01$, $p_1 = 0.10$, $\alpha = 0.05$, and $\beta = 0.20$.

(a) Determine the acceptance and rejection numbers for $n = 1, 2, \ldots ,$ and 50.

(b) Use random numbers and the acceptance and rejection numbers obtained in part (a) to simulate the inspection of a very large lot containing 20 per cent defectives.

16

APPLICATIONS TO
RELIABILITY AND
LIFE TESTING

16.1 Introduction

The task of designing and supervising the manufacture of a product has been made increasingly difficult by rapid strides in the sophistication of modern products and the severity of the environmental conditions under which they must perform. No longer can an engineer be satisfied if the operation of a product is technically feasible, or if it can be made to "work" under optimum conditions. In addition to such considerations as cost and ease of manufacture, increasing attention must now be paid to size and weight, ease of maintenance, and reliability. The magnitude of the problem of maintainability and reliability is illustrated by surveys which have uncovered the fact that frequently a high percentage of space-age electronic equipment has been in inoperative condition. Military surveys have further shown that maintenance and repair expenses for electronic equipment often exceed the original cost of procurement, even during the first year of operation.

The problem of assuring and maintaining reliability has many facets, including original equipment design, control of quality during production, acceptance inspection, field trials, life testing, and design modifications. To complicate matters further, reliability competes directly or indirectly with a host of other engineering considerations, chiefly cost, complexity, size and weight, and maintainability. In spite of its complicated engineering aspects, it is possible to give a relatively simple mathematical definition of reliability. To motivate this definition, we call the reader's attention to the fact that a product may function satisfactorily under one set of conditions but not under other conditions, and that satisfactory performance for one purpose does not assure adequate performance for another purpose. For example, a vacuum tube which is perfectly satisfactory for use in a home radio may be entirely unsatisfactory for use in the airborne guidance system of a missile. Accordingly, we shall define the reliability of a product as *the probability that it will function within specified limits for at least a specified period of time under specified environmental conditions*. Thus, the reliability of a "standard equipment" automobile tire is close to unity for 10,000 miles of normal operation on a passenger car, but it is virtually zero for use at the Indianapolis "500."

Since reliability has been defined as a probability, the theoretical treatment of this subject is based essentially on the material introduced in the early chapters of this book. Thus, the rules of probability introduced in Chapter 2 can be applied directly to the calculation of the reliability of a complex system, if the reliabilities of the individual components are known. (Estimates of the reliabilities of the individual components are usually obtained from statistical life tests, such as those discussed in Sections 16.4 and 16.5.)

Many systems can be considered to be series or parallel systems, or a combination of both. A *series system* is one in which all components are so interrelated that the entire system will fail if any one of its components fails; a *parallel system* is one that will fail only if all of its components fail.

Let us first discuss a system of n components connected in series, and let us suppose that the components are *independent*, namely, that the performance of any one part does not affect the reliability of the others. Under these conditions, the probability that the system will function is given by the special rule of multiplication for probabilities, and we have

$$\blacklozenge \qquad R_s = \prod_{i=1}^{n} R_i \qquad \blacklozenge$$

where R_i is the reliability of the ith component and R_s is the reliability of the series system. This simple *product law of reliabilities*, applicable to series systems of independent components, vividly demonstrates the effect of increased complexity on reliability. If a system consists of five independent components in series, each having a reliability of 0.970, then the reliability of the whole series system is $(0.970)^5 = 0.859$. Now, if the system complexity were increased so that it contained 10 similar components, its reliability would be reduced to $(0.970)^{10} = 0.738$. Looking at the effect of increasing complexity in another way, we find that each of the components in the ten-component system would have to have a reliability of 0.985, instead of 0.970, for the ten-component system to have a reliability equal to that of the original five-component system.

One way to increase the reliability of a system is to replace certain components by several similar components connected in parallel. If a system consists of n independent components connected in parallel, it will fail to function only if all n components fail. Thus, if $F_i = 1 - R_i$ is the "unreliability" of the ith component, we can again apply the special rule of multiplication for probabilities to obtain

$$F_p = \prod_{i=1}^{n} F_i$$

where F_p is the unreliability of the parallel system, and $R_p = 1 - F_p$ is the reliability of the parallel system. Thus, for parallel systems we have a *product law of unreliabilities* analogous to the product law of reliabilities for series systems. Writing this law in another way, we get

♦
$$R_p = 1 - \prod_{i=1}^{n} (1 - R_i)$$
♦

for the reliability of a parallel system.

The two basic formulas for the reliability of series and parallel systems can be used in combination to calculate the reliability of a system having both series and parallel parts. To illustrate such a calculation, consider the system diagrammed in Figure 16.1, which consists of eight components

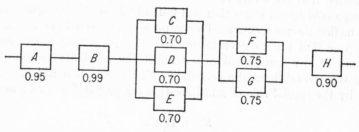

FIG. 16.1 Systems reliability

having the reliabilities shown in that figure. The parallel assembly C, D, E can be replaced by an equivalent component C' having the reliability $1 - (1 - 0.70)^3 = 0.973$, without affecting the over-all reliability of the system. Similarly, the parallel assembly F, G can be replaced by a single component F' having the reliability $1 - (1 - 0.75)^2 = 0.9375$. The resulting series system A, B, C', F', H, equivalent to the original system, has the reliability

$$(0.95)(0.99)(0.973)(0.9375)(0.90) = 0.772.$$

16.2 Failure-time Distributions

According to the definition of reliability given in the preceding section, the reliability of a system or a component will often depend on the length of time it has been in service. Thus, of fundamental importance in reliability studies is the *distribution of the time to failure* of a component under given environmental conditions. A useful way to characterize this distribution is by means of its associated *instantaneous failure rate*, defined as follows: If $f(t)$ is the probability density of the time to failure of a given component, that is, the probability that the component will fail between times t and $t + \Delta t$ is given by $f(t) \cdot \Delta t$, then the probability that the component will fail on the interval from 0 to t is given by

$$F(t) = \int_0^t f(x)\, dx$$

and the *reliability function*, expressing the probability that it survives to time t, is given by

$$R(t) = 1 - F(t)$$

Thus, the probability that the component will fail in the interval from t to $t + \Delta t$ is $F(t + \Delta t) - F(t)$, and the conditional probability of failure in this interval, *given that the component survived to time t*, is expressed by

$$\frac{F(t + \Delta t) - F(t)}{R(t)}$$

Dividing by Δt, we obtain the average rate of failure in the interval from t to $t + \Delta t$, given that the component survived to time t:

$$\frac{F(t + \Delta t) - F(t)}{\Delta t} \cdot \frac{1}{R(t)}$$

Taking the limit as $\Delta t \to 0$, we get the *instantaneous failure rate*, or simply the *failure rate*

$$Z(t) = \frac{F'(t)}{R(t)}$$

where $F'(t)$ is the derivative of $F(t)$ with respect to t. Finally, observing that $f(t) = F'(t)$ (see page 66) we get the relation

$$Z(t) = \frac{f(t)}{R(t)} = \frac{f(t)}{1 - F(t)}$$

which expressed the failure rate in terms of the distribution of failure times.

A failure-rate curve that is typical of many manufactured items is shown in Figure 16.2. The curve is conveniently divided into three parts. The first part is characterized by a decreasing failure rate and it represents the period during which poorly manufactured items are weeded out. (It is common in the electronics industry to "burn in" components prior to actual use in order to eliminate any early failures.) The second part, which is often characterized by a constant failure rate, is normally regarded as

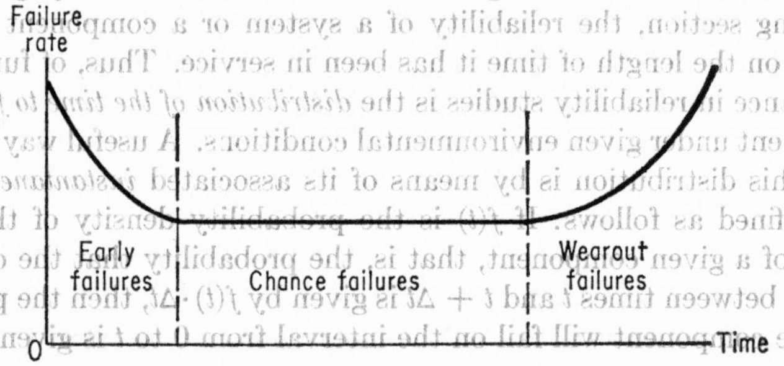

FIG. 16.2 Typical failure-rate curve

the period of useful life during which only chance failures occur. The third part is characterized by an increasing failure rate, and it is the period during which components fail primarily because they are worn out. Note that the same general failure-rate curve is typical of human mortality, where the first part represents infant mortality, and the third part corresponds to old-age mortality.

Let us now derive an important relationship expressing the failure-time density in terms of the failure-rate function. Making use of the fact that $R(t) = 1 - F(t)$ and, hence, that $F'(t) = -R'(t)$, we can write

$$Z(t) = -\frac{R'(t)}{R(t)} = -\frac{d[\ln R(t)]}{dt}$$

Solving this differential equation for $R(t)$, we obtain

$$R(t) = e^{-\int_0^t Z(x)dx}$$

and, making use of the relation $f(t) = Z(t) \cdot R(t)$, we finally get

$$\blacklozenge \qquad f(t) = Z(t) \cdot e^{-\int_0^t Z(x)dx} \qquad \blacklozenge$$

As illustrated in Figure 16.2, it is often assumed that the failure rate is constant during the period of useful life of a component. Denoting this constant failure rate by α, where $\alpha > 0$, and substituting α for $Z(t)$ in the formula for $f(t)$, we obtain

$$f(t) = \alpha \cdot e^{-\alpha t} \quad t > 0$$

Thus, we observe that the distribution of failure times is an *exponential distribution* when it can be assumed that the failure rate is constant. For this reason, the assumption of constant failure rates is sometimes also called the "exponential assumption." Interpreting the time to failure as a *waiting time*, we can use the results of Section 5.3 to conclude that the occurrence of failures is a Poisson process, if a component which fails is immediately replaced with a new one having the same constant failure rate α. As we observed on page 93, the mean waiting time between successive failures is $1/\alpha$, or the reciprocal of the failure rate. Thus, the constant $1/\alpha$ is often referred to as the *mean time between failures*, and it is abbreviated *MTBF*.

There are situations in which the assumption of a constant failure rate is not realistic, and in many of these situations one assumes instead that the failure-rate function increases or decreases "smoothly" with time. In other words, it is assumed that there are no discontinuities or turning points. This assumption would be consistent with the initial and last stages of the failure-rate curve shown in Figure 16.2.

A useful function that is often used to approximate such failure-rate curves is given by

$$Z(t) = \alpha\beta t^{\beta-1} \quad t > 0$$

where α and β are positive constants. Note the generality of this function: If $\beta < 1$ the failure rate *decreases* with time, if $\beta > 1$ it *increases* with time, and if $\beta = 1$ the failure rate equals α. Note that the assumption of a constant failure rate, the exponential assumption, is thus included as a special case.

If we substitute the above expression for $Z(t)$ into the formula for $f(t)$ on page 366, we obtain

$$f(t) = \alpha\beta t^{\beta-1} e^{-\alpha t^\beta} \quad t > 0$$

where α and β are positive constants. We refer to this density, or distribution, as the *Weibull distribution*, and we shall discuss its application to problems of life testing in Section 16.5.

16.3 The Exponential Model in Reliability

If we make the exponential assumption about the distribution of failure times, some very useful results can be derived concerning the *MTBF*, the mean time between failure, of series and parallel systems. In order to use the product laws of Section 16.1, we shall first have to obtain a relation expressing the reliability of a component in terms of its service time t. Making use of the fact that

$$R(t) = 1 - F(t) = 1 - \int_0^t f(t)\, dt$$

we obtain

$$R(t) = 1 - \int_0^t \alpha e^{-\alpha x}\, dx = e^{-\alpha t}$$

for the reliability function of the exponential model. Thus, if a component has a failure rate of 0.05 per thousand hours, the probability that it will survive at least 10,000 hours of operation is $e^{-(0.05)10} = 0.607$.

Suppose now that a system consists of n components connected in series, and that these components have the respective failure rates $\alpha_1, \alpha_2, \ldots,$ and α_n. The product law of reliabilities can be written as

$$\blacklozenge \qquad R_s(t) = \prod_{i=1}^{n} e^{-\alpha_i t} = e^{-\left(\sum_{i=1}^{n} \alpha_i\right)t} \qquad \blacklozenge$$

and it can be seen that the reliability function of the series system also satisfies the exponential assumption. The failure rate of the entire series system is readily identified as $\sum_{i=1}^{n} \alpha_i$, the *sum* of the failure rates of its components. Since the $MTBF$ is the reciprocal of the failure rate when each component which fails is replaced immediately with another having the identical failure rate, we obtain the formula

$$\blacklozenge \qquad \mu_s = \frac{1}{\dfrac{1}{\mu_1} + \dfrac{1}{\mu_2} + \ldots + \dfrac{1}{\mu_n}} \qquad \blacklozenge$$

expressing the $MTBF$ μ_s of a series system in terms of the $MTBF$'s μ_i of its components. In the special case where all n components have the same failure rate α and hence the same $MTBF$ μ, the system failure rate is $n\alpha$, and the system $MTBF$ is $1/n\alpha = \mu/n$.

For parallel systems the results are not quite so simple. If a system consists of n components in parallel, having the respective failure rates $\alpha_1, \alpha_2, \ldots, \alpha_n$, the system "unreliability" to time t is given by

$$F_p(t) = \prod_{i=1}^{n} (1 - e^{-\alpha_i t})$$

Thus, the failure-time distribution of a parallel system is not exponential even when each of its components satisfies the exponential assumption. The system failure-rate function can be obtained by means of the formula $Z_p(t) = F_p'(t)/R_p(t)$, but the result is fairly complicated. Note, however, that the system failure rate is not constant, but depends on t, the "age" of the system.

The mean time to failure of a parallel system is also difficult to obtain in general, but in the special case where all components have the same failure rate α, an interesting and useful result can be obtained. In this special case the system reliability function becomes

$$R_p(t) = 1 - (1 - e^{-\alpha t})^n$$

$$= \binom{n}{1} e^{-\alpha t} - \binom{n}{2} e^{-2\alpha t} + \ldots + (-1)^{n-1} e^{-n\alpha t}$$

after using the binomial theorem to expand $(1 - e^{-\alpha t})^n$. Then, making use of the fact that $f_p(t) = -R_p'(t)$, we obtain

$$f_p(t) = \alpha \binom{n}{1} e^{-\alpha t} - 2\alpha \binom{n}{2} e^{-2\alpha t} + \ldots + (-1)^{n-1} n\alpha e^{-n\alpha t}$$

and the mean of the failure time distribution is given by

$$\mu_p = \int_0^\infty t \cdot f_p(t) \, dt$$

$$= \alpha \binom{n}{1} \int_0^\infty t e^{-\alpha t} \, dt - 2\alpha \binom{n}{2} \int_0^\infty t e^{-2\alpha t} \, dt + \ldots$$

$$+ (-1)^{n-1} n\alpha \int_0^\infty t e^{-n\alpha t} \, dt$$

$$= \frac{1}{\alpha} \binom{n}{1} - \frac{1}{2\alpha} \binom{n}{2} + \ldots + (-1)^{n-1} \frac{1}{n\alpha}$$

It can be proved by induction that this expression is equivalent to

$$\blacklozenge \qquad \mu_p = \frac{1}{\alpha} \left(1 + \frac{1}{2} + \ldots + \frac{1}{n} \right) \qquad \blacklozenge$$

Thus, if a parallel system consists of n components having the identical failure rate α, the mean time between failures of the system equals $\left(1 + \frac{1}{2} + \ldots + \frac{1}{n} \right)$ times the common $MTBF$ of its components, provided each defective component is replaced whenever the whole parallel system fails. Thus, if we use two parallel components rather than one, the mean time to failure of the pair exceeds that of the single component by 50 per cent, rather than doubling it. In general, the above formula for μ_p expresses a rather severe law of diminishing returns for parallel redundancy.

To illustrate how the formulas derived in this section can be used in system design, let us again consider the system diagrammed in Figure 16.1 on page 364. Assuming the exponential model and that the reliabilities are given for 10 hours of operation, we can calculate the failure rate of component A by solving the equation $0.95 = e^{-10\alpha}$ for α, and we obtain $\alpha = (5.1)10^{-3}$ failures per hour, or 5.1 failures per thousand hours. The failure rates of all eight components (in failures per thousand hours) are as shown in the following table:

Component	A	B	C	D	E	F	G	H
Failure rate	5.1	1.0	35.7	35.7	35.7	28.8	28.8	10.5

To compute the mean time to failure for the entire system, we first obtain the mean failure times for the parallel assemblies C, D, E, and F, G, respectively. For C, D, E we have $\mu_{CDE} = \frac{1}{35.7}\left(1 + \frac{1}{2} + \frac{1}{3}\right) = 0.051$ thousand hours, or 51 hours; for F, G we have $\mu_{FG} = \frac{1}{28.8}\left(1 + \frac{1}{2}\right) = 0.052$ thousand hours, or 52 hours. Although the two parallel assemblies do not have constant failure rates, we shall approximate their respective failure rates by $1/0.051 = 19.6$ and $1/0.052 = 19.2$ failures per thousand hours, and treat the entire system as a series system. Thus, the system failure rate is given approximately by $5.1 + 1.0 + 19.6 + 19.2 + 10.5 = 55.4$ failures per thousand hours, and the mean time to failure of the system is approximately $1/55.4 = 0.018$ or 18 hours.

EXERCISES

1. A system consists of 5 identical components connected in parallel. What must be the reliability of each component, if the over-all reliability of the system is to be 0.99?

2. An old-fashioned string of Christmas-tree lights has 10 bulbs connected in series. What would have to be the reliability of each bulb if there is to be a 90 per cent chance of the string's lighting after a year's storage?

3. A system consists of 5 components connected as in Figure 16.3. Find the over-

FIG. 16.3 Exercise 3

all reliability of the system, given that the reliabilities of A, B, C, D, and E are, respectively, 0.99, 0.99, 0.95, 0.95, and 0.98.

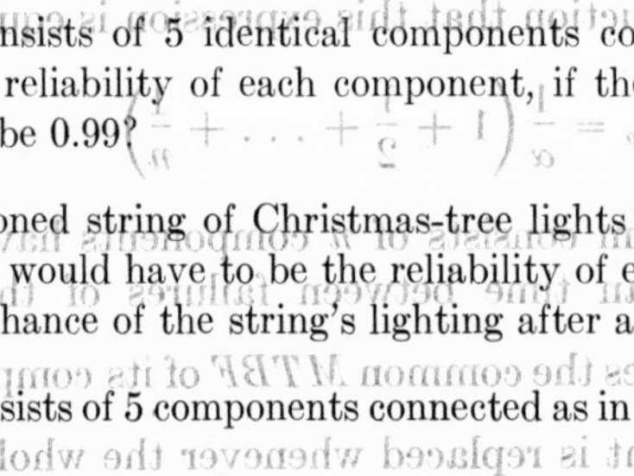

4. Suppose a carrier-based bomber is regarded as a system having the three main components A (aircraft), B (pilot), and C (carrier). Suppose, furthermore, that component B can be regarded as a parallel subsystem consisting of B_1 (pilot), B_2 (copilot), and B_3 (navigator); and C is a parallel subsystem consisting of C_1 (home carrier) and C_2 (alternate landing point). Under given combat conditions, the reliabilities of components A, B_1, B_2, B_3, C_1, and C_2 (defined as the probabilities that they can contribute to the successful completion of the bomber's mission and its safe return) are, respectively, 0.75, 0.95, 0.90, 0.10, 0.85, and 0.50.

(a) What is the reliability of the system?

(b) What is the effect on the system reliability of having a navigator who is also a trained pilot, so that the reliability of B_3 is increased from 0.10 to 0.90?

(c) If the bomber's crew did not have a copilot, what would then be the effect of increasing the reliability of B_3 from 0.10 to 0.90?

5. As has been indicated in the text, one often distinguishes between initial failures, random failures during the useful life of the product, and wear-out failures. Thus, suppose that for a given product the probability of an initial failure (a failure prior to time $t = \alpha$) is θ_1, the probability of a wear-out failure (a failure beyond time $t = \beta$) is θ_2, and that for the interval $\alpha \leq t \leq \beta$ the failure-time density is given by

$$f(t) = \frac{(1 - \theta_1 - \theta_2)}{\beta - \alpha}$$

(a) Find an expression for $F(t)$ for the interval $\alpha \leq t \leq \beta$.

(b) Show that for the interval $\alpha \leq t \leq \beta$ the failure rate is given by

$$Z(t) = \frac{1 - \theta_1 - \theta_2}{(\beta - \alpha)(1 - \theta_1) - (1 - \theta_1 - \theta_2)(t - \alpha)}$$

(c) Suppose that the failure of an automobile tire is considered to be an initial failure if it occurs during the first 500 miles and a wear-out failure if it occurs after 10,000 miles. Assuming that the model given in this exercise holds and that θ_1 and θ_2 equal 0.03 and 0.85, respectively, sketch the graph of the failure-rate function from $t = 500$ to $t = 10,000$. Note that here t is the number of miles driven rather than time.

6. In some reliability problems we are concerned only with initial failures, treating a component as if (for all practical purposes) it never failed, once it has survived past a certain time $t = \alpha$. In a problem like this, it may be reasonable to use the failure rate

$$Z(t) = \begin{cases} \beta \left(1 - \dfrac{t}{\alpha} \right) & \text{for } 0 < t < \alpha \\ 0 & \text{elsewhere} \end{cases}$$

(a) Find expressions for $f(t)$ and $F(t)$.

(b) Show that the probability of an initial failure is given by

$$1 - e^{-\alpha\beta/2}$$

7. A certain component has an exponential life distribution with a failure rate of $\alpha = 0.0025$ failures per hour.

(a) What is the probability that the component will fail during the first 400 hours it is in operation?

(b) What is the probability that two such components will both survive the first 200 hours of operation?

8. A transistor has a constant failure rate of 0.01 per thousand hours.

(a) What is the probability that it will operate satisfactorily for at least 25,000 hours?

(b) What is the 10,000-hour reliability of a circuit consisting of five such transistors connected in series?

9. A system consists of five different components connected in series. Find the $MTBF$ of the system if the five components have exponential time-to-failure distributions with failure rates of 1.2, 1.6, 1.8, 1.0, and 1.5 failures per 1000 hours, respectively.

10. A system containing several identical components in parallel is to have a failure rate of at most 10^{-4} per hour. What is the least number of components that must be used if each has a constant failure rate of 2.5×10^{-4} per hour?

11. A certain part has an exponential life distribution with a mean life, that is, an $MTBF$, of 500 hours.

(a) What is the probability that such a part will last at least 600 hours?

(b) What is the probability that among three such parts at least one will fail during the first 400 hours?

(c) What is the probability that among four such parts exactly two will fail during the first 300 hours?

12. If a component has the Weibull failure-time distribution with the parameters $\alpha = 0.01$ and $\beta = 0.50$, find the probability that it will operate successfully for at least 10,000 hours.

13. Throughout Sections 16.2 and 16.3 we assumed that the products with which we were concerned were in continuous operation. Consequently, the models discussed in these sections do not apply if we want to investigate the ability of electron tubes to withstand successive voltage overloads, the performance of switches which are repeatedly turned on and off, or the ability of a mattress to withstand repeated pounding in a torture test. In each of these cases failure can occur on the xth trial ($x = 1, 2, 3, \ldots$), and it is often assumed

that the probability of failure on the xth trial equals some constant p, provided the item has not failed prior to that trial.

(a) Show that the probability of failure on the xth trial is given by

$$f(x) = p(1 - p)^{x-1}$$

for $x = 1, 2, 3, \ldots$. Why is this probability distribution usually referred to as a *geometric distribution?*

(b) Find $F(x)$ for the probability distribution obtained in part (a).

(c) What is the probability that an electron tube will survive 20 voltage overloads, if the above model holds and the constant probability of failure as the result of any one of the voltage overloads is $p = 0.08$?

16.4 The Exponential Model in Life Testing

An effective and widely used method of handling problems of reliability is that of life testing. For the purpose of such tests, a random sample of n components is selected from a lot, put on test under specified environmental conditions, and the times to failure of the individual components are observed. If each component that fails is immediately replaced by a new one, the resulting life test is called a *replacement test;* otherwise, the life test is called a *nonreplacement test.* Whenever the mean lifetime of the components is so large that it is not practical, or economically feasible, to test each component to failure, the life test may be *truncated*, that is, it may be terminated after the first r failures have occurred ($r \leq n$), or after a fixed period of time has been accumulated.

A special method that is often used when early results are required in connection with very-high-reliability components is that of *accelerated life testing.* In an accelerated life test the components are put on test under environmental conditions that are far more severe than those normally encountered in practice. This causes the components to fail more quickly, and it can drastically reduce both the time required for the test and the number of components that must be placed on test. Accelerated life testing can be used to compare two or more types of components for the purpose of obtaining a rapid assessment of which is the most reliable. Sometimes, preliminary experimentation is carried out to determine the relationship between the proportion of failures that can be expected under nominal conditions and under various levels of accelerated environmental conditions. The methods of Sections 12.4 and 14.2 can be applied in this connection to determine "derating curves," relating the reliability of the component to the severity of the environmental conditions under which it is to operate.

In the remainder of this section we shall assume that the exponential model holds, namely, that the failure-time distribution of each component is given by

$$f(t) = \alpha \cdot e^{-\alpha t} \qquad t > 0, \alpha > 0$$

In what follows, we shall assume that n components are put on test, life testing is discontinued after a fixed number, r ($r \leq n$), of components have failed, and that the observed failure times are $t_1 \leq t_2 \leq \ldots \leq t_r$. We shall be concerned with estimating and testing hypotheses about the mean life of the component, namely, $\mu = 1/\alpha$.

Using theory developed in the article by B. Epstein mentioned in the Bibliography, it can be shown that unbiased estimates of the mean life of the component are given by

$$\hat{\mu} = \frac{T_r}{r}$$

where T_r is the accumulated life on test until the rth failure occurs, and hence

$$T_r = \sum_{i=1}^{r} t_i + (n - r)t_r$$

for *nonreplacement tests* and

$$T_r = nt_r$$

if the test is *with replacement*. Note that if the test is without replacement and $r = n$, $\hat{\mu}$ is simply the mean of the observed times to failure.

To make inferences concerning the mean life μ of the component, we use the fact that $2T_r/\mu$ is a value of a random variable having the chi-square distribution with $2r$ degrees of freedom (see reference to B. Epstein in the Bibliography). With the appropriate expression substituted for T_r, this is true regardless of whether the test is conducted with or without replacement. Thus, in either case a two-sided $1 - \alpha$ confidence interval for μ is given by

$$\frac{2T_r}{\chi_2^2} < \mu < \frac{2T_r}{\chi_1^2}$$

where χ_1^2 and χ_2^2 cut off left- and right-hand tails of area $\alpha/2$ under the chi-square distribution with $2r$ degrees of freedom. (See Exercise 6 on page 381.)

Tests of the null hypothesis that $\mu = \mu_0$ can also be based on the sampling distribution of $2T_r/\mu$, using the appropriate expression for T_r depending on whether the test is with or without replacement. Thus, if the alternative hypothesis is $\mu > \mu_0$, we reject the null hypothesis at the level of significance α when $2T_r/\mu_0$ exceeds χ_α^2, or

◆ $$T_r > \frac{1}{2}\mu_0\chi_\alpha^2$$ ◆

where χ_α^2, to be determined for $2r$ degrees of freedom, is as defined on page 139. In Exercises 2 and 3 on page 380, the reader will be asked to construct and perform similar tests corresponding to the alternative hypotheses $\mu < \mu_0$ and $\mu \neq \mu_0$.

An alternate life-testing procedure consists of discontinuing the test after a fixed accumulated amount of lifetime T has elapsed, and treating the observed number of failures k as the value of a random variable. (In the important special case where n items are tested with replacement for a length of time t^*, we have $T = nt^*$.) Regardless of whether the test is with or without replacement, an *approximate* $1 - \alpha$ confidence interval for the mean life of the component is given by

◆ $$\frac{2T}{\chi_4^2} < \mu < \frac{2T}{\chi_3^2}$$ ◆

Here χ_4^2 cuts off a right-hand tail of area $\alpha/2$ under the chi-square distribution with $2k + 2$ degrees of freedom, while χ_3^2 cuts off a left-hand tail of area $\alpha/2$ under the chi-square distribution with $2k$ degrees of freedom.

To illustrate some of the methods presented in this section, let us consider the following example. Suppose that 50 units are placed on life test (without replacement) and that the test is to be truncated after $r = 10$ of them have failed. We shall suppose, furthermore, that the first 10 failure times are 65, 110, 380, 420, 505, 580, 650, 840, 910, and 950 hours. Thus, $n = 50$, $r = 10$,

$$T_{10} = (65 + 110 + \ldots + 950) + (50 - 10)950$$
$$= 43{,}410 \quad \text{hours}$$

and we estimate the mean life of the component as $\hat{\mu} = \dfrac{43{,}410}{10} = 4341$ hours. The failure rate α is estimated by $1/\hat{\mu} = 0.00023$ failures per hour, or 0.23 failures per thousand hours. Also, a 0.90 confidence interval for μ is given by

$$\frac{2(43{,}410)}{31.410} < \mu < \frac{2(43{,}410)}{10.851}$$

or

$$2764 < \mu < 8001$$

Suppose it were also desired to use the above sample to test whether the failure rate is 0.40 failures per thousand hours against the alternative that the failure rate is less. This is equivalent to a test of the null hypothesis $\mu = 1000/0.40 = 2500$ hours against the alternative that $\mu > 2500$ hours. Using a level of significance of 0.05, we find that the critical value for T_{10}

for this test is given by $\frac{1}{2}(2500)(31.410) = 39{,}263$ hours, and since this is exceeded by the observed value $T_{10} = 43{,}410$, the null hypothesis must be rejected. We conclude that the mean lifetime exceeds 2500 hours, or equivalently, that the failure rate is less than 0.40 failures per thousand hours.

16.5 The Weibull Model in Life Testing

Although life testing of components during the period of useful life is generally based on the exponential model, we have already pointed out that the failure rate of a component may not be constant throughout a period under investigation. In some instances the period of initial failure may be so long that the component's main use is during this period, and in other instances the main purpose of life testing may be that of determining the time to wear-out failure rather than chance failure. In such cases the exponential model generally does not apply, and it is necessary to substitute a more general assumption for that of a constant failure rate.

As we observed on page 367, the Weibull distribution adequately describes the failure times of components when their failure rate either increases or decreases with time. It has the parameters α and β, its formula is given by

$$\blacklozenge \qquad f(t) = \alpha\beta t^{\beta-1} e^{-\alpha t^\beta} \qquad t > 0, \alpha > 0, \beta > 0 \qquad \blacklozenge$$

and it follows (see Exercise 11 on page 381) that the reliability function associated with the Weibull distribution is given by

$$\blacklozenge \qquad R(t) = e^{-\alpha t^\beta} \qquad \blacklozenge$$

We already showed on page 367 that the failure rate leading to the Weibull distribution is given by

$$\blacklozenge \qquad Z(t) = \alpha\beta t^{\beta-1} \qquad \blacklozenge$$

The range of shapes a graph of the Weibull density can take on is very broad, depending primarily on the value of the parameter β. As illustrated in Figure 16.4, the Weibull curve is asymptotic to both axes and highly skewed to the right for values of β less than 1; it is identical to that of the exponential density for $\beta = 1$, and it is "bell-shaped" but skewed for values of β greater than 1.

The mean of the Weibull distribution having the parameters α and β may be obtained by evaluating the integral

$$\mu = \int_0^\infty t \cdot \alpha\beta t^{\beta-1} e^{-\alpha t^\beta} \, dt$$

Making the change of variable $u = \alpha t^\beta$, we get

$$\mu = \alpha^{-1/\beta} \int_0^\infty u^{1/\beta} e^{-u}\, du$$

Recognizing the integral as $\Gamma\left(1 + \dfrac{1}{\beta}\right)$, we find that the mean time to failure for the Weibull model is

♦ $$\mu = \alpha^{-1/\beta}\Gamma\left(1 + \frac{1}{\beta}\right)$$ ♦

The reader will be asked to show in Exercise 12 on page 382 that the variance of this distribution is given by

♦ $$\sigma^2 = \alpha^{-2/\beta}\left\{\Gamma\left(1 + \frac{2}{\beta}\right) - \left[\Gamma\left(1 + \frac{1}{\beta}\right)\right]^2\right\}$$ ♦

Estimates of the parameters α and β of the Weibull distribution are somewhat difficult to obtain. Although there exist analytical methods for

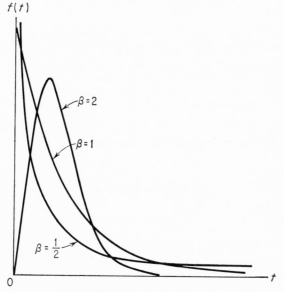

FIG. 16.4 Weibull density functions ($\alpha = 1$)

estimating these parameters, they involve the solution of a system of transcendental equations, and they will not be presented here. Instead, a more rapid and commonly used method, based on a graphical technique, will be described. This method is based on the fact that the reliability function of the Weibull distribution can be transformed into a linear function of $\ln t$ by means of a double-logarithmic transformation. Taking the natural logarithm of $R(t)$, we obtain

$$\ln R(t) = -\alpha t^\beta \qquad \text{or} \qquad \ln \frac{1}{R(t)} = \alpha t^\beta$$

Again taking logarithms, we have

$$\blacklozenge \qquad \ln \ln \frac{1}{R(t)} = \ln \alpha + \beta \cdot \ln t \qquad \blacklozenge$$

and it can be seen that the right-hand side is linear in $\ln t$.

To estimate α and β we require estimates of $R(t)$ for various values of t, and the usual procedure is to place n units on life test and observe their failure times. If the ith unit fails at time t_i, we estimate $F(t_i) = 1 - R(t_i)$ by the same method as on page 112, namely, we use the estimator

$$\widehat{F(t_i)} = \frac{i - 1/2}{n}$$

Before going any further, it is customary to check whether it is actually reasonable to use the Weibull model. To this end, we plot points having the coordinates t_i and $\widehat{F(t_i)}$ on special graph paper having its scales transformed so that the divisions on the horizontal axis are proportional to $\ln t$ and those on the vertical scale are proportional to $\ln \ln \dfrac{1}{1 - F(t)}$. If the points fall reasonably close to a straight line, it can be assumed that the underlying failure-time distribution is of the Weibull type. The parameters α and β of this distribution can then be estimated by applying the linear regression methods of Chapter 12 to fit a straight line to the transformed data.

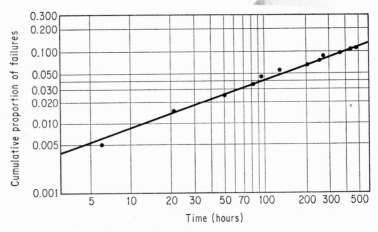

FIG. 16.5 Weibull failure-time distribution

To illustrate this procedure, let us consider the following numerical example. Suppose that a sample of 100 components is put on life test for 500 hours and that the times to failure of the 12 components that failed during the test are as follows: 6, 21, 50, 84, 95, 130, 205, 260, 270, 370, 440, and 480 hours. These points are plotted in Figure 16.5 on the transformed scales previously described, and it can be seen that they fall fairly close to a straight line.

The parameters α and β are estimated by applying the method of least squares to the transformed points (x_i, y_i), where

$$x_i = \ln t_i$$

$$y_i = \ln \ln \frac{1}{1 - \widehat{F}(t_i)}$$

Thus, in our numerical example we obtain

$\widehat{F}(t_i)$	t_i	x_i	y_i
0.005	6	1.79	-5.30
0.015	21	3.04	-4.20
0.025	50	3.91	-3.68
0.035	84	4.43	-3.33
0.045	95	4.55	-3.08
0.055	130	4.87	-2.87
0.065	205	5.32	-2.70
0.075	260	5.56	-2.55
0.085	270	5.60	-2.42
0.095	370	5.91	-2.30
0.105	440	6.09	-2.20
0.115	480	6.17	-2.10

and, by the methods of Section 12.1, the regression line becomes

$$y = -6.44 + 0.71x$$

Note that in calculating the values of y_i for the above table, it is convenient to use the approximation $\ln \ln \frac{1}{1 - z} \simeq \ln z$ (see Exercise 13 on page 382) for small values of $\widehat{F}(t_i)$.

Thus, the parameter β of the underlying Weibull distribution is estimated as $\hat{\beta} = 0.71$, and α is estimated as $\hat{\alpha} = e^{-6.44} = 0.0016$. It follows that the mean time to failure is estimated as

$$\hat{\mu} = (0.0016)^{-1/0.71} \Gamma\left(1 + \frac{1}{0.71}\right)$$

which equals approximately 11,000 hours. Also, values of the failure-rate function may be obtained by substituting for t into

$$\widehat{Z(t)} = (0.0016)(0.71)t^{-0.29}$$

Since $\hat{\beta} < 1$ the failure rate is decreasing with time. After one hour ($t = 1$), units are failing at the rate of $(0.0016)(0.71) = 0.00114$ units per hour, and after 1000 hours the failure rate has decreased to $(0.00114)(1000)^{-0.29} = 0.00015$ units per hour.

EXERCISES

1. In a life test with replacement, 20 small electric motors were put into continuous operation, and the first five failures occurred after 22, 37, 61, 95, and 130 hours.

   (a) Assuming the exponential model, construct a 0.99 confidence interval for the mean life of this kind of motor.

   (b) To check the manufacturer's claim that the mean life of these motors is at least 500 hours, test the null hypothesis $\mu = 500$ against an appropriate alternative, so that the burden of proof is put on the manufacturer. Use $\alpha = 0.05$.

2. Suppose that 100 units are put on life test, each unit that fails is immediately replaced, and the test is discontinued after 10 units have failed. If the tenth failure occurred at 580 hours,

   (a) construct a 0.95 confidence interval for the mean life of the units;

   (b) test at the 0.05 level of significance whether or not the mean life is less than 8000 hours.

3. To investigate the average time to failure of a certain airplane part subjected to continuous vibrations, eight such parts were subjected to specified environmental conditions and their times to failure were 112, 160, 174, 210, 238, 280, 315, and 360 hours.

   (a) Assuming the exponential model, construct a 0.95 confidence interval for the mean life of the part under the given environmental conditions.

   (b) Assuming the exponential model, test the null hypothesis that the mean life of the part under the given environmental conditions is 300 hours against the alternative hypothesis that $\mu \neq 300$ hours. Use a level of significance of 0.01.

4. Twenty assemblies are put on life test without replacement, and the test is truncated after five failures. If the first five failures occurred at 156, 179, 212, 350, and 485 hours,

   (a) find a 0.90 confidence interval for the failure rate of these assemblies;

   (b) test the null hypothesis that the failure rate is 0.0005 failures per hour against the alternative that it is less than 0.0005, using the 0.01 level of significance.

5. In life testing we are sometimes interested in establishing *tolerance limits* for the life of a component (see Section 15.5); in particular, we may be interested in a one-sided tolerance limit t^*, for which we can assert with a degree of confidence $1 - \alpha$ that at least $100 \cdot P$ per cent of the components have a life exceeding t^*. Using the exponential model, it can be shown that a good approximation is given by

$$t^* = \frac{-2T_r(\ln P)}{\chi_\alpha^2}$$

where T_r is as defined on page 374 and the value of χ_α^2 is to be obtained from Table V with $2r$ degrees of freedom.

(a) Using the data of Exercise 1, establish a lower tolerance limit for which one can assert with a degree of confidence of 0.95 that it is exceeded by at least 80 per cent of the lifetimes of the motors.

(b) Using the data of Exercise 3, establish a lower tolerance limit for which one can assert with a degree of confidence of 0.99 that it is exceeded by at least 90 per cent of the lifetimes of the given airplane parts.

6. Using the fact that $2T_r/\mu$ is a value of a random variable having the chi-square distribution with $2r$ degrees of freedom, derive the confidence interval for μ given on page 374.

7. A sample of 500 high-reliability capacitors was placed on life test for 1000 hours and there were no failures; the test was then terminated. Find a 0.95 *lower* confidence limit for the mean life of the capacitors.

8. Two hundred devices are put on life test, and the times to failure (in hours) of the first 10 that fail are as follows: 0.7, 1.4, 1.9, 3.0, 5.5, 8.0, 17.5, 26.0, 44.0, and 80.0. Assuming a Weibull failure-time distribution, estimate the parameters α and β as well as the failure rate at 100 hours. How does this value of the failure rate compare with the value we would obtain if we assumed the exponential model?

9. To investigate the performance of a missile component, a laboratory puts 50 of the components on life test (without replacement) under specified environmental conditions, and the first 10 failures are observed after 18, 36, 40, 53, 71, 90, 106, 127, 149, and 165 minutes. Using the Weibull model, estimate the mean life of the component. How does this value compare with the mean life we would obtain assuming the exponential model?

10. Using the estimates of the parameters of the Weibull model obtained in Exercise 9, estimate the probability that this kind of missile component will perform satisfactorily for at least 100 minutes.

11. Show that the reliability function associated with the Weibull failure-time distribution is given by

$$R(t) = e^{-\alpha t^\beta}$$

12. Derive the formula for the variance of the Weibull distribution given on page 377.

13. Show that $\ln \ln \dfrac{1}{1-z}$ can be approximated by $\ln z$ for small values of z.

[*Hint:* Note that $\dfrac{1}{1-z} = 1 + z + z^2 + z^3 \ldots$ for $|z| < 1$, and then use the Maclaurin's series for $\ln (1 + x)$.]

BIBLIOGRAPHY

1. Engineering Statistics

Bowker, A. H., and Lieberman, G. J., *Engineering Statistics*. Englewood Cliffs, N.J.: Prentice-Hall, 1959.

Brownlee, K. A., *Statistical Theory and Methodology in Science and Engineering*. New York: John Wiley, 1960.

Derman, C., and Klein, M., *Probability and Statistical Inference for Engineers*. New York: Oxford University Press, 1959.

Ehrenfeld, S., and Littauer, S. B., *Introduction to Statistical Method*. New York: McGraw-Hill, 1964.

Hald, A., *Statistical Theory with Engineering Applications*. New York: John Wiley, 1952.

2. Theoretical Statistics

Anderson, R. L., and Bancroft, T. A., *Statistical Theory in Research*. New York: McGraw-Hill, 1952.

Brunk, H. D., *An Introduction to Mathematical Statistics*. Boston: Ginn and Co., 1960.

Feller, W., *An Introduction to Probability Theory and Its Applications*, 2nd ed. New York: John Wiley, 1957.

Freund, J. E., *Mathematical Statistics*. Englewood Cliffs, N.J.: Prentice-Hall, 1962.

Goldberg, S., *Probability, An Introduction*. Englewood Cliffs, N.J.: Prentice-Hall, 1960.

Hoel, P., *Introduction to Mathematical Statistics*, 3rd ed. New York: John Wiley, 1962.

Mann, H. B., *Analysis and Design of Experiments*. New York: Dover, 1949.

Mood, A. M., and Graybill, F. A., *Introduction to the Theory of Statistics*, 2nd ed. New York: McGraw-Hill, 1963.

3. Experimental Designs and Analysis of Variance

Chew, V., *Experimental Designs in Industry*. New York: John Wiley, 1958.

Cochran, W. G., and Cox, G. M., *Experimental Designs*, 2nd ed. New York: John Wiley, 1957.

Davies, O. L., *The Design and Analysis of Industrial Experiments*. New York: Hafner, 1956.

Federer, W. T., *Experimental Designs, Theory and Application*. New York: Macmillan, 1955.

Finney, D. J., *Experimental Design and Its Statistical Basis*. Chicago: University of Chicago Press, 1955.

Fisher, R. A., *The Design of Experiments*, 4th ed. New York: Hafner, 1947.

Freund, J. E., Livermore, P. E., and Miller, I., *Manual of Experimental Statistics*. Englewood Cliffs, N.J.: Prentice-Hall, 1960.

Graybill, F. A., *An Introduction to Linear Statistical Models*, Vol. I. New York: McGraw-Hill, 1961. P. 163

Snedecor, G. W., *Statistical Methods*, 5th ed. Ames, Iowa: Iowa State University Press, 1956.

4. Special Topics

Ackoff, R. L., *Progress in Operations Research*, Vol. I. New York: John Wiley, 1961.

Bazovsky, I., *Reliability: Theory and Practice*. Englewood Cliffs, N.J.: Prentice-Hall, 1961.

Burr, I. W., *Engineering Statistics and Quality Control*. New York: McGraw-Hill, 1953.

Charnes, A., and Cooper, W. W., *Management Models and Industrial Applications of Linear Programming*, Vols. I and II. New York: John Wiley, 1961.

Cowden, D. J., *Statistical Methods in Quality Control.* Englewood Cliffs, N.J.: Prentice-Hall, 1957.

Epstein, B., "Statistical Life Test Acceptance Procedures," *Technometrics*, Vol. 2, November 1960.

Wald, A., *Sequential Analysis.* New York: John Wiley, 1947.

Zelen, M., *Statistical Theory of Reliability.* Madison, Wisc.: University of Wisconsin Press, 1963.

5. Statistical Tables

Kitagawa, T., and Mitome, M., *Tables for the Design of Factorial Experiments.* New York: Dover, 1955.

Military Standard 105D. Washington, D.C.: U.S. Government Printing Office, 1963.

National Bureau of Standards, *Tables of the Binomial Distribution.* Washington, D.C.: U.S. Government Printing Office, 1950.

Owen, D. B., *Handbook of Statistical Tables.* Reading, Mass.: Addison-Wesley, 1962.

Pearson, E. S., and Hartley, H. O., *Biometrika Tables for Statisticians.* Cambridge: Cambridge University Press, 1954.

RAND Corporation, *A Million Random Digits with 100,000 Normal Deviates.* New York: Free Press of Glencoe, 1955.

Romig, H. G., *50–100 Binomial Tables.* New York: John Wiley, 1953.

STATISTICAL TABLES

387

Table I

BINOMIAL DISTRIBUTION FUNCTION

at most

$$B(x; n, p) = \sum_{k=0}^{x} \binom{n}{k} p^k (1 - p)^{n-k}$$

n	x	0.05	0.10	0.15	0.20	0.25	0.30	0.35	0.40	0.45	0.50
2	0	0.9025	0.8100	0.7225	0.6400	0.5625	0.4900	0.4225	0.3600	0.3025	0.2500
	1	0.9975	0.9900	0.9775	0.9600	0.9375	0.9100	0.8775	0.8400	0.7975	0.7500
3	0	0.8574	0.7290	0.6141	0.5120	0.4219	0.3430	0.2746	0.2160	0.1664	0.1250
	1	0.9928	0.9720	0.9392	0.8960	0.8438	0.7840	0.7182	0.6480	0.5748	0.5000
	2	0.9999	0.9990	0.9966	0.9920	0.9844	0.9730	0.9571	0.9360	0.9089	0.8750
4	0	0.8145	0.6561	0.5220	0.4096	0.3164	0.2401	0.1785	0.1296	0.0915	0.0625
	1	0.9860	0.9477	0.8905	0.8192	0.7383	0.6517	0.5630	0.4752	0.3910	0.3125
	2	0.9995	0.9963	0.9880	0.9728	0.9492	0.9163	0.8735	0.8208	0.7585	0.6875
	3	1.0000	0.9999	0.9995	0.9984	0.9961	0.9919	0.9850	0.9744	0.9590	0.9375
5	0	0.7738	0.5905	0.4437	0.3277	0.2373	0.1681	0.1160	0.0778	0.0503	0.0312
	1	0.9774	0.9185	0.8352	0.7373	0.6328	0.5282	0.4284	0.3370	0.2562	0.1875
	2	0.9988	0.9914	0.9734	0.9421	0.8965	0.8369	0.7648	0.6826	0.5931	0.5000
	3	1.0000	0.9995	0.9978	0.9933	0.9844	0.9692	0.9460	0.9130	0.8688	0.8125
	4	1.0000	1.0000	0.9999	0.9997	0.9990	0.9976	0.9947	0.9898	0.9815	0.9688
6	0	0.7351	0.5314	0.3771	0.2621	0.1780	0.1176	0.0754	0.0467	0.0277	0.0156
	1	0.9672	0.8857	0.7765	0.6554	0.5339	0.4202	0.3191	0.2333	0.1636	0.1094
	2	0.9978	0.9842	0.9527	0.9011	0.8306	0.7443	0.6471	0.5443	0.4415	0.3438
	3	0.9999	0.9987	0.9941	0.9830	0.9624	0.9295	0.8826	0.8208	0.7447	0.6562
	4	1.0000	0.9999	0.9996	0.9984	0.9954	0.9891	0.9777	0.9590	0.9308	0.8906
	5	1.0000	1.0000	1.0000	0.9999	0.9998	0.9993	0.9982	0.9959	0.9917	0.9844
7	0	0.6983	0.4783	0.3206	0.2097	0.1335	0.0824	0.0490	0.0280	0.0152	0.0078
	1	0.9556	0.8503	0.7166	0.5767	0.4449	0.3294	0.2338	0.1586	0.1024	0.0625
	2	0.9962	0.9743	0.9262	0.8520	0.7564	0.6471	0.5323	0.4199	0.3164	0.2266
	3	0.9998	0.9973	0.9879	0.9667	0.9294	0.8740	0.8002	0.7102	0.6083	0.5000
	4	1.0000	0.9998	0.9988	0.9953	0.9871	0.9712	0.9444	0.9037	0.8471	0.7734
	5	1.0000	1.0000	0.9999	0.9996	0.9987	0.9962	0.9910	0.9812	0.9643	0.9375
	6	1.0000	1.0000	1.0000	1.0000	0.9999	0.9998	0.9994	0.9984	0.9963	0.9922
8	0	0.6634	0.4305	0.2725	0.1678	0.1001	0.0576	0.0319	0.0168	0.0084	0.0039
	1	0.9428	0.8131	0.6572	0.5033	0.3671	0.2553	0.1691	0.1064	0.0632	0.0352
	2	0.9942	0.9619	0.8948	0.7969	0.6785	0.5518	0.4278	0.3154	0.2201	0.1445
	3	0.9996	0.9950	0.9786	0.9437	0.8862	0.8059	0.7064	0.5941	0.4770	0.3633
	4	1.0000	0.9996	0.9971	0.9896	0.9727	0.9420	0.8939	0.8263	0.7396	0.6367
	5	1.0000	1.0000	0.9998	0.9988	0.9958	0.9887	0.9747	0.9502	0.9115	0.8555
	6	1.0000	1.0000	1.0000	0.9999	0.9996	0.9987	0.9964	0.9915	0.9819	0.9648
	7	1.0000	1.0000	1.0000	1.0000	1.0000	0.9999	0.9998	0.9993	0.9983	0.9961
9	0	0.6302	0.3874	0.2316	0.1342	0.0751	0.0404	0.0207	0.0101	0.0046	0.0020
	1	0.9288	0.7748	0.5995	0.4362	0.3003	0.1960	0.1211	0.0705	0.0385	0.0195
	2	0.9916	0.9470	0.8591	0.7382	0.6007	0.4628	0.3373	0.2318	0.1495	0.0898
	3	0.9994	0.9917	0.9661	0.9144	0.8343	0.7297	0.6089	0.4826	0.3614	0.2539
	4	1.0000	0.9991	0.9944	0.9804	0.9511	0.9012	0.8283	0.7334	0.6214	0.5000
	5	1.0000	0.9999	0.9994	0.9969	0.9900	0.9747	0.9464	0.9006	0.8342	0.7461
	6	1.0000	1.0000	1.0000	0.9997	0.9987	0.9957	0.9888	0.9750	0.9502	0.9102
	7	1.0000	1.0000	1.0000	1.0000	0.9999	0.9996	0.9986	0.9962	0.9909	0.9805
	8	1.0000	1.0000	1.0000	1.0000	1.0000	1.0000	0.9999	0.9997	0.9992	0.9980

at most ; p > .5 : $B(x; n, p) = 1 - B(n - x - 1; n, 1 - p)$

exactly $b(x; n, p) = B(x; n, p) - B(x - 1; n, p)$

exactly ; p > .5 : $b(x; n, p) = B(n - x; n, 1 - p) - B(n - x - 1; n, 1 - p)$

Table I

BINOMIAL DISTRIBUTION FUNCTION (*Continued*)

n	x	0.05	0.10	0.15	0.20	0.25	0.30	0.35	0.40	0.45	0.50
10	0	0.5987	0.3487	0.1969	0.1074	0.0563	0.0282	0.0135	0.0060	0.0025	0.0010
	1	0.9139	0.7361	0.5443	0.3758	0.2440	0.1493	0.0860	0.0464	0.0232	0.0107
	2	0.9885	0.9298	0.8202	0.6778	0.5256	0.3828	0.2616	0.1673	0.0996	0.0547
	3	0.9990	0.9872	0.9500	0.8791	0.7759	0.6496	0.5138	0.3823	0.2660	0.1719
	4	0.9999	0.9984	0.9901	0.9672	0.9219	0.8497	0.7515	0.6331	0.5044	0.3770
	5	1.0000	0.9999	0.9986	0.9936	0.9803	0.9527	0.9051	0.8338	0.7384	0.6230
	6	1.0000	1.0000	0.9999	0.9991	0.9965	0.9894	0.9740	0.9452	0.8980	0.8281
	7	1.0000	1.0000	1.0000	0.9999	0.9996	0.9984	0.9952	0.9877	0.9726	0.9453
	8	1.0000	1.0000	1.0000	1.0000	1.0000	0.9999	0.9995	0.9983	0.9955	0.9893
	9	1.0000	1.0000	1.0000	1.0000	1.0000	1.0000	1.0000	0.9999	0.9997	0.9990
11	0	0.5688	0.3138	0.1673	0.0859	0.0422	0.0198	0.0088	0.0036	0.0014	0.0005
	1	0.8981	0.6974	0.4922	0.3221	0.1971	0.1130	0.0606	0.0302	0.0139	0.0059
	2	0.9848	0.9104	0.7788	0.6174	0.4552	0.3127	0.2001	0.1189	0.0652	0.0327
	3	0.9984	0.9815	0.9306	0.8389	0.7133	0.5696	0.4256	0.2963	0.1911	0.1133
	4	0.9999	0.9972	0.9841	0.9496	0.8854	0.7897	0.6683	0.5328	0.3971	0.2744
	5	1.0000	0.9997	0.9973	0.9883	0.9657	0.9218	0.8513	0.7535	0.6331	0.5000
	6	1.0000	1.0000	0.9997	0.9980	0.9924	0.9784	0.9499	0.9006	0.8262	0.7256
	7	1.0000	1.0000	1.0000	0.9998	0.9988	0.9957	0.9878	0.9707	0.9390	0.8867
	8	1.0000	1.0000	1.0000	1.0000	0.9999	0.9994	0.9980	0.9941	0.9852	0.9673
	9	1.0000	1.0000	1.0000	1.0000	1.0000	1.0000	0.9998	0.9993	0.9978	0.9941
	10	1.0000	1.0000	1.0000	1.0000	1.0000	1.0000	1.0000	1.0000	0.9998	0.9995
12	0	0.5404	0.2824	0.1422	0.0687	0.0317	0.0138	0.0057	0.0022	0.0008	0.0002
	1	0.8816	0.6590	0.4435	0.2749	0.1584	0.0850	0.0424	0.0196	0.0083	0.0032
	2	0.9804	0.8891	0.7358	0.5583	0.3907	0.2528	0.1513	0.0834	0.0421	0.0193
	3	0.9978	0.9744	0.9078	0.7946	0.6488	0.4925	0.3467	0.2253	0.1345	0.0730
	4	0.9998	0.9957	0.9761	0.9274	0.8424	0.7237	0.5833	0.4382	0.3044	0.1938
	5	1.0000	0.9995	0.9954	0.9806	0.9456	0.8822	0.7873	0.6652	0.5269	0.3872
	6	1.0000	0.9999	0.9993	0.9961	0.9857	0.9614	0.9154	0.8418	0.7393	0.6128
	7	1.0000	1.0000	0.9999	0.9994	0.9972	0.9905	0.9745	0.9427	0.8883	0.8062
	8	1.0000	1.0000	1.0000	0.9999	0.9996	0.9983	0.9944	0.9847	0.9644	0.9270
	9	1.0000	1.0000	1.0000	1.0000	1.0000	0.9998	0.9992	0.9972	0.9921	0.9807
	10	1.0000	1.0000	1.0000	1.0000	1.0000	1.0000	0.9999	0.9997	0.9989	0.9968
	11	1.0000	1.0000	1.0000	1.0000	1.0000	1.0000	1.0000	1.0000	0.9999	0.9998
13	0	0.5133	0.2542	0.1209	0.0550	0.0238	0.0097	0.0037	0.0013	0.0004	0.0001
	1	0.8646	0.6213	0.3983	0.2336	0.1267	0.0637	0.0296	0.0126	0.0049	0.0017
	2	0.9755	0.8661	0.6920	0.5017	0.3326	0.2025	0.1132	0.0579	0.0269	0.0112
	3	0.9969	0.9658	0.8820	0.7473	0.5843	0.4206	0.2783	0.1686	0.0929	0.0461
	4	0.9997	0.9935	0.9658	0.9009	0.7940	0.6543	0.5005	0.3530	0.2279	0.1334
	5	1.0000	0.9991	0.9925	0.9700	0.9198	0.8346	0.7159	0.5744	0.4268	0.2905
	6	1.0000	0.9999	0.9987	0.9930	0.9757	0.9376	0.8705	0.7712	0.6437	0.5000
	7	1.0000	1.0000	0.9998	0.9988	0.9944	0.9818	0.9538	0.9023	0.8212	0.7095
	8	1.0000	1.0000	1.0000	0.9998	0.9990	0.9960	0.9874	0.9679	0.9302	0.8666
	9	1.0000	1.0000	1.0000	1.0000	0.9999	0.9993	0.9975	0.9922	0.9797	0.9539
	10	1.0000	1.0000	1.0000	1.0000	1.0000	0.9999	0.9997	0.9987	0.9959	0.9888
	11	1.0000	1.0000	1.0000	1.0000	1.0000	1.0000	1.0000	0.9999	0.9995	0.9983
	12	1.0000	1.0000	1.0000	1.0000	1.0000	1.0000	1.0000	1.0000	1.0000	0.9999
14	0	0.4877	0.2288	0.1028	0.0440	0.0178	0.0068	0.0024	0.0008	0.0002	0.0001
	1	0.8470	0.5846	0.3567	0.1979	0.1010	0.0475	0.0205	0.0081	0.0029	0.0009

at least x of n : $\sum\limits_{x}^{m} b(x; n, p)$ if $p > .5$ $1 - \sum\limits_{x}^{2} b(n-x-1; n, 1-p)$

$B(x; n, p) =$ at most

Table I

BINOMIAL DISTRIBUTION FUNCTION (*Continued*)

n	x	0.05	0.10	0.15	0.20	0.25	p 0.30	0.35	0.40	0.45	0.50
14	2	0.9699	0.8416	0.6479	0.4481	0.2811	0.1608	0.0839	0.0398	0.0170	0.0065
	3	0.9958	0.9559	0.8535	0.6982	0.5213	0.3552	0.2205	0.1243	0.0632	0.0287
	4	0.9996	0.9908	0.9533	0.8702	0.7415	0.5842	0.4227	0.2793	0.1672	0.0898
	5	1.0000	0.9985	0.9885	0.9561	0.8883	0.7805	0.6405	0.4859	0.3373	0.2120
	6	1.0000	0.9998	0.9978	0.9884	0.9617	0.9067	0.8164	0.6925	0.5461	0.3953
	7	1.0000	1.0000	0.9997	0.9976	0.9897	0.9685	0.9247	0.8499	0.7414	0.6047
	8	1.0000	1.0000	1.0000	0.9996	0.9978	0.9917	0.9757	0.9417	0.8811	0.7880
	9	1.0000	1.0000	1.0000	1.0000	0.9997	0.9983	0.9940	0.9825	0.9574	0.9102
	10	1.0000	1.0000	1.0000	1.0000	1.0000	0.9998	0.9989	0.9961	0.9886	0.9713
	11	1.0000	1.0000	1.0000	1.0000	1.0000	1.0000	0.9999	0.9994	0.9978	0.9935
	12	1.0000	1.0000	1.0000	1.0000	1.0000	1.0000	1.0000	0.9999	0.9997	0.9991
	13	1.0000	1.0000	1.0000	1.0000	1.0000	1.0000	1.0000	1.0000	1.0000	0.9999
15	0	0.4633	0.2059	0.0874	0.0352	0.0134	0.0047	0.0016	0.0005	0.0001	0.0000
	1	0.8290	0.5490	0.3186	0.1671	0.0802	0.0353	0.0142	0.0052	0.0017	0.0005
	2	0.9638	0.8159	0.6042	0.3980	0.2361	0.1268	0.0617	0.0271	0.0107	0.0037
	3	0.9945	0.9444	0.8227	0.6482	0.4613	0.2969	0.1727	0.0905	0.0424	0.0176
	4	0.9994	0.9873	0.9383	0.8358	0.6865	0.5155	0.3519	0.2173	0.1204	0.0592
	5	0.9999	0.9978	0.9832	0.9389	0.8516	0.7216	0.5643	0.4032	0.2608	0.1509
	6	1.0000	0.9997	0.9964	0.9819	0.9434	0.8689	0.7548	0.6098	0.4522	0.3036
	7	1.0000	1.0000	0.9996	0.9958	0.9827	0.9500	0.8868	0.7869	0.6535	0.5000
	8	1.0000	1.0000	0.9999	0.9992	0.9958	0.9848	0.9578	0.9050	0.8182	0.6964
	9	1.0000	1.0000	1.0000	0.9999	0.9992	0.9963	0.9876	0.9662	0.9231	0.8491
	10	1.0000	1.0000	1.0000	1.0000	0.9999	0.9993	0.9972	0.9907	0.9745	0.9408
	11	1.0000	1.0000	1.0000	1.0000	1.0000	0.9999	0.9995	0.9981	0.9937	0.9824
	12	1.0000	1.0000	1.0000	1.0000	1.0000	1.0000	0.9999	0.9997	0.9989	0.9963
	13	1.0000	1.0000	1.0000	1.0000	1.0000	1.0000	1.0000	1.0000	0.9999	0.9995
	14	1.0000	1.0000	1.0000	1.0000	1.0000	1.0000	1.0000	1.0000	1.0000	1.0000
16	0	0.4401	0.1853	0.0743	0.0281	0.0100	0.0033	0.0010	0.0003	0.0001	0.0000
	1	0.8108	0.5147	0.2839	0.1407	0.0635	0.0261	0.0098	0.0033	0.0010	0.0003
	2	0.9571	0.7892	0.5614	0.3518	0.1971	0.0994	0.0451	0.0183	0.0066	0.0021
	3	0.9930	0.9316	0.7899	0.5981	0.4050	0.2459	0.1339	0.0651	0.0281	0.0106
	4	0.9991	0.9830	0.9209	0.7982	0.6302	0.4499	0.2892	0.1666	0.0853	0.0384
	5	0.9999	0.9967	0.9765	0.9183	0.8103	0.6598	0.4900	0.3288	0.1976	0.1051
	6	1.0000	0.9995	0.9944	0.9733	0.9204	0.8247	0.6881	0.5272	0.3660	0.2272
	7	1.0000	0.9999	0.9989	0.9930	0.9729	0.9256	0.8406	0.7161	0.5629	0.4018
	8	1.0000	1.0000	0.9998	0.9985	0.9925	0.9743	0.9329	0.8577	0.7441	0.5982
	9	1.0000	1.0000	1.0000	0.9998	0.9984	0.9929	0.9771	0.9417	0.8759	0.7728
	10	1.0000	1.0000	1.0000	1.0000	0.9997	0.9984	0.9938	0.9809	0.9514	0.8949
	11	1.0000	1.0000	1.0000	1.0000	1.0000	0.9997	0.9987	0.9951	0.9851	0.9616
	12	1.0000	1.0000	1.0000	1.0000	1.0000	1.0000	0.9998	0.9991	0.9965	0.9894
	13	1.0000	1.0000	1.0000	1.0000	1.0000	1.0000	1.0000	0.9999	0.9994	0.9979
	14	1.0000	1.0000	1.0000	1.0000	1.0000	1.0000	1.0000	1.0000	1.0000	0.9997
	15	1.0000	1.0000	1.0000	1.0000	1.0000	1.0000	1.0000	1.0000	1.0000	1.0000
17	0	0.4181	0.1668	0.0631	0.0225	0.0075	0.0023	0.0007	0.0002	0.0000	0.0000
	1	0.7922	0.4818	0.2525	0.1182	0.0501	0.0193	0.0067	0.0021	0.0006	0.0001
	2	0.9497	0.7618	0.5198	0.3096	0.1637	0.0774	0.0327	0.0123	0.0041	0.0012
	3	0.9912	0.9174	0.7556	0.5489	0.3530	0.2019	0.1028	0.0464	0.0184	0.0064
	4	0.9988	0.9779	0.9013	0.7582	0.5739	0.3887	0.2348	0.1260	0.0596	0.0245

Table I

BINOMIAL DISTRIBUTION FUNCTION (*Continued*)

n	x	0.05	0.10	0.15	0.20	0.25	0.30	0.35	0.40	0.45	0.50
17	5	0.9999	0.9953	0.9681	0.8943	0.7653	0.5968	0.4197	0.2639	0.1471	0.0717
	6	1.0000	0.9992	0.9917	0.9623	0.8929	0.7752	0.6188	0.4478	0.2902	0.1662
	7	1.0000	0.9999	0.9983	0.9891	0.9598	0.8954	0.7872	0.6405	0.4743	0.3145
	8	1.0000	1.0000	0.9997	0.9974	0.9876	0.9597	0.9006	0.8011	0.6626	0.5000
	9	1.0000	1.0000	1.0000	0.9995	0.9969	0.9873	0.9617	0.9081	0.8166	0.6855
	10	1.0000	1.0000	1.0000	0.9999	0.9994	0.9968	0.9880	0.9652	0.9174	0.8338
	11	1.0000	1.0000	1.0000	1.0000	0.9999	0.9993	0.9970	0.9894	0.9699	0.9283
	12	1.0000	1.0000	1.0000	1.0000	1.0000	0.9999	0.9994	0.9975	0.9914	0.9755
	13	1.0000	1.0000	1.0000	1.0000	1.0000	1.0000	0.9999	0.9995	0.9981	0.9936
	14	1.0000	1.0000	1.0000	1.0000	1.0000	1.0000	1.0000	0.9999	0.9997	0.9988
	15	1.0000	1.0000	1.0000	1.0000	1.0000	1.0000	1.0000	1.0000	1.0000	0.9999
	16	1.0000	1.0000	1.0000	1.0000	1.0000	1.0000	1.0000	1.0000	1.0000	1.0000
18	0	0.3972	0.1501	0.0536	0.0180	0.0056	0.0016	0.0004	0.0001	0.0000	0.0000
	1	0.7735	0.4503	0.2241	0.0991	0.0395	0.0142	0.0046	0.0013	0.0003	0.0001
	2	0.9419	0.7338	0.4797	0.2713	0.1353	0.0600	0.0236	0.0082	0.0025	0.0007
	3	0.9891	0.9018	0.7202	0.5010	0.3057	0.1646	0.0783	0.0328	0.0120	0.0038
	4	0.9985	0.9718	0.8794	0.7164	0.5187	0.3327	0.1886	0.0942	0.0411	0.0154
	5	0.9998	0.9936	0.9581	0.8671	0.7175	0.5344	0.3550	0.2088	0.1077	0.0481
	6	1.0000	0.9988	0.9882	0.9487	0.8610	0.7217	0.5491	0.3743	0.2258	0.1189
	7	1.0000	0.9998	0.9973	0.9837	0.9431	0.8593	0.7283	0.5634	0.3915	0.2403
	8	1.0000	1.0000	0.9995	0.9957	0.9807	0.9404	0.8609	0.7368	0.5778	0.4073
	9	1.0000	1.0000	0.9999	0.9991	0.9946	0.9790	0.9403	0.8653	0.7473	0.5927
	10	1.0000	1.0000	1.0000	0.9998	0.9988	0.9939	0.9788	0.9424	0.8720	0.7597
	11	1.0000	1.0000	1.0000	1.0000	0.9998	0.9986	0.9938	0.9797	0.9463	0.8811
	12	1.0000	1.0000	1.0000	1.0000	1.0000	0.9997	0.9986	0.9942	0.9817	0.9519
	13	1.0000	1.0000	1.0000	1.0000	1.0000	1.0000	0.9997	0.9987	0.9951	0.9846
	14	1.0000	1.0000	1.0000	1.0000	1.0000	1.0000	1.0000	0.9998	0.9990	0.9962
	15	1.0000	1.0000	1.0000	1.0000	1.0000	1.0000	1.0000	1.0000	0.9999	0.9993
	16	1.0000	1.0000	1.0000	1.0000	1.0000	1.0000	1.0000	1.0000	1.0000	0.9999
19	0	0.3774	0.1351	0.0456	0.0144	0.0042	0.0011	0.0003	0.0001	0.0000	0.0000
	1	0.7547	0.4203	0.1985	0.0829	0.0310	0.0104	0.0031	0.0008	0.0002	0.0000
	2	0.9335	0.7054	0.4413	0.2369	0.1113	0.0462	0.0170	0.0055	0.0015	0.0004
	3	0.9868	0.8850	0.6841	0.4551	0.2630	0.1332	0.0591	0.0230	0.0077	0.0022
	4	0.9980	0.9648	0.8556	0.6733	0.4654	0.2822	0.1500	0.0696	0.0280	0.0096
	5	0.9998	0.9914	0.9463	0.8369	0.6678	0.4739	0.2968	0.1629	0.0777	0.0318
	6	1.0000	0.9983	0.9837	0.9324	0.8251	0.6655	0.4812	0.3081	0.1727	0.0835
	7	1.0000	0.9997	0.9959	0.9767	0.9225	0.8180	0.6656	0.4878	0.3169	0.1796
	8	1.0000	1.0000	0.9992	0.9933	0.9713	0.9161	0.8145	0.6675	0.4940	0.3238
	9	1.0000	1.0000	0.9999	0.9984	0.9911	0.9674	0.9125	0.8139	0.6710	0.5000
	10	1.0000	1.0000	1.0000	0.9997	0.9977	0.9895	0.9653	0.9115	0.8159	0.6762
	11	1.0000	1.0000	1.0000	1.0000	0.9995	0.9972	0.9886	0.9648	0.9129	0.8204
	12	1.0000	1.0000	1.0000	1.0000	0.9999	0.9994	0.9969	0.9884	0.9658	0.9165
	13	1.0000	1.0000	1.0000	1.0000	1.0000	0.9999	0.9993	0.9969	0.9891	0.9682
	14	1.0000	1.0000	1.0000	1.0000	1.0000	1.0000	0.9999	0.9994	0.9972	0.9904
	15	1.0000	1.0000	1.0000	1.0000	1.0000	1.0000	1.0000	0.9999	0.9995	0.9978
	16	1.0000	1.0000	1.0000	1.0000	1.0000	1.0000	1.0000	1.0000	0.9999	0.9996
	17	1.0000	1.0000	1.0000	1.0000	1.0000	1.0000	1.0000	1.0000	1.0000	1.0000

Table I

BINOMIAL DISTRIBUTION FUNCTION *(Continued)*

n	x	0.05	0.10	0.15	0.20	0.25	0.30	0.35	0.40	0.45	0.50
20	0	0.3585	0.1216	0.0388	0.0115	0.0032	0.0008	0.0002	0.0000	0.0000	0.0000
	1	0.7358	0.3917	0.1756	0.0692	0.0243	0.0076	0.0021	0.0005	0.0001	0.0000
	2	0.9245	0.6769	0.4049	0.2061	0.0913	0.0355	0.0121	0.0036	0.0009	0.0002
	3	0.9841	0.8670	0.6477	0.4114	0.2252	0.1071	0.0444	0.0160	0.0049	0.0013
	4	0.9974	0.9568	0.8298	0.6296	0.4148	0.2375	0.1182	0.0510	0.0189	0.0059
	5	0.9997	0.9887	0.9327	0.8042	0.6172	0.4164	0.2454	0.1256	0.0553	0.0207
	6	1.0000	0.9976	0.9781	0.9133	0.7858	0.6080	0.4166	0.2500	0.1299	0.0577
	7	1.0000	0.9996	0.9941	0.9679	0.8982	0.7723	0.6010	0.4159	0.2520	0.1316
	8	1.0000	0.9999	0.9987	0.9900	0.9591	0.8867	0.7624	0.5956	0.4143	0.2517
	9	1.0000	1.0000	0.9998	0.9974	0.9861	0.9520	0.8782	0.7553	0.5914	0.4119
	10	1.0000	1.0000	1.0000	0.9994	0.9961	0.9829	0.9468	0.8725	0.7507	0.5881
	11	1.0000	1.0000	1.0000	0.9999	0.9991	0.9949	0.9804	0.9435	0.8692	0.7483
	12	1.0000	1.0000	1.0000	1.0000	0.9998	0.9987	0.9940	0.9790	0.9420	0.8684
	13	1.0000	1.0000	1.0000	1.0000	1.0000	0.9997	0.9985	0.9935	0.9786	0.9423
	14	1.0000	1.0000	1.0000	1.0000	1.0000	1.0000	0.9997	0.9984	0.9936	0.9793
	15	1.0000	1.0000	1.0000	1.0000	1.0000	1.0000	1.0000	0.9997	0.9985	0.9941
	16	1.0000	1.0000	1.0000	1.0000	1.0000	1.0000	1.0000	1.0000	0.9997	0.9987
	17	1.0000	1.0000	1.0000	1.0000	1.0000	1.0000	1.0000	1.0000	1.0000	0.9998
	18	1.0000	1.0000	1.0000	1.0000	1.0000	1.0000	1.0000	1.0000	1.0000	1.0000

Table II

POISSON DISTRIBUTION FUNCTION*

$$F(x; \lambda) = \sum_{k=0}^{x} e^{-\lambda} \frac{\lambda^k}{k!}$$

λ \ x	0	1	2	3	4	5	6	7	8	9
0.02	0.980	1.000								
0.04	0.961	0.999	1.000							
0.06	0.942	0.998	1.000							
0.08	0.923	0.997	1.000							
0.10	0.905	0.995	1.000							
0.15	0.861	0.990	0.999	1.000						
0.20	0.819	0.982	0.999	1.000						
0.25	0.779	0.974	0.998	1.000						
0.30	0.741	0.963	0.996	1.000						
0.35	0.705	0.951	0.994	1.000						
0.40	0.670	0.938	0.992	0.999	1.000					
0.45	0.638	0.925	0.989	0.999	1.000					
0.50	0.607	0.910	0.986	0.998	1.000					
0.55	0.577	0.894	0.982	0.998	1.000					
0.60	0.549	0.878	0.977	0.997	1.000					
0.65	0.522	0.861	0.972	0.996	0.999	1.000				
0.70	0.497	0.844	0.966	0.994	0.999	1.000				
0.75	0.472	0.827	0.959	0.993	0.999	1.000				
0.80	0.449	0.809	0.953	0.991	0.999	1.000				
0.85	0.427	0.791	0.945	0.989	0.998	1.000				
0.90	0.407	0.772	0.937	0.987	0.998	1.000				
0.95	0.387	0.754	0.929	0.984	0.997	1.000				
1.00	0.368	0.736	0.920	0.981	0.996	0.999	1.000			
1.1	0.333	0.699	0.900	0.974	0.995	0.999	1.000			
1.2	0.301	0.663	0.879	0.966	0.992	0.998	1.000			
1.3	0.273	0.627	0.857	0.957	0.989	0.998	1.000			
1.4	0.247	0.592	0.833	0.946	0.986	0.997	0.999	1.000		
1.5	0.223	0.558	0.809	0.934	0.981	0.996	0.999	1.000		
1.6	0.202	0.525	0.783	0.921	0.976	0.994	0.999	1.000		
1.7	0.183	0.493	0.757	0.907	0.970	0.992	0.998	1.000		
1.8	0.165	0.463	0.731	0.891	0.964	0.990	0.997	0.999	1.000	
1.9	0.150	0.434	0.704	0.875	0.956	0.987	0.997	0.999	1.000	
2.0	0.135	0.406	0.677	0.857	0.947	0.983	0.995	0.999	1.000	

* Reprinted by kind permission from E. C. Molina, *Poisson's Exponential Binomial Limit*, D. Van Nostrand Company, Inc., Princeton, N.J., 1947.

Table II

POISSON DISTRIBUTION FUNCTION (*Continued*)

λ \ x	0	1	2	3	4	5	6	7	8	9
2.2	0.111	0.355	0.623	0.819	0.928	0.975	0.993	0.998	1.000	
2.4	0.091	0.308	0.570	0.779	0.9C4	0.964	0.988	0.997	0.999	1.000
2.6	0.074	0.267	0.518	0.736	0.877	0.951	C.983	0.995	0.999	1.000
2.8	0.061	0.231	0.469	0.692	0.848	0.935	0.976	0.992	0.998	0.999
3.0	0.050	0.199	0.423	0.647	0.815	0.916	0.966	0.988	0.996	0.999
3.2	0.041	0.171	0.380	0.603	0.781	0.895	0.955	0.983	0.994	0.998
3.4	0.033	0.147	0.340	0.558	0.744	0.871	0.942	0.977	0.992	0.997
3.6	0.027	0.126	0.303	0.515	0.7C6	0.844	0.927	0.969	0.988	0.996
3.8	0.022	0.107	0.269	0.473	0.668	0.816	0.909	0.960	0.984	0.994
4.0	0.018	0.092	0.238	0.433	0.629	0.785	0.889	0.949	0.979	0.992
4.2	0.015	0.078	0.210	0.395	0.590	0.753	0.867	0.936	0.972	0.989
4.4	0.012	0.066	0.185	0.359	0.551	0.720	0.844	0.921	0.964	0.985
4.6	0.010	0.056	0.163	0.326	0.513	0.686	0.818	0.905	0.955	0.980
4.8	0.008	0.048	0.143	0.294	0.476	0.651	0.791	0.887	0.944	0.975
5.0	0.007	0.040	0.125	0.265	0.440	0.616	0.762	0.867	0.932	0.968
5.2	0.006	0.034	0.109	0.238	0.406	0.581	0.732	0.845	0.918	0.960
5.4	0.005	0.029	0.095	0.213	0.373	0.546	0.702	0.822	0.903	0.951
5.6	0.004	0.024	0.082	0.191	0.342	0.512	0.670	0.797	0.886	0.941
5.8	0.003	0.021	0.072	0.170	0.313	0.478	0.638	0.771	0.867	0.929
6.0	0.002	0.017	0.062	0.151	0.285	0.446	0.606	0.744	0.847	0.916

λ \ x	10	11	12	13	14	15	16
2.8	1.000						
3.0	1.000						
3.2	1.000						
3.4	0.999	1.000					
3.6	0.999	1.000					
3.8	0.998	0.999	1.000				
4.0	0.997	0.999	1.000				
4.2	0.996	0.999	1.000				
4.4	0.994	0.998	0.999	1.000			
4.6	0.992	0.997	0.999	1.000			
4.8	0.990	0.996	0.999	1.000			
5.0	0.986	0.995	0.998	0.999	1.000		
5.2	0.982	0.993	0.997	0.999	1.000		
5.4	0.977	0.990	0.996	0.999	1.000		
5.6	0.972	0.988	0.995	0.998	0.999	1.000	
5.8	0.965	0.984	0.993	0.997	0.999	1.000	
6.0	0.957	0.980	0.991	0.996	0.999	0.999	1.000

Table II

POISSON DISTRIBUTION FUNCTION (*Continued*)

λ \ x	0	1	2	3	4	5	6	7	8	9
6.2	0.002	0.015	0.054	0.134	0.259	0.414	0.574	0.716	0.826	0.902
6.4	0.002	0.012	0.046	0.119	0.235	0.384	0.542	0.687	0.803	0.886
6.6	0.001	0.010	0.040	0.105	0.213	0.355	0.511	0.658	0.780	0.869
6.8	0.001	0.009	0.034	0.093	0.192	0.327	0.480	0.628	0.755	0.850
7.0	0.001	0.007	0.030	0.082	0.173	0.301	0.450	0.599	0.729	0.830
7.2	0.001	0.006	0.025	0.072	0.156	0.276	0.420	0.569	0.703	0.810
7.4	0.001	0.005	0.022	0.063	0.140	0.253	0.392	0.539	0.676	0.788
7.6	0.001	0.004	0.019	0.055	0.125	0.231	0.365	0.510	0.648	0.765
7.8	0.000	0.004	0.016	0.048	0.112	0.210	0.338	0.481	0.620	0.741
8.0	0.000	0.003	0.014	0.042	0.100	0.191	0.313	0.453	0.593	0.717
8.5	0.000	0.002	0.009	0.030	0.074	0.150	0.256	0.386	0.523	0.653
9.0	0.000	0.001	0.006	0.021	0.055	0.116	0.207	0.324	0.456	0.587
9.5	0.000	0.001	0.004	0.015	0.040	0.089	0.165	0.269	0.392	0.522
10.0	0.000	0.000	0.003	0.010	0.029	0.067	0.130	0.220	0.333	0.458

λ \ x	10	11	12	13	14	15	16	17	18	19
6.2	0.949	0.975	0.989	0.995	0.998	0.999	1.000			
6.4	0.939	0.969	0.986	0.994	0.997	0.999	1.000			
6.6	0.927	0.963	0.982	0.992	0.997	0.999	0.999	1.000		
6.8	0.915	0.955	0.978	0.990	0.996	0.998	0.999	1.000		
7.0	0.901	0.947	0.973	0.987	0.994	0.998	0.999	1.000		
7.2	0.887	0.937	0.967	0.984	0.993	0.997	0.999	0.999	1.000	
7.4	0.871	0.926	0.961	0.980	0.991	0.996	0.998	0.999	1.000	
7.6	0.854	0.915	0.954	0.976	0.989	0.995	0.998	0.999	1.000	
7.8	0.835	0.902	0.945	0.971	0.986	0.993	0.997	0.999	1.000	
8.0	0.816	0.888	0.936	0.966	0.983	0.992	0.996	0.998	0.999	1.000
8.5	0.763	0.849	0.909	0.949	0.973	0.986	0.993	0.997	0.999	0.999
9.0	0.706	0.803	0.876	0.926	0.959	0.978	0.989	0.995	0.998	0.999
9.5	0.645	0.752	0.836	0.898	0.940	0.967	0.982	0.991	0.996	0.998
10.0	0.583	0.697	0.792	0.864	0.917	0.951	0.973	0.986	0.993	0.997

λ \ x	20	21	22
8.5	1.000		
9.0	1.000		
9.5	0.999	1.000	
10.0	0.998	0.999	1.000

Table II

POISSON DISTRIBUTION FUNCTION (*Continued*)

λ \ x	0	1	2	3	4	5	6	7	8	9
10.5	0.000	0.000	0.002	0.007	0.021	0.050	0.102	0.179	0.279	0.397
11.0	0.000	0.000	0.001	0.005	0.015	0.038	0.079	0.143	0.232	0.341
11.5	0.000	0.000	0.001	0.003	0.011	0.028	0.060	0.114	0.191	0.289
12.0	0.000	0.000	0.001	0.002	0.008	0.020	0.046	0.090	0.155	0.242
12.5	0.000	0.000	0.000	0.002	0.005	0.015	0.035	0.070	0.125	0.201
13.0	0.000	0.000	0.000	0.001	0.004	0.011	0.026	0.054	0.100	0.166
13.5	0.000	0.000	0.000	0.001	0.003	0.008	0.019	0.041	0.079	0.135
14.0	0.000	0.000	0.000	0.000	0.002	0.006	0.014	0.032	0.062	0.109
14.5	0.000	0.000	0.000	0.000	0.001	0.004	0.010	0.024	0.048	0.088
15.0	0.000	0.000	0.000	0.000	0.001	0.003	0.008	0.018	0.037	0.070

λ \ x	10	11	12	13	14	15	16	17	18	19
10.5	0.521	0.639	0.742	0.825	0.888	0.932	0.960	0.978	0.988	0.994
11.0	0.460	0.579	0.689	0.781	0.854	0.907	0.944	0.968	0.982	0.991
11.5	0.402	0.520	0.633	0.733	0.815	0.878	0.924	0.954	0.974	0.986
12.0	0.347	0.462	0.576	0.682	0.772	0.844	0.899	0.937	0.963	0.979
12.5	0.297	0.406	0.519	0.628	0.725	0.806	0.869	0.916	0.948	0.969
13.0	0.252	0.353	0.463	0.573	0.675	0.764	0.835	0.890	0.930	0.957
13.5	0.211	0.304	0.409	0.518	0.623	0.718	0.798	0.861	0.908	0.942
14.0	0.176	0.260	0.358	0.464	0.570	0.669	0.756	0.827	0.883	0.923
14.5	0.145	0.220	0.311	0.413	0.518	0.619	0.711	0.790	0.853	0.901
15.0	0.118	0.185	0.268	0.363	0.466	0.568	0.664	0.749	0.819	0.875

λ \ x	20	21	22	23	24	25	26	27	28	29
10.5	0.997	0.999	0.999	1.000						
11.0	0.995	0.998	0.999	1.000						
11.5	0.992	0.996	0.998	0.999	1.000					
12.0	0.988	0.994	0.997	0.999	0.999	1.000				
12.5	0.983	0.991	0.995	0.998	0.999	0.999	1.000			
13.0	0.975	0.986	0.992	0.996	0.998	0.999	1.000			
13.5	0.965	0.980	0.989	0.994	0.997	0.998	0.999	1.000		
14.0	0.952	0.971	0.983	0.991	0.995	0.997	0.999	0.999	1.000	
14.5	0.936	0.960	0.976	0.986	0.992	0.996	0.999	0.999	0.999	1.000
15.0	0.917	0.947	0.967	0.981	0.989	0.994	0.997	0.998	0.999	1.000

Table II

POISSON DISTRIBUTION FUNCTION *(Continued)*

λ \ x	4	5	6	7	8	9	10	11	12	13
16	0.000	0.001	0.004	0.010	0.022	0.043	0.077	0.127	0.193	0.275
17	0.000	0.001	0.002	0.005	0.013	0.026	0.049	0.085	0.135	0.201
18	0.000	0.000	0.001	0.003	0.007	0.015	0.030	0.055	0.092	0.143
19	0.000	0.000	0.001	0.002	0.004	0.009	0.018	0.035	0.061	0.098
20	0.000	0.000	0.000	0.001	0.002	0.005	0.011	0.021	0.039	0.066
21	0.000	0.000	0.000	0.000	0.001	0.003	0.006	0.013	0.025	0.043
22	0.000	0.000	0.000	0.000	0.001	0.002	0.004	0.008	0.015	0.028
23	0.000	0.000	0.000	0.000	0.000	0.001	0.002	0.004	0.009	0.017
24	0.000	0.000	0.000	0.000	0.000	0.000	0.001	0.003	0.005	0.011
25	0.000	0.000	0.000	0.000	0.000	0.000	0.001	0.001	0.003	0.006

λ \ x	14	15	16	17	18	19	20	21	22	23
16	0.368	0.467	0.566	0.659	0.742	0.812	0.868	0.911	0.942	0.963
17	0.281	0.371	0.468	0.564	0.655	0.736	0.805	0.861	0.905	0.937
18	0.208	0.287	0.375	0.469	0.562	0.651	0.731	0.799	0.855	0.899
19	0.150	0.215	0.292	0.378	0.469	0.561	0.647	0.725	0.793	0.849
20	0.105	0.157	0.221	0.297	0.381	0.470	0.559	0.644	0.721	0.787
21	0.072	0.111	0.163	0.227	0.302	0.384	0.471	0.558	0.640	0.716
22	0.048	0.077	0.117	0.169	0.232	0.306	0.387	0.472	0.556	0.637
23	0.031	0.052	0.082	0.123	0.175	0.238	0.310	0.389	0.472	0.555
24	0.020	0.034	0.056	0.087	0.128	0.180	0.243	0.314	0.392	0.473
25	0.012	0.022	0.038	0.060	0.092	0.134	0.185	0.247	0.318	0.394

λ \ x	24	25	26	27	28	29	30	31	32	33
16	0.978	0.987	0.993	0.996	0.998	0.999	0.999	1.000	1.000	
17	0.959	0.975	0.985	0.991	0.995	0.997	0.999	0.999	1.000	1.000
18	0.932	0.955	0.972	0.983	0.990	0.994	0.997	0.998	0.999	1.000
19	0.893	0.927	0.951	0.969	0.980	0.988	0.993	0.996	0.998	0.999
20	0.843	0.888	0.922	0.948	0.966	0.978	0.987	0.992	0.995	0.997
21	0.782	0.838	0.883	0.917	0.944	0.963	0.976	0.985	0.991	0.994
22	0.712	0.777	0.832	0.877	0.913	0.940	0.959	0.973	0.983	0.989
23	0.635	0.708	0.772	0.827	0.873	0.908	0.936	0.956	0.971	0.981
24	0.554	0.632	0.704	0.768	0.823	0.868	0.904	0.932	0.953	0.969
25	0.473	0.553	0.629	0.700	0.763	0.818	0.863	0.900	0.929	0.950

λ \ x	34	35	36	37	38	39	40	41	42	43
19	0.999	1.000								
20	0.999	0.999	1.000							
21	0.997	0.998	0.999	0.999	1.000					
22	0.994	0.996	0.998	0.999	0.999	1.000				
23	0.988	0.993	0.996	0.997	0.999	0.999	1.000			
24	0.979	0.987	0.992	0.995	0.997	0.998	0.999	0.999	1.000	
25	0.966	0.978	0.985	0.991	0.994	0.997	0.998	0.999	0.999	1.000

Table III

NORMAL DISTRIBUTION FUNCTION

$$F(z) = \frac{1}{\sqrt{2\pi}} \int_{-\infty}^{z} e^{-\frac{1}{2}t^2}\, dt$$

z	0.00	0.01	0.02	0.03	0.04	0.05	0.06	0.07	0.08	0.09
0.0	0.5000	0.5040	0.5080	0.5120	0.5160	0.5199	0.5239	0.5279	0.5319	0.5359
0.1	0.5398	0.5438	0.5478	0.5517	0.5557	0.5596	0.5636	0.5675	0.5714	0.5753
0.2	0.5793	0.5832	0.5871	0.5910	0.5948	0.5987	0.6026	0.6064	0.6103	0.6141
0.3	0.6179	0.6217	0.6255	0.6293	0.6331	0.6368	0.6406	0.6443	0.6480	0.6517
0.4	0.6554	0.6591	0.6628	0.6664	0.6700	0.6736	0.6772	0.6808	0.6844	0.6879
0.5	0.6915	0.6950	0.6985	0.7019	0.7054	0.7088	0.7123	0.7157	0.7190	0.7224
0.6	0.7257	0.7291	0.7324	0.7357	0.7389	0.7422	0.7454	0.7486	0.7517	0.7549
0.7	0.7580	0.7611	0.7642	0.7673	0.7704	0.7734	0.7764	0.7794	0.7823	0.7852
0.8	0.7881	0.7910	0.7939	0.7967	0.7995	0.8023	0.8051	0.8078	0.8106	0.8133
0.9	0.8159	0.8186	0.8212	0.8238	0.8264	0.8289	0.8315	0.8340	0.8365	0.8389
1.0	0.8413	0.8438	0.8461	0.8485	0.8508	0.8531	0.8554	0.8577	0.8599	0.8621
1.1	0.8643	0.8665	0.8686	0.8708	0.8729	0.8749	0.8770	0.8790	0.8810	0.8830
1.2	0.8849	0.8869	0.8888	0.8907	0.8925	0.8944	0.8962	0.8980	0.8997	0.9015
1.3	0.9032	0.9049	0.9066	0.9082	0.9099	0.9115	0.9131	0.9147	0.9162	0.9177
1.4	0.9192	0.9207	0.9222	0.9236	0.9251	0.9265	0.9279	0.9292	0.9306	0.9319
1.5	0.9332	0.9345	0.9357	0.9370	0.9382	0.9394	0.9406	0.9418	0.9429	0.9441
1.6	0.9452	0.9463	0.9474	0.9484	0.9495	0.9505	0.9515	0.9525	0.9535	0.9545
1.7	0.9554	0.9564	0.9573	0.9582	0.9591	0.9599	0.9608	0.9616	0.9625	0.9633
1.8	0.9641	0.9649	0.9656	0.9664	0.9671	0.9678	0.9686	0.9693	0.9699	0.9706
1.9	0.9713	0.9719	0.9726	0.9732	0.9738	0.9744	0.9750	0.9756	0.9761	0.9767
2.0	0.9772	0.9778	0.9783	0.9788	0.9793	0.9798	0.9803	0.9808	0.9812	0.9817
2.1	0.9821	0.9826	0.9830	0.9834	0.9838	0.9842	0.9846	0.9850	0.9854	0.9857
2.2	0.9861	0.9864	0.9868	0.9871	0.9875	0.9878	0.9881	0.9884	0.9887	0.9890
2.3	0.9893	0.9896	0.9898	0.9901	0.9904	0.9906	0.9909	0.9911	0.9913	0.9916
2.4	0.9918	0.9920	0.9922	0.9925	0.9927	0.9929	0.9931	0.9932	0.9934	0.9936
2.5	0.9938	0.9940	0.9941	0.9943	0.9945	0.9946	0.9948	0.9949	0.9951	0.9952
2.6	0.9953	0.9955	0.9956	0.9957	0.9959	0.9960	0.9961	0.9962	0.9963	0.9964
2.7	0.9965	0.9966	0.9967	0.9968	0.9969	0.9970	0.9971	0.9972	0.9973	0.9974
2.8	0.9974	0.9975	0.9976	0.9977	0.9977	0.9978	0.9979	0.9979	0.9980	0.9981
2.9	0.9981	0.9982	0.9982	0.9983	0.9984	0.9984	0.9985	0.9985	0.9986	0.9986
3.0	0.9987	0.9987	0.9987	0.9988	0.9988	0.9989	0.9989	0.9989	0.9990	0.9990
3.1	0.9990	0.9991	0.9991	0.9991	0.9992	0.9992	0.9992	0.9992	0.9993	0.9993
3.2	0.9993	0.9993	0.9994	0.9994	0.9994	0.9994	0.9994	0.9995	0.9995	0.9995
3.3	0.9995	0.9995	0.9995	0.9996	0.9996	0.9996	0.9996	0.9996	0.9997	0.9997
3.4	0.9997	0.9997	0.9997	0.9997	0.9997	0.9997	0.9997	0.9997	0.9997	0.9998

$$t = \frac{\bar{x} - \mu}{s/\sqrt{n}}$$

Table IV

VALUES OF $t_\alpha{}^*$

ν	$\alpha = 0.10$	$\alpha = 0.05$	$\alpha = 0.025$	$\alpha = 0.01$	$\alpha = 0.005$	ν
1	3.078	6.314	12.706	31.821	63.657	1
2	1.886	2.920	4.303	6.965	9.925	2
3	1.638	2.353	3.182	4.541	5.841	3
4	1.533	2.132	2.776	3.747	4.604	4
5	1.476	2.015	2.571	3.365	4.032	5
6	1.440	1.943	2.447	3.143	3.707	6
7	1.415	1.895	2.365	2.998	3.499	7
8	1.397	1.860	2.306	2.896	3.355	8
9	1.383	1.833	2.262	2.821	3.250	9
10	1.372	1.812	2.228	2.764	3.169	10
11	1.363	1.796	2.201	2.718	3.106	11
12	1.356	1.782	2.179	2.681	3.055	12
13	1.350	1.771	2.160	2.650	3.012	13
14	1.345	1.761	2.145	2.624	2.977	14
15	1.341	1.753	2.131	2.602	2.947	15
16	1.337	1.746	2.120	2.583	2.921	16
17	1.333	1.740	2.110	2.567	2.898	17
18	1.330	1.734	2.101	2.552	2.878	18
19	1.328	1.729	2.093	2.539	2.861	19
20	1.325	1.725	2.086	2.528	2.845	20
21	1.323	1.721	2.080	2.518	2.831	21
22	1.321	1.717	2.074	2.508	2.819	22
23	1.319	1.714	2.069	2.500	2.807	23
24	1.318	1.711	2.064	2.492	2.797	24
25	1.316	1.708	2.060	2.485	2.787	25
26	1.315	1.706	2.056	2.479	2.779	26
27	1.314	1.703	2.052	2.473	2.771	27
28	1.313	1.701	2.048	2.467	2.763	28
29	1.311	1.699	2.045	2.462	2.756	29
inf.	1.282	1.645	1.960	2.326	2.576	inf.

* This table is abridged from Table IV of R. A. Fisher, *Statistical Methods for Research Workers*, published by Oliver and Boyd, Ltd., Edinburgh, by permission of the author and publishers.

CHI - SQUARE DIST.

$$\chi^2 = \frac{(N-1)s^2}{\sigma^2}$$

Table V

VALUES OF χ_α^2*

ν	$\alpha = 0.995$	$\alpha = 0.99$	$\alpha = 0.975$	$\alpha = 0.95$	$\alpha = 0.05$	$\alpha = 0.025$	$\alpha = 0.01$	$\alpha = 0.005$	ν
1	0.0000393	0.000157	0.000982	0.00393	3.841	5.024	6.635	7.879	1
2	0.0100	0.0201	0.0506	0.103	5.991	7.378	9.210	10.597	2
3	0.0717	0.115	0.216	0.352	7.815	9.348	11.345	12.838	3
4	0.207	0.297	0.484	0.711	9.488	11.143	13.277	14.860	4
5	0.412	0.554	0.831	1.145	11.070	12.832	15.086	16.750	5
6	0.676	0.872	1.237	1.635	12.592	14.449	16.812	18.548	6
7	0.989	1.239	1.690	2.167	14.067	16.013	18.475	20.278	7
8	1.344	1.646	2.180	2.733	15.507	17.535	20.090	21.955	8
9	1.735	2.088	2.700	3.325	16.919	19.023	21.666	23.589	9
10	2.156	2.558	3.247	3.940	18.307	20.483	23.209	25.188	10
11	2.603	3.053	3.816	4.575	19.675	21.920	24.725	26.757	11
12	3.074	3.571	4.404	5.226	21.026	23.337	26.217	28.300	12
13	3.565	4.107	5.009	5.892	22.362	24.736	27.688	29.819	13
14	4.075	4.660	5.629	6.571	23.685	26.119	29.141	31.319	14
15	4.601	5.229	6.262	7.261	24.996	27.488	30.578	32.801	15
16	5.142	5.812	6.908	7.962	26.296	28.845	32.000	34.267	16
17	5.697	6.408	7.564	8.672	27.587	30.191	33.409	35.718	17
18	6.265	7.015	8.231	9.390	28.869	31.526	34.805	37.156	18
19	6.844	7.633	8.907	10.117	30.144	32.852	36.191	38.582	19
20	7.434	8.260	9.591	10.851	31.410	34.170	37.566	39.997	20
21	8.034	8.897	10.283	11.591	32.671	35.479	38.932	41.401	21
22	8.643	9.542	10.982	12.338	33.924	36.781	40.289	42.796	22
23	9.260	10.196	11.689	13.091	35.172	38.076	41.638	44.181	23
24	9.886	10.856	12.401	13.848	36.415	39.364	42.980	45.558	24
25	10.520	11.524	13.120	14.611	37.652	40.646	44.314	46.928	25
26	11.160	12.198	13.844	15.379	38.885	41.923	45.642	48.290	26
27	11.808	12.879	14.573	16.151	40.113	43.194	46.963	49.645	27
28	12.461	13.565	15.308	16.928	41.337	44.461	48.278	50.993	28
29	13.121	14.256	16.047	17.708	42.557	45.722	49.588	52.336	29
30	13.787	14.953	16.791	18.493	43.773	46.979	50.892	53.672	30

* This table is based on Table 8 of *Biometrika Tables for Statisticians*, Vol. I, by permission of the *Biometrika* trustees.

area = α

χ_α^2

400

Table VI(a)

VALUES OF $F_{.05}$*

n_1 = Degrees of freedom for numerator

n_2 = Degrees of freedom for denominator	1	2	3	4	5	6	7	8	9	10	12	15	20	24	30	40	60	120	∞
1	161	200	216	225	230	234	237	239	241	242	244	246	248	249	250	251	252	253	254
2	18.50	19.00	19.20	19.20	19.30	19.30	19.40	19.40	19.40	19.40	19.40	19.40	19.40	19.50	19.50	19.50	19.50	19.50	19.50
3	10.10	9.55	9.28	9.12	9.01	8.94	8.89	8.85	8.81	8.79	8.74	8.70	8.66	8.64	8.62	8.59	8.57	8.55	8.53
4	7.71	6.94	6.59	6.39	6.26	6.16	6.09	6.04	6.00	5.96	5.91	5.86	5.80	5.77	5.75	5.72	5.69	5.66	5.63
5	6.61	5.79	5.41	5.19	5.05	4.95	4.88	4.82	4.77	4.74	4.68	4.62	4.56	4.53	4.50	4.46	4.43	4.40	4.37
6	5.99	5.14	4.76	4.53	4.39	4.28	4.21	4.15	4.10	4.06	4.00	3.94	3.87	3.84	3.81	3.77	3.74	3.70	3.67
7	5.59	4.74	4.35	4.12	3.97	3.87	3.79	3.73	3.68	3.64	3.57	3.51	3.44	3.41	3.38	3.34	3.30	3.27	3.23
8	5.32	4.46	4.07	3.84	3.69	3.58	3.50	3.44	3.39	3.35	3.28	3.22	3.15	3.12	3.08	3.04	3.01	2.97	2.93
9	5.12	4.26	3.86	3.63	3.48	3.37	3.29	3.23	3.18	3.14	3.07	3.01	2.94	2.90	2.86	2.83	2.79	2.75	2.71
10	4.96	4.10	3.71	3.48	3.33	3.22	3.14	3.07	3.02	2.98	2.91	2.85	2.77	2.74	2.70	2.66	2.62	2.58	2.54
11	4.84	3.98	3.59	3.36	3.20	3.09	3.01	2.95	2.90	2.85	2.79	2.72	2.65	2.61	2.57	2.53	2.49	2.45	2.40
12	4.75	3.89	3.49	3.26	3.11	3.00	2.91	2.85	2.80	2.75	2.69	2.62	2.54	2.51	2.47	2.43	2.38	2.34	2.30
13	4.67	3.81	3.41	3.18	3.03	2.92	2.83	2.77	2.71	2.67	2.60	2.53	2.46	2.42	2.38	2.34	2.30	2.25	2.21
14	4.60	3.74	3.34	3.11	2.96	2.85	2.76	2.70	2.65	2.60	2.53	2.46	2.39	2.35	2.31	2.27	2.22	2.18	2.13
15	4.54	3.68	3.29	3.06	2.90	2.79	2.71	2.64	2.59	2.54	2.48	2.40	2.33	2.29	2.25	2.20	2.16	2.11	2.07
16	4.49	3.63	3.24	3.01	2.85	2.74	2.66	2.59	2.54	2.49	2.42	2.35	2.28	2.24	2.19	2.15	2.11	2.06	2.01
17	4.45	3.59	3.20	2.96	2.81	2.70	2.61	2.55	2.49	2.45	2.38	2.31	2.23	2.19	2.15	2.10	2.06	2.01	1.96
18	4.41	3.55	3.16	2.93	2.77	2.66	2.58	2.51	2.46	2.41	2.34	2.27	2.19	2.15	2.11	2.06	2.02	1.97	1.92
19	4.38	3.52	3.13	2.90	2.74	2.63	2.54	2.48	2.42	2.38	2.31	2.23	2.16	2.11	2.07	2.03	1.98	1.93	1.88
20	4.35	3.49	3.10	2.87	2.71	2.60	2.51	2.45	2.39	2.35	2.28	2.20	2.12	2.08	2.04	1.99	1.95	1.90	1.84
21	4.32	3.47	3.07	2.84	2.68	2.57	2.49	2.42	2.37	2.32	2.25	2.18	2.10	2.05	2.01	1.96	1.92	1.87	1.81
22	4.30	3.44	3.05	2.82	2.66	2.55	2.46	2.40	2.34	2.30	2.23	2.15	2.07	2.03	1.98	1.94	1.89	1.84	1.78
23	4.28	3.42	3.03	2.80	2.64	2.53	2.44	2.37	2.32	2.27	2.20	2.13	2.05	2.01	1.96	1.91	1.86	1.81	1.76
24	4.26	3.40	3.01	2.78	2.62	2.51	2.42	2.36	2.30	2.25	2.18	2.11	2.03	1.98	1.94	1.89	1.84	1.79	1.73
25	4.24	3.39	2.99	2.76	2.60	2.49	2.40	2.34	2.28	2.24	2.16	2.09	2.01	1.96	1.92	1.87	1.82	1.77	1.71
30	4.17	3.32	2.92	2.69	2.53	2.42	2.33	2.27	2.21	2.16	2.09	2.01	1.93	1.89	1.84	1.79	1.74	1.68	1.62
40	4.08	3.23	2.84	2.61	2.45	2.34	2.25	2.18	2.12	2.08	2.00	1.92	1.84	1.79	1.74	1.69	1.64	1.58	1.51
60	4.00	3.15	2.76	2.53	2.37	2.25	2.17	2.10	2.04	1.99	1.92	1.84	1.75	1.70	1.65	1.59	1.53	1.47	1.39
120	3.92	3.07	2.68	2.45	2.29	2.18	2.09	2.02	1.96	1.91	1.83	1.75	1.66	1.61	1.55	1.50	1.43	1.35	1.25
∞	3.84	3.00	2.60	2.37	2.21	2.10	2.01	1.94	1.88	1.83	1.75	1.67	1.57	1.52	1.46	1.39	1.32	1.22	1.00

*This table is reproduced from M. Merrington and C. M. Thompson, "Tables of percentage points of the inverted beta (F) distribution," *Biometrika*, Vol. 33 (1943), by permission of the *Biometrika* trustees.

401

Table VI(b)

VALUES OF $F_{.01}$*

v_1 = Degrees of freedom for numerator

v_2 = Degrees of freedom for denominator	1	2	3	4	5	6	7	8	9	10	12	15	20	24	30	40	60	120	∞
1	4,052	5,000	5,403	5,625	5,764	5,859	5,928	5,982	6,023	6,056	6,106	6,157	6,209	6,235	6,261	6,287	6,313	6,339	6,366
2	98.50	99.00	99.20	99.20	99.30	99.30	99.40	99.40	99.40	99.40	99.40	99.40	99.40	99.50	99.50	99.50	99.50	99.50	99.50
3	34.10	30.80	29.50	28.70	28.20	27.90	27.70	27.50	27.30	27.20	27.10	26.90	26.70	26.60	26.50	26.40	26.30	26.20	26.10
4	21.20	18.00	16.70	16.00	15.50	15.20	15.00	14.80	14.70	14.50	14.40	14.20	14.00	13.90	13.80	13.70	13.70	13.60	13.50
5	16.30	13.30	12.10	11.40	11.00	10.70	10.50	10.30	10.20	10.10	9.89	9.72	9.55	9.47	9.38	9.29	9.20	9.11	9.02
6	13.70	10.90	9.78	9.15	8.75	8.47	8.26	8.10	7.98	7.87	7.72	7.56	7.40	7.31	7.23	7.14	7.06	6.97	6.88
7	12.20	9.55	8.45	7.85	7.46	7.19	6.99	6.84	6.72	6.62	6.47	6.31	6.16	6.07	5.99	5.91	5.82	5.74	5.65
8	11.30	8.65	7.59	7.01	6.63	6.37	6.18	6.03	5.91	5.81	5.67	5.52	5.36	5.28	5.20	5.12	5.03	4.95	4.83
9	10.60	8.02	6.99	6.42	6.06	5.80	5.61	5.47	5.35	5.26	5.11	4.96	4.81	4.73	4.65	4.57	4.48	4.40	4.31
10	10.00	7.56	6.55	5.99	5.64	5.39	5.20	5.06	4.94	4.85	4.71	4.56	4.41	4.33	4.25	4.17	4.08	4.00	3.91
11	9.65	7.21	6.22	5.67	5.32	5.07	4.89	4.74	4.63	4.54	4.40	4.25	4.10	4.02	3.94	3.86	3.78	3.69	3.60
12	9.33	6.93	5.95	5.41	5.06	4.82	4.64	4.50	4.39	4.30	4.16	4.01	3.86	3.78	3.70	3.62	3.54	3.45	3.36
13	9.07	6.70	5.74	5.21	4.86	4.62	4.44	4.30	4.19	4.10	3.96	3.82	3.66	3.59	3.51	3.43	3.34	3.25	3.17
14	8.86	6.51	5.56	5.04	4.70	4.46	4.28	4.14	4.03	3.94	3.80	3.66	3.51	3.43	3.35	3.27	3.18	3.09	3.00
15	8.68	6.36	5.42	4.89	4.56	4.32	4.14	4.00	3.89	3.80	3.67	3.52	3.37	3.29	3.21	3.13	3.05	2.96	2.87
16	8.53	6.23	5.29	4.77	4.44	4.20	4.03	3.89	3.78	3.69	3.55	3.41	3.26	3.18	3.10	3.02	2.93	2.84	2.75
17	8.40	6.11	5.19	4.67	4.34	4.10	3.93	3.79	3.68	3.59	3.46	3.31	3.16	3.08	3.00	2.92	2.83	2.75	2.65
18	8.29	6.01	5.09	4.58	4.25	4.01	3.84	3.71	3.60	3.51	3.37	3.23	3.08	3.00	2.92	2.84	2.75	2.66	2.57
19	8.19	5.93	5.01	4.50	4.17	3.94	3.77	3.63	3.52	3.43	3.30	3.15	3.00	2.92	2.84	2.76	2.67	2.58	2.49
20	8.10	5.85	4.94	4.43	4.10	3.87	3.70	3.56	3.46	3.37	3.23	3.09	2.94	2.86	2.78	2.69	2.61	2.52	2.42
21	8.02	5.78	4.87	4.37	4.04	3.81	3.64	3.51	3.40	3.31	3.17	3.03	2.88	2.80	2.72	2.64	2.55	2.46	2.36
22	7.95	5.72	4.82	4.31	3.99	3.76	3.59	3.45	3.35	3.26	3.12	2.98	2.83	2.75	2.67	2.58	2.50	2.40	2.31
23	7.88	5.66	4.76	4.26	3.94	3.71	3.54	3.41	3.30	3.21	3.07	2.93	2.78	2.70	2.62	2.54	2.45	2.35	2.26
24	7.82	5.61	4.72	4.22	3.90	3.67	3.50	3.36	3.26	3.17	3.03	2.89	2.74	2.66	2.58	2.49	2.40	2.31	2.21
25	7.77	5.57	4.68	4.18	3.86	3.63	3.46	3.32	3.22	3.13	2.99	2.85	2.70	2.62	2.53	2.45	2.36	2.27	2.17
30	7.56	5.39	4.51	4.02	3.70	3.47	3.30	3.17	3.07	2.98	2.84	2.70	2.55	2.47	2.39	2.30	2.21	2.11	2.01
40	7.31	5.18	4.31	3.83	3.51	3.29	3.12	2.99	2.89	2.80	2.66	2.52	2.37	2.29	2.20	2.11	2.02	1.92	1.80
60	7.08	4.98	4.13	3.65	3.34	3.12	2.95	2.82	2.72	2.63	2.50	2.35	2.20	2.12	2.03	1.94	1.84	1.73	1.60
120	6.85	4.79	3.95	3.48	3.17	2.96	2.79	2.66	2.56	2.47	2.34	2.19	2.03	1.95	1.86	1.76	1.66	1.53	1.38
∞	6.63	4.61	3.78	3.32	3.02	2.80	2.64	2.51	2.41	2.32	2.18	2.04	1.88	1.79	1.70	1.59	1.47	1.32	1.00

*This table is reproduced from M. Merrington and C. M. Thompson, "Tables of percentage points of the inverted beta (F) distribution," Biometrika, Vol. 33 (1913). by permission of the Biometrika trustees.

Table VII

RANDOM DIGITS*

1306	1189	5731	3968	5606	5084	8947	3897	1636	7810
0422	2431	0649	8085	5053	4722	6598	5044	9040	5121
6597	2022	6168	5060	8656	6733	6364	7649	1871	4328
7965	6541	5645	6243	7658	6903	9911	5740	7824	8520
7695	6937	0406	8894	0441	8135	9797	7285	5905	9539
5160	7851	8464	6789	3938	4197	6511	0407	9239	2232
2961	0551	0539	8288	7478	7565	5581	5771	5442	8761
1428	4183	4312	5445	4854	9157	9158	5218	1464	3634
3666	5642	4539	1561	7849	7520	2547	0756	1206	2033
6543	6799	7454	9052	6689	1946	2574	9386	0304	7945
9975	6080	7423	3175	9377	6951	6519	8287	8994	5532
4866	0956	7545	7723	8085	4948	2228	9583	4415	7065
8239	7068	6694	5168	3117	1586	0237	6160	9585	1133
8722	9191	3386	3443	0434	4586	4150	1224	6204	0937
1330	9120	8785	8382	2929	7089	3109	6742	2468	7025
2296	2952	4764	9070	6356	9192	4012	0618	2219	1109
3582	7052	3132	4519	9250	2486	0830	8472	2160	7046
5872	9207	7222	6494	8973	3545	6967	8490	5264	9821
1134	6324	6201	3792	5651	0538	4676	2064	0584	7996
1403	4497	7390	8503	8239	4236	8022	2914	4368	4529
3393	7025	3381	3553	2128	1021	8353	6413	5161	8583
1137	7896	3602	0060	7850	7626	0854	6565	4260	6220
7437	5198	8772	6927	8527	6851	2709	5992	7383	1071
8414	8820	3917	7238	9821	6073	6658	1280	9643	7761
8398	5224	2749	7311	5740	9771	7826	9533	3800	4553
0995	8935	2939	3092	2496	0359	0318	4697	7181	4035
6657	0755	9685	4017	6581	7292	5643	5064	1142	1297
8875	8369	7868	0190	9278	1709	4253	9346	4335	3769
8399	6702	0586	6428	7985	2979	4513	1970	1989	3105
6703	1024	2064	0393	6815	8502	1375	4171	6970	1201
4730	1653	9032	9855	0957	7366	0325	5178	7959	5371
8400	6834	3187	8688	1079	1480	6776	9888	7585	9998
3647	8002	6726	0877	4552	3238	7542	7804	3933	9475
6789	5197	8037	2354	9262	5497	0005	3986	1767	7981
2630	2721	2810	2185	6323	5679	4931	8336	6662	3566
1374	8625	1644	3342	1587	0762	6057	8011	2666	3759
1572	7625	9110	4409	0239	7059	3415	5537	2250	7292
9678	2877	7579	4935	0449	8119	6969	5383	1717	6719
0882	6781	3538	4090	3092	2365	6001	3446	9985	6007
0006	4205	2389	4365	1981	8158	7784	6256	3842	5603
4611	9861	7916	9305	2074	9462	0254	4827	9198	3974
1093	3784	4190	6332	1175	8599	9735	8584	6581	7194
3374	3545	6865	8819	3342	1676	2264	6014	5012	2458
3650	9676	1436	4374	4716	5548	8276	6235	6742	2154
7292	5749	7977	7602	9205	3599	3880	9537	4423	2330
2353	8319	2850	4026	3027	1708	3518	7034	7132	6903
1094	2009	8919	5676	7283	4982	9642	7235	8167	3366
0568	4002	0587	7165	1094	2006	7471	0940	4366	9554
5606	4070	5233	4339	6543	6695	5799	5821	3953	9458
8285	7537	1181	2300	5294	6892	1627	3372	1952	3028

* From Donald B. Owen, *Handbook of Statistical Tables*. Reading, Mass.: Addison-Wesley, 1962.

Table VII

RANDOM DIGITS *(Continued)*

2444	9039	4803	8568	1590	2420	2547	2470	8179	4617
5748	7767	2800	6289	2814	8381	1549	9519	3341	1192
7761	8583	0852	5619	6864	8506	9643	7763	9611	1289
6838	9280	2654	0812	3988	2146	5095	0150	8043	9079
6440	2631	3033	9167	4998	7036	0133	7428	9702	1376
8829	0094	2887	3802	5497	0318	5168	6377	9216	2802
9845	4796	2951	4449	1999	2691	5328	7674	7004	6212
5072	9000	3887	5739	7920	6074	4715	3681	2721	2701
9035	0553	1272	2600	3828	8197	8852	9092	8027	6144
5562	1080	2222	0336	1411	0303	7424	3713	9278	1918
2757	2650	8727	3953	9579	2442	8041	9869	2887	3933
6397	1848	1476	0787	4990	4666	1208	2769	3922	1158
9208	7641	3575	4279	1282	1840	5999	1806	7809	5885
2418	9289	6120	8141	3908	5577	3590	2317	8975	4593
7300	9006	5659	8258	3662	0332	5369	3640	0563	7939
6870	2535	8916	3245	2256	4350	6064	2438	2002	1272
2914	7309	4045	7513	3195	4166	0878	5184	6680	2655
0868	8657	8118	6340	9452	7460	3291	5778	1167	0312
7994	6579	6461	2292	9554	8309	5036	0974	9517	8293
8587	0764	6687	9150	1642	2050	4934	0027	1376	5040
8016	8345	2257	5084	8004	7949	3205	3972	7640	3478
5581	5775	7517	9076	4699	8313	8401	7147	9416	7184
2015	3364	6688	2631	2152	2220	1637	8333	4838	5699
7327	8987	5741	0102	1173	7350	7080	7420	1847	0741
3589	1991	1764	8355	9684	9423	7101	1063	4151	4875
2188	6454	7319	1215	0473	6589	2355	9579	7004	6209
2924	0472	9878	7966	2491	5662	5635	2789	2564	1249
1961	1669	2219	1113	9175	0260	4046	8142	4432	2664
2393	9637	0410	7536	0972	5153	0708	1935	1143	1704
7585	4424	2648	6728	2233	3518	7267	1732	1926	3833
0197	4021	9207	7327	9212	7017	8060	6216	1942	6817
9719	5336	5532	8537	2980	8252	4971	0110	6209	1556
8866	4785	6007	8006	9043	4109	5570	9249	9905	2152
5744	3957	8786	9023	1472	7275	1014	1104	0832	7680
7149	5721	1389	6581	7196	7072	6360	3084	7009	0239
7710	8479	9345	7773	9086	1202	8845	3163	7937	6163
5246	5651	0432	8644	6341	9661	2361	8377	8673	6098
3576	0013	7381	0124	8559	9813	9080	6984	0926	2169
3026	1464	2671	4691	0353	5289	8754	2442	7799	8983
6591	4365	8717	2365	5686	8377	8675	9798	7745	6360
0402	3257	0480	5038	1998	2935	1306	1190	2406	2596
7105	7654	4745	4482	8471	1424	2031	7803	4367	6816
7181	4140	1046	0885	1264	7755	1653	8924	5822	4401
3655	3282	2178	8134	3291	7262	8229	2866	7065	4806
5121	6717	3117	1901	5184	6467	8954	3884	0279	8635
3618	3098	9208	7429	1578	1917	7927	2696	3704	0833
0166	3638	4947	1414	4799	9189	2459	5056	5982	6154
6187	9653	3658	4730	1652	8096	8288	9368	5531	7788
1234	1448	0276	7290	1667	2823	3755	5642	4854	8844
8949	8731	4875	5724	2962	1182	2930	7539	4526	7252

Table VII

RANDOM DIGITS (*Continued*)

4357	4146	8353	9952	8004	7945	1530	5207	4730	1967
5339	7325	6862	7584	8634	3485	2278	5832	0612	8118
6583	8433	0717	0606	9284	2719	1888	2889	0285	2765
6564	3526	2171	3809	3428	5523	9078	0648	7768	3326
4811	1933	3763	6265	8931	0649	8085	6177	4450	2139
6931	7236	1230	0441	4013	1352	6563	1499	7332	3068
8755	3390	6120	7825	9005	7012	1643	9934	4044	7022
6742	2260	3443	0190	9278	1816	7697	7933	0067	2906
6655	3930	9014	6032	7574	1685	5258	3100	5358	1929
8514	4806	4124	9286	0449	5051	4772	4651	0038	1580
8135	5004	7299	8981	4689	1950	2271	2201	8344	3852
4414	6855	0127	5489	5157	6386	7492	3736	7164	0498
3727	7959	5056	5983	8021	0204	7616	4325	7454	5039
5434	7342	0314	7252	0067	2800	6292	4706	3454	6881
7195	8828	9869	2785	3186	8375	7414	7232	0401	2483
2705	8245	6251	9611	1077	0641	0195	7024	6202	3899
1547	8981	4972	1280	4286	5678	0338	8096	8284	7010
3424	1435	1354	7631	7260	7361	0151	8903	9056	8684
8969	7551	3695	4915	7921	2913	3840	9031	9747	9735
5225	8720	8898	2478	3342	9200	8836	7269	2992	6284
6432	9861	1516	2849	2539	2208	4595	8616	6170	5865
3085	5903	8319	2744	0814	7318	8619	7614	3265	5999
0264	1246	3687	9759	6995	6565	3949	1012	0179	0059
8710	2419	6065	0036	9650	2027	6042	5467	1839	5577
5736	9001	3132	4521	9973	5070	8078	4150	2276	5059
7529	1339	4802	5751	3785	7125	4922	8877	9530	6499
5133	7995	8030	7408	2186	0725	5554	5664	6791	9677
3170	9915	6960	2621	6718	4059	9919	1007	6469	5410
3024	0680	1127	8088	0200	5868	0084	6362	6808	3727
4398	3121	7749	8191	2087	8270	5233	3980	6774	8522
0082	5419	7659	2061	2506	7573	1157	3979	2309	0811
4351	6516	6814	5898	3973	8103	3616	2049	7843	0568
3268	0086	7580	1337	3884	5679	4830	4509	9587	2184
4391	8487	4884	1488	2249	6661	5774	7205	2717	0730
7328	0705	0652	9424	7082	8579	5647	5571	9667	5855
3835	2938	2671	4691	0559	8382	2825	4928	5379	8635
8731	4980	8674	4506	7262	8127	2022	2178	7463	4842
2995	7868	0683	3768	0625	9887	7060	0514	0034	8600
5597	9028	5660	5006	8325	9677	2169	3196	0357	7811
3081	5876	8150	1360	1868	9265	3277	8465	7502	6458
7406	4439	5683	6877	2920	9588	3002	2869	3746	3690
5969	9442	7696	7510	1620	4973	1911	1288	6160	9797
4765	9647	4364	1037	4975	1998	1359	1346	6125	5078
3219	2532	7577	2815	8696	9248	9410	9282	6572	3940
6906	8859	5044	8826	6218	3206	9034	0843	9832	2703
7993	3141	0103	4528	7988	4635	8478	9094	9077	5306
2549	3737	7686	0723	4505	6841	1379	6460	1869	5700
3672	7033	4844	0149	7412	6370	1884	0717	5740	8477
2217	0293	3978	5933	1032	5192	1732	2137	9357	5941
3162	9968	6369	1258	0416	4326	7840	6525	2608	5255

Table VII

RANDOM DIGITS (*Continued*)

1758	1489	2774	6033	9813	1052	1816	7484	1699	7350
6430	8803	0478	4157	5626	1603	1339	4666	1207	2135
4893	8857	1717	1533	6572	8408	2173	4754	0272	1305
1516	2733	7326	8674	9233	1799	5281	0797	0885	0947
4950	3171	5756	3036	9047	8719	8498	1312	7124	4787
0549	6775	9360	6639	0990	0037	7309	4702	0812	4195
1018	7027	7569	7549	2539	2315	8030	7663	3881	8264
2241	9965	9729	7092	4891	9239	0738	1804	3025	1030
1602	0708	2201	9848	6241	1084	8142	8555	7291	5016
5840	8381	1549	9902	6935	3681	6420	0214	8489	5911
1676	0367	7484	1595	5693	3008	9816	7311	6162	1024
6048	4175	8940	9029	8306	8892	4127	1709	4043	6591
5549	9621	2563	0515	0560	9021	0632	4309	4044	7010
5317	4584	9418	4600	0640	9668	6379	6515	6310	7916
2532	7784	6469	4793	5957	4123	6555	3237	6915	6960
2300	5412	3106	4877	6936	4109	8060	1896	6881	7028
1499	8699	4534	5367	7557	2701	2587	2521	2159	6991
6201	3791	2946	2863	5684	5517	7448	2227	8991	7505
6839	9736	8312	8068	7339	5395	9559	3416	6169	5484
0092	5537	1933	3186	8482	6680	2656	1864	4535	2193
1862	3253	6515	6299	2929	2219	9145	7511	2146	4962
9886	6744	3097	8894	0446	3494	8211	1723	6138	3181
5289	9071	1231	0651	9109	7448	2228	9700	0224	4595
2685	7104	7193	5506	2993	7028	4830	3866	8698	0277
6055	7092	4786	6847	4543	7448	2017	4114	8385	3625
4092	4995	0280	9371	3375	3503	4496	8642	5388	1831
5951	4937	3670	5797	5030	6524	2265	7748	7875	6976
7687	3849	4821	2373	1157	4208	3623	9399	7349	6663
8665	3463	2055	4872	2702	1807	9056	8576	4237	8757
3193	3011	8899	6721	0086	2623	7977	7578	4024	1997
9181	7365	9135	1669	2007	7784	6363	6913	6017	6588
9459	2175	5728	4933	0111	6703	1234	2410	1620	4859
9874	5278	2849	3163	6372	2600	9887	7060	3919	1111
7729	2099	7513	2774	6030	8260	9023	1368	9513	6122
4699	8102	3001	7947	1659	6571	1969	7152	7356	1062
1872	7244	3954	7422	2688	8649	0156	1965	5012	2461
9636	0123	2438	1757	4204	1650	2486	0002	4724	7412
6403	9054	7632	7469	8973	3332	0294	5062	0303	7315
4433	3293	2314	7431	2389	4094	5062	0118	0046	6070
2361	3933	8026	0431	8012	3214	8927	7355	0585	7638
4077	8463	6580	6983	0181	3327	6812	1755	3387	4569
6678	0006	3686	8478	9187	2291	9032	9852	1450	7940
6499	2582	5207	4627	0456	4245	3583	8996	1006	5839
6663	9021	0319	7908	1241	9977	7042	6923	2539	2103
9999	4503	6105	5525	1068	6272	7036	0200	6291	2841
9048	6982	3845	6865	9029	8700	0349	3416	8236	1129
5136	9653	3654	2863	5565	8923	5596	8389	9927	9092
9906	1070	5693	3012	1218	7309	4361	3041	4327	8423
4198	7035	8182	6270	6461	2079	2998	5507	9605	6734
2030	5878	8989	6789	4359	1820	5063	9199	7751	6337

Table VIII(a)

0.95 CONFIDENCE INTERVALS FOR PROPORTIONS*

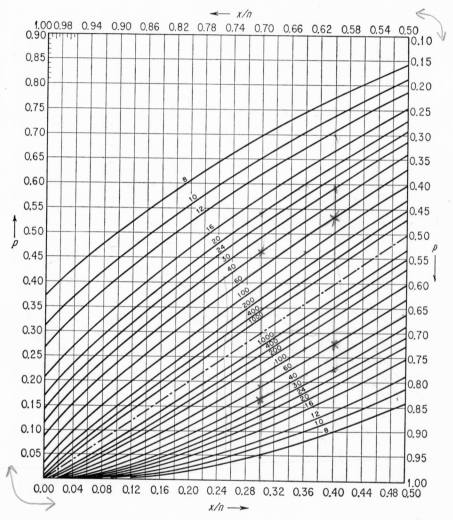

* This table is reproduced from Table 41 of the *Biometrika Tables for Statisticians*, Vol. I (New York: Cambridge University Press, 1954) by permission of the *Biometrika* trustees.

use left side for $\frac{X}{n} < .50$

use right side for $\frac{X}{n} > .50$

Table VIII(b)

0.99 CONFIDENCE INTERVALS FOR PROPORTIONS*

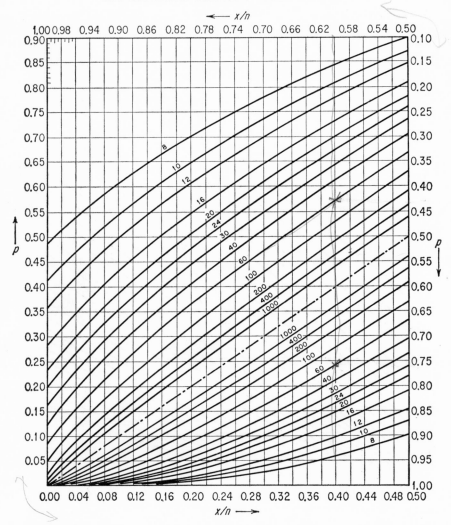

Table IX

CRITICAL VALUES OF D^*

Sample size n	$D_{.10}$	$D_{.05}$	$D_{.01}$
1	0.950	0.975	0.995
2	0.776	0.842	0.929
3	0.642	0.708	0.828
4	0.564	0.624	0.733
5	0.510	0.565	0.669
6	0.470	0.521	0.618
7	0.438	0.486	0.577
8	0.411	0.457	0.543
9	0.388	0.432	0.514
10	0.368	0.410	0.490
11	0.352	0.391	0.468
12	0.338	0.375	0.450
13	0.325	0.361	0.433
14	0.314	0.349	0.418
15	0.304	0.338	0.404
16	0.295	0.328	0.392
17	0.286	0.318	0.381
18	0.278	0.309	0.371
19	0.272	0.301	0.363
20	0.264	0.294	0.356
25	0.24	0.27	0.32
30	0.22	0.24	0.29

* Adapted from F. J. Massey, Jr., "The Kolgomorov-Smirnov test for goodness of fit," *J. Amer. Statist. Ass.*, Vol. 46 (1951), p. 70, with the kind permission of the author and publisher.

Table X(a)

VALUES OF r_p FOR $\alpha = 0.05^*$

p / d.f.	2	3	4	5	6	7	8	9	10
1	17.97								
2	6.09	6.09							
3	4.50	4.52	4.52						
4	3.93	4.01	4.03	4.03					
5	3.64	3.75	3.80	3.81	3.81				
6	3.46	3.59	3.65	3.68	3.69	3.70			
7	3.34	3.48	3.55	3.59	3.61	3.62	3.63		
8	3.26	3.40	3.48	3.52	3.55	3.57	3.57	3.58	
9	3.20	3.34	3.42	3.47	3.50	3.52	3.54	3.54	3.55
10	3.15	3.29	3.38	3.43	3.47	3.49	3.51	3.52	3.52
11	3.11	3.26	3.34	3.40	3.44	3.46	3.48	3.49	3.50
12	3.08	3.23	3.31	3.37	3.41	3.44	3.46	3.47	3.48
13	3.06	3.20	3.29	3.35	3.39	3.42	3.44	3.46	3.47
14	3.03	3.18	3.27	3.33	3.37	3.40	3.43	3.44	3.46
15	3.01	3.16	3.25	3.31	3.36	3.39	3.41	3.43	3.45
16	3.00	3.14	3.23	3.30	3.34	3.38	3.40	3.42	3.44
17	2.98	3.13	3.22	3.28	3.33	3.37	3.39	3.41	3.43
18	2.97	3.12	3.21	3.27	3.32	3.36	3.38	3.40	3.42
19	2.96	3.11	3.20	3.26	3.31	3.35	3.38	3.40	3.41
20	2.95	3.10	3.19	3.25	3.30	3.34	3.37	3.39	3.41
24	2.92	3.07	3.16	3.23	3.28	3.31	3.35	3.37	3.39
30	2.89	3.03	3.13	3.20	3.25	3.29	3.32	3.35	3.37
40	2.86	3.01	3.10	3.17	3.22	3.27	3.30	3.33	3.35
60	2.83	2.98	3.07	3.14	3.20	3.24	3.28	3.31	3.33
120	2.80	2.95	3.04	3.12	3.17	3.22	3.25	3.29	3.31
∞	2.77	2.92	3.02	3.09	3.15	3.19	3.23	3.27	3.29

* This table is reproduced from H. L. Harter, "Critical values for Duncan's new multiple range test." It contains some corrected values to replace those given by D. B. Duncan in "Multiple Range and Multiple F Tests," *Biometrics*, Vol. 11 (1955). The above table is reproduced with the permission of the author and the editor of *Biometrics*.

Table X(b)

VALUES OF r_p FOR $\alpha = 0.01^*$

d.f. \\ p	2	3	4	5	6	7	8	9	10
1	90.02								
2	14.04	14.04							
3	8.26	8.32	8.32						
4	6.51	6.68	6.74	6.76					
5	5.70	5.90	5.99	6.04	6.07				
6	5.24	5.44	5.53	5.62	5.66	5.68			
7	4.95	5.15	5.26	5.33	5.38	5.42	5.44		
8	4.74	4.94	5.06	5.13	5.19	5.23	5.26	5.28	
9	4.60	4.79	4.91	4.99	5.04	5.09	5.12	5.14	5.16
10	4.48	4.67	4.79	4.88	4.93	4.98	5.01	5.04	5.06
11	4.39	4.58	4.70	4.78	4.84	4.89	4.92	4.95	4.97
12	4.32	4.50	4.62	4.71	4.77	4.81	4.85	4.88	4.91
13	4.26	4.44	4.56	4.64	4.71	4.75	4.79	4.82	4.85
14	4.21	4.39	4.51	4.59	4.66	4.70	4.74	4.77	4.80
15	4.17	4.34	4.46	4.55	4.61	4.66	4.70	4.73	4.76
16	4.13	4.31	4.43	4.51	4.57	4.62	4.66	4.70	4.72
17	4.10	4.27	4.39	4.47	4.54	4.59	4.63	4.66	4.69
18	4.07	4.25	4.36	4.45	4.51	4.56	4.60	4.64	4.66
19	4.05	4.22	4.33	4.42	4.48	4.53	4.57	4.61	4.64
20	4.02	4.20	4.31	4.40	4.46	4.51	4.55	4.59	4.62
24	3.96	4.13	4.24	4.32	4.39	4.44	4.48	4.52	4.55
30	3.89	4.06	4.17	4.25	4.31	4.36	4.41	4.45	4.48
40	3.82	3.99	4.10	4.18	4.24	4.29	4.33	4.38	4.41
60	3.76	3.92	4.03	4.11	4.18	4.23	4.27	4.31	4.34
120	3.70	3.86	3.97	4.04	4.11	4.16	4.20	4.24	4.27
∞	3.64	3.80	3.90	3.98	4.04	4.09	4.13	4.17	4.21

* This table is reproduced from H. L. Harter, "Critical values for Duncan's new multiple range test." It contains some corrected values to replace those given by D. B. Duncan in "Multiple Range and Multiple F Tests," *Biometrics*, Vol. 11 (1955). The above table is reproduced with the permission of the author and the editor of *Biometrics*.

Table XI

CONTROL CHART CONSTANTS*

Number of observations in sample, n	Chart for averages			Chart for standard deviations					Chart for ranges				
	Factors for control limits			Factor for central line	Factors for control limits				Factor for central line	Factors for control limits			
	A	A_1	A_2	c_2	B_1	B_2	B_3	B_4	d_2	D_1	D_2	D_3	D_4
2	2.121	3.760	1.880	0.5642	0	1.843	0	3.267	1.128	0	3.686	0	3.267
3	1.732	2.394	1.023	0.7236	0	1.858	0	2.568	1.693	0	4.358	0	2.575
4	1.500	1.880	0.729	0.7979	0	1.808	0	2.266	2.059	0	4.698	0	2.282
5	1.342	1.596	0.577	0.8407	0	1.756	0	2.089	2.326	0	4.918	0	2.115
6	1.225	1.410	0.483	0.8686	0.026	1.711	0.030	1.970	2.534	0	5.078	0	2.004
7	1.134	1.277	0.419	0.8882	0.105	1.672	0.118	1.882	2.704	0.205	5.203	0.076	1.924
8	1.061	1.175	0.373	0.9027	0.167	1.638	0.185	1.815	2.847	0.387	5.307	0.136	1.864
9	1.000	1.094	0.337	0.9139	0.219	1.609	0.239	1.761	2.970	0.546	5.394	0.184	1.816
10	0.949	1.028	0.308	0.9227	0.262	1.584	0.284	1.716	3.078	0.687	5.469	0.223	1.777
11	0.905	0.973	0.285	0.9300	0.299	1.561	0.321	1.679	3.173	0.812	5.534	0.256	1.744
12	0.866	0.925	0.266	0.9359	0.331	1.541	0.354	1.646	3.258	0.924	5.592	0.284	1.716
13	0.832	0.884	0.249	0.9410	0.359	1.523	0.382	1.618	3.336	1.026	5.646	0.308	1.692
14	0.802	0.848	0.235	0.9453	0.384	1.507	0.406	1.594	3.407	1.121	5.693	0.329	1.671
15	0.775	0.816	0.223	0.9490	0.406	1.492	0.428	1.572	3.472	1.207	5.737	0.348	1.652

* This table is reproduced, by permission, from the *ASTM Manual on Quality Control of Materials*, American Society for Testing and Materials, Philadelphia, Pa., 1951.

Table XII

FACTORS FOR TWO-SIDED TOLERANCE LIMITS[*]

	$1 - \alpha = 0.95$			$1 - \alpha = 0.99$		
n \ P	0.90	0.95	0.99	0.90	0.95	0.99
2	32.019	37.674	48.430	160.193	188.491	242.300
3	8.380	9.916	12.861	18.930	22.401	29.055
4	5.369	6.370	8.299	9.398	11.150	14.527
5	4.275	5.079	6.634	6.612	7.855	10.260
6	3.712	4.414	5.775	5.337	6.345	8.301
7	3.369	4.007	5.248	4.613	5.488	7.187
8	3.136	3.732	4.891	4.147	4.936	6.468
9	2.967	3.532	4.631	3.822	4.550	5.966
10	2.839	3.379	4.433	3.582	4.265	5.594
11	2.737	3.259	4.277	3.397	4.045	5.308
12	2.655	3.162	4.150	3.250	3.870	5.079
13	2.587	3.081	4.044	3.130	3.727	4.893
14	2.529	3.012	3.955	3.029	3.608	4.737
15	2.480	2.954	3.878	2.945	3.507	4.605
16	2.437	2.903	3.812	2.872	3.421	4.492
17	2.400	2.858	3.754	2.808	3.345	4.393
18	2.366	2.819	3.702	2.753	3.279	4.307
19	2.337	2.784	3.656	2.703	3.221	4.230
20	2.310	2.752	3.615	2.659	3.168	4.161
25	2.208	2.631	3.457	2.494	2.972	3.904
30	2.140	2.549	3.350	2.385	2.841	3.733
35	2.090	2.490	3.272	2.306	2.748	3.611
40	2.052	2.445	3.213	2.247	2.677	3.518
45	2.021	2.408	3.165	2.200	2.621	3.444
50	1.996	2.379	3.126	2.162	2.576	3.385
55	1.976	2.354	3.094	2.130	2.538	3.335
60	1.958	2.333	3.066	2.103	2.506	3.293
65	1.943	2.315	3.042	2.080	2.478	3.257
70	1.929	2.299	3.021	2.060	2.454	3.225
75	1.917	2.285	3.002	2.042	2.433	3.197
80	1.907	2.272	2.986	2.026	2.414	3.173
85	1.897	2.261	2.971	2.012	2.397	3.150
90	1.889	2.251	2.958	1.999	2.382	3.130
95	1.881	2.241	2.945	1.987	2.368	3.112
100	1.874	2.233	2.934	1.977	2.355	3.096
150	1.825	2.175	2.859	1.905	2.270	2.983
200	1.798	2.143	2.816	1.865	2.222	2.921
250	1.780	2.121	2.788	1.839	2.191	2.880
300	1.767	2.106	2.767	1.820	2.169	2.850
400	1.749	2.084	2.739	1.794	2.138	2.809
500	1.737	2.070	2.721	1.777	2.117	2.783
600	1.729	2.060	2.707	1.764	2.102	2.763
700	1.722	2.052	2.697	1.755	2.091	2.748
800	1.717	2.046	2.688	1.747	2.082	2.736
900	1.712	2.040	2.682	1.741	2.075	2.726
1000	1.709	2.036	2.676	1.736	2.068	2.718
∞	1.645	1.960	2.576	1.645	1.960	2.576

[*] Adapted by permission from *Techniques of Statistical Analysis* by C. Eisenhart, M. W. Hastay, and W. A. Wallis. Copyright 1947, McGraw-Hill Book Company, Inc.

Table XIII

SAMPLE SIZE CODE LETTERS FROM MIL-STD-105 D

Lot or batch size			General inspection levels		
			I	II	III
2	to	8	A	A	B
9	to	15	A	B	C
16	to	25	B	C	D
26	to	50	C	D	E
51	to	90	C	E	F
91	to	150	D	F	G
151	to	280	E	G	H
281	to	500	F	H	J
501	to	1,200	G	J	K
1,201	to	3,200	H	K	L
3,201	to	10,000	J	L	M
10,001	to	35,000	K	M	N
35,001	to	150,000	L	N	P
150,001	to	500,000	M	P	Q
500,001	and	over	N	Q	R

Table XIV

MASTER TABLE FOR SINGLE SAMPLING (NORMAL INSPECTION)
MIL-STD-105 D

Acceptable Quality Levels (normal inspection)

Sample size code letter	Sample size	0.010 Ac	0.010 Re	0.015 Ac	0.015 Re	0.025 Ac	0.025 Re	0.040 Ac	0.040 Re	0.065 Ac	0.065 Re	0.10 Ac	0.10 Re	0.15 Ac	0.15 Re	0.25 Ac	0.25 Re	0.40 Ac	0.40 Re	0.65 Ac	0.65 Re	1.0 Ac	1.0 Re	1.5 Ac	1.5 Re	2.5 Ac	2.5 Re	4.0 Ac	4.0 Re	6.5 Ac	6.5 Re	10 Ac	10 Re	15 Ac	15 Re	25 Ac	25 Re	40 Ac	40 Re	65 Ac	65 Re	100 Ac	100 Re	150 Ac	150 Re	250 Ac	250 Re	400 Ac	400 Re	650 Ac	650 Re	1000 Ac	1000 Re
A	2	↓		↓		↓		↓		↓		↓		↓		↓		↓		↓		↓		↓		↓		↓		↓		↓		0	1	1	2	2	3	3	4	5	6	7	8	10	11	14	15	21	22	30	31
B	3	↓		↓		↓		↓		↓		↓		↓		↓		↓		↓		↓		↓		↓		↓		↓		0	1	1	2	2	3	3	4	5	6	7	8	10	11	14	15	21	22	30	31	44	45
C	5	↓		↓		↓		↓		↓		↓		↓		↓		↓		↓		↓		↓		↓		↓		0	1	1	2	2	3	3	4	5	6	7	8	10	11	14	15	21	22	30	31	44	45	↑	
D	8	↓		↓		↓		↓		↓		↓		↓		↓		↓		↓		↓		↓		↓		0	1	1	2	2	3	3	4	5	6	7	8	10	11	14	15	21	22	30	31	44	45	↑		↑	
E	13	↓		↓		↓		↓		↓		↓		↓		↓		↓		↓		↓		↓		0	1	1	2	2	3	3	4	5	6	7	8	10	11	14	15	21	22	30	31	44	45	↑		↑		↑	
F	20	↓		↓		↓		↓		↓		↓		↓		↓		↓		↓		↓		0	1	1	2	2	3	3	4	5	6	7	8	10	11	14	15	21	22	30	31	44	45	↑		↑		↑		↑	
G	32	↓		↓		↓		↓		↓		↓		↓		↓		↓		↓		0	1	1	2	2	3	3	4	5	6	7	8	10	11	14	15	21	22	30	31	44	45	↑		↑		↑		↑		↑	
H	50	↓		↓		↓		↓		↓		↓		↓		↓		↓		0	1	1	2	2	3	3	4	5	6	7	8	10	11	14	15	21	22	30	31	44	45	↑		↑		↑		↑		↑		↑	
J	80	↓		↓		↓		↓		↓		↓		↓		↓		0	1	1	2	2	3	3	4	5	6	7	8	10	11	14	15	21	22	30	31	44	45	↑		↑		↑		↑		↑		↑		↑	
K	125	↓		↓		↓		↓		↓		↓		↓		0	1	1	2	2	3	3	4	5	6	7	8	10	11	14	15	21	22	30	31	44	45	↑		↑		↑		↑		↑		↑		↑		↑	
L	200	↓		↓		↓		↓		↓		↓		0	1	1	2	2	3	3	4	5	6	7	8	10	11	14	15	21	22	30	31	44	45	↑		↑		↑		↑		↑		↑		↑		↑		↑	
M	315	↓		↓		↓		↓		↓		0	1	1	2	2	3	3	4	5	6	7	8	10	11	14	15	21	22	30	31	44	45	↑		↑		↑		↑		↑		↑		↑		↑		↑		↑	
N	500	↓		↓		↓		↓		0	1	1	2	2	3	3	4	5	6	7	8	10	11	14	15	21	22	30	31	44	45	↑		↑		↑		↑		↑		↑		↑		↑		↑		↑		↑	
P	800	↓		↓		↓		0	1	1	2	2	3	3	4	5	6	7	8	10	11	14	15	21	22	30	31	44	45	↑		↑		↑		↑		↑		↑		↑		↑		↑		↑		↑		↑	
Q	1250	↓		↓		0	1	1	2	2	3	3	4	5	6	7	8	10	11	14	15	21	22	30	31	44	45	↑		↑		↑		↑		↑		↑		↑		↑		↑		↑		↑		↑		↑	
R	2000	↓		0	1	1	2	2	3	3	4	5	6	7	8	10	11	14	15	21	22	30	31	44	45	↑		↑		↑		↑		↑		↑		↑		↑		↑		↑		↑		↑		↑		↑	

↓ = Use first sampling plan below arrow. If sample size equals, or exceeds, lot or batch size, do 100 percent inspection.

↑ = Use first sampling plan above arrow.

Ac = Acceptance number.

Re = Rejection number.

ANSWERS TO ODD-NUMBERED EXERCISES

In Exercises involving extensive numerical calculations, the reader may get answers differing from those given here due to rounding at various intermediate stages.

Page 12

1. 60.   3. 9 possible outcomes.

7. (a) {Bailey, Clark, Edwards, Fox}; (b) {Clark}; (c) {Dodds};
   (e) {Andrews, Clark, Dodds, Edwards, Fox}.

9. (a) $(1, 1)$, $(1, 2)$, $(1, 3)$, $(1, 4)$, $(2, 1)$, $(2, 2)$, $(2, 3)$, $(2, 4)$, $(3, 1)$, $(3, 2)$, $(3, 3)$, $(3, 4)$, $(4, 1)$, $(4, 2)$, $(4, 3)$, $(4, 4)$;
   (b) $(1, 1)$, $(1, 2)$, $(1, 3)$, $(1, 4)$, $(2, 1)$, $(3, 1)$, $(4, 1)$;
   (c) $(1, 1)$, $(2, 2)$, $(3, 3)$, $(4, 4)$;   (d) $(2, 2)$, $(4, 4)$, $(2, 4)$, $(4, 2)$;
   (e) $(2, 2)$, $(2, 3)$, $(2, 4)$, $(3, 2)$, $(3, 3)$, $(3, 4)$, $(4, 2)$, $(4, 3)$, $(4, 4)$;
   (f) $(1, 1)$, $(2, 2)$, $(3, 3)$, $(4, 4)$, $(2, 4)$, $(4, 2)$;
   (g) $(1, 1)$;   (h) ϕ

417

Page 22

1. ϕ, $M \cap G'$, $M \cap G$, $M' \cap G$, $M' \cap G'$, M, $(M \cap G') \cup (M' \cap G)$, G', G, $(M \cap G) \cup (M' \cap G')$, M', $M' \cup G$, $M' \cup G'$, $M \cup G'$, $M \cup G$, S.

3. (a) 85; (b) 40; (c) 70; (d) 55; (e) 10; (f) 30.

5. (a) Yes; (b) No; (c) No; (d) Yes.

7. (a) $\dfrac{4547}{5804}$; (b) $\dfrac{267}{1451}$; (c) $\dfrac{1661}{2902}$; (d) $\dfrac{1099}{5804}$.

9. (a) 0.30; (b) 0.10; (c) 0.20; (d) 0.06; (e) 0.44; (f) 0.73.

11. (a) 1/26; (b) 1/2; (c) 3/13; (d) 1/13.

13. (a) 13/25; (b) 31/75; (c) 9/25; (d) 8/75.

15. (a) 0.92; (b) 0.14; (c) 0.84; (d) 0.62.

17. 0.0051.

19. (a) $P(A \cup C)$ cannot be less than $P(A)$; (b) $P(B \cap C)$ cannot be greater than $P(B)$; (c) $P(A \cap B') = P(A)$ since A and B are mutually exclusive.

Page 32

1. 2/3 and 4/7.

3. (a) 16/31; (b) 4/13; (c) 8/13; (d) 2/11; (e) 2/3; (f) 25/49.

5. (a) 6/25; (b) 1/2; (c) 394/709.

7. (a) 16/25; (b) 156/245.   9. 0.415.

11. 0.651 and 0.274.   13. 0.51.

15. 5/13.

Page 44

1. $f(0) = 1/20, f(1) = 2/20, f(2) = 3/20, f(3) = 4/20, f(4) = 4/20, f(5) = 3/20,$ $f(6) = 2/20, f(7) = 1/20$.

3. (a) Yes; (b) Yes; (c) No; (d) No.

9. (a) 0.4032; (b) 0.1859; (c) 0.5075; (d) 0.2312; (e) 0.0432; (f) 0.9997.

11. (a) 0.3741; (b) 0.9912; (c) 0.2078.

13. (a) 0.9419; (b) 0.7338; (c) 0.4797; (d) 0.2713.

Page 51

1. (a) 60/143; (b) 102/143; (c) 102/143; (d) 999/1001.

3. (a) 385/969; (b) 682/969; (c) 53/969.

5. (a) 0.5120; (b) 0.2160; (c) 0.0640; (d) 0.0080.

7. 0.135, 0.271, 0.271, 0.180, 0.090, 0.036, 0.012, 0.004, 0.001, 0.000, etc.

9. (a) 0.070; (b) 0.033; (c) 0.900.

11. 0.368, 0.368, and 0.184.   13. 0.005.

Page 59

1. $\mu = 26/31$ and $\sigma^2 = 1122/961$.   3. $\mu = 2.4$ and $\sigma^2 = 0.24$.

7. $\mu = \dfrac{n+1}{2}$ and $\sigma^2 = \dfrac{n^2-1}{12}$.   9. 0.8889 and 0.9994.

11. 250.

Page 61

1. 35/34,992.   3. 0.003.

Page 68

3. (a) $k = 1/5$; (b) $F(x) = 0$ for $x \le 0$ and $F(x) = 1 - e^{-x/5}$ for $x > 0$; (c) 0.1809; (d) 0.5507; (e) 0.3012.

5. $1/\pi$.   7. $\mu = 4/5$ and $\sigma^2 = 2/75$.

9. $\mu = 1/2$ and $\sigma^2 = 1/20$.

Page 74

3. (a) 0.9772; (b) 0.0250; (c) 0.0049; (d) 0.9901; (e) 0.3413; (f) 0.2640; (g) 0.1510; (h) 0.9608.

7. (a) 0.0465; (b) 0.2743; (c) 0.6594; (d) 0.1979.

9. (a) 0.0202; (b) 0.8788.   11. 0.8531.

13. 18.1%.

Page 81

1. $F(x) = 0$ for $x \le \alpha$, $F(x) = \dfrac{x - \alpha}{\beta - \alpha}$ for $\alpha < x < \beta$, $F(x) = 1$ for $x \ge \beta$.

3. 0.76.

5. $F(x) = 0$ for $x \le 0$, $F(x) = 1 - e^{-x/\beta}$ for $x > 0$; 0.135.

11. $k = \alpha\beta$, $\mu = \alpha^{-1/\beta}\Gamma\left(1 + \dfrac{1}{\beta}\right)$, and $\sigma^2 = \alpha^{-2/\beta}\left\{\Gamma\left(1 + \dfrac{2}{\beta}\right) - \left[\Gamma\left(1 + \dfrac{1}{\beta}\right)\right]^2\right\}$.

13. 0.228.

Page 84

1. (a) 3/256; (b) 1/2.

3. (a) $k = 1$; (b) $\dfrac{1}{2}\left(1 - \dfrac{1}{e}\right)$; (c) $1/e^2$.

5. (a) $F_1(x) = 0$ for $x \le 0$, $F_1(x) = \dfrac{x^3 + 43x}{156}$ for $0 < x < 3$, $F_1(x) = 1$ for $x \ge 3$;

   (b) $F_2(y) = 0$ for $y \le 1$, $F_2(y) = \dfrac{9y + y^3 - 10}{260}$ for $1 < y < 6$, $F_2(y) = 1$ for $y \ge 6$.

7. 0.722.

9. 14.48.

Page 90

1. No, expectation is only $12.18.

3. (b) A gets $11 and B gets $5.

5. When 3 per cent are defective it is cheaper to install without testing; when 6 per cent are defective it is cheaper to test.

7. Stock 3, the maximum expected profit is $3.825.

9. 50%.

Page 98

1. 0.082.

5. (a) 2; (b) 4/3; (c) 2/3; (d) 5/9.

7. 11/16.

9. (a) 1/3; (b) 1/3.

11. (a) 0.94; (b) 0.76; (c) 0.57; when odds are against you bet as much as possible each time.

Page 114

1. *A possible answer is:* Class interval is 2; the lower class limits are 15.0, 17.0, 19.0, 21.0, 23.0, 25.0, 27.0, 29.0; the upper class limits are 16.9, 18.9, 20.9, 22.9, 24.9, 26.9, 28.9, 30.9; the class boundaries are 14.95, 16.95, 18.95, 20.95, 22.95, 24.95, 26.95, 28.95, 30.95; the class marks are 15.95, 17.95, 19.95, 21.95, 23.95, 25.95, 27.95, 29.95.

3. The classes $0.10 - 0.14$, $0.15 - 0.19$, $\ldots$, and $0.45 - 0.49$ have respective frequencies of 2, 5, 14, 28, 32, 13, 5, and 1.

5. Yes, close to a normal distribution.

9. Yes, they follow the pattern of a normal distribution.

13. (a) 0, 1, 2, 3, 4, 5, and 6 imperfections occur with respective frequencies of 12, 11, 9, 6, 8, 3, and 1; the cumulative "or more" frequencies are 50, 38, 27, 18, 12, 4, 1, and 0, respectively.

15. Each dimension should be multiplied by $\sqrt{2}$ rather than by 2.

Page 123

7. $\bar{x} = 45{,}753$ and $s = 14{,}203$.

11. $s = 0.0665$.

9. $\bar{x} = 2.00$ and $s = 1.69$.

13. (a) \$29,500.

Page 134

7. $\mu_{\bar{x}} = 2.5$ and $\sigma_{\bar{x}}^2 = 0.625$.

13. 0.8904.

11. 0.8664.

Page 141

1. $t = -3.08$, information refutes the claim.

3. $t = 4.74$, process not in control.

7. 0.02.

5. 0.95.

9. 0.308.

Page 149

1. Error will not exceed 0.0067 calories.

3. (a) Error will not exceed 1.55 minutes; (b) $41.1 - 43.9$.

5. $n = 246$.

7. $12.79 - 12.83$.

9. Largest error is 0.181; $5.50 - 5.86$.

11. 0.92.

13. $n = 18$.

15. (a) $\{3, 3\}$, $\{3, 6\}$, $\{3, 9\}$, $\{3, 12\}$, $\{3, 15\}$, $\{6, 6\}$, $\{6, 9\}$, $\{6, 12\}$, $\{6, 15\}$, $\{9, 9\}$, $\{9, 12\}$, $\{9, 15\}$, $\{12, 12\}$, $\{12, 15\}$, $\{15, 15\}$.

17. The probabilities for $\mu = 46$, $\mu = 50$, and $\mu = 55$ are, respectively, 0.0118, 0.2436, and 0.7446; the Bayesian estimate of μ is 53.7.

Page 160

1. $\alpha = 0.106$ and $\beta = 0.106$.

3. (b) Values of β are 0.56, 0.09, and 0.002.

5. $n = 100$; $\beta = 0.09$ for $\mu = 0.30$.

7. (b) Values of β are 0.91, 0.25, and 0.05.

9. Reject for $\bar{x} < -0.39$ or $\bar{x} > 0.39$.   11. 568.

Page 170

1. (a) $\mu_2 - \mu_1 > 0$; (b) $\mu_2 - \mu_1 < 0$; (c) $\mu_2 \neq \mu_1$.

3. $z = 2.06$; Yes.

5. $t = -3.28$; No.

7. $t = -1.95$; cannot reject H_0.

11. (a) $\mu = 0.006$ and $\sigma = 0.0036$; (b) 0.0475.

13. $t = -3.74$; reject null hypothesis.

15. $z = 3.77$; reject null hypothesis.

17. $t = 1.94$; cannot accept hypothesis that plastic pins last on the average 1,000 hours longer.

19. $t = 2.20$; difference is not significant.

21. $\bar{x}_1 - \bar{x}_2 \pm t_{\alpha/2} \sqrt{\dfrac{[(n_1 - 1)s_1^2 + (n_2 - 1)s_2^2](n_1 + n_2)}{n_1 n_2 (n_1 + n_2 - 2)}}$.

Page 178

1. (a) 34.0; (b) 35.5.

3. $1.15 - 5.52$.

5. (a) $13.2 - 23.6$; (b) $13.3 - 23.4$.

7. $0.033 - 0.057$.

Page 183

1. $\chi^2 = 5.12$; cannot reject the hypothesis that $\sigma = 1.5$.

3. $\chi^2 = 5.5$; cannot reject the hypothesis that $\sigma = 0.01$.

5. $z = -2.01$; reject the null hypothesis.

7. $F = 1.48$; claim not reasonable on the basis of given data

9. $F = 2.25$; null hypothesis cannot be rejected.

Page 190

3. $0.58 - 0.71$.

5. (a) $0.48 - 0.61$; (b) $0.490 - 0.614$.

7. $n = 385$; $n = 351$.

9. $0.181 - 0.407$.

11. 0.0155.

Page 197

1. $z = 2.47$; the new muscle relaxant is effective.

3. (b) 0.035.

5. $z = -3.13$; claim is refuted.

9. $z = -2.79$; reject the null hypothesis.

11. $z = -1.84$; yes.

13. $\chi^2 = 3.18$; differences not significant.

15. $\chi^2 = 11.81$; yes.

Page 203

1. $\chi^2 = 7.69$; cannot reject null hypothesis.
3. $\chi^2 = 15.0$; differences are significant.
5. $\chi^2 = 4.80$; reject H_0.
9. (a) 0.0305, 0.1056, 0.2171, 0.2812, 0.2171, 0.1056, 0.0305;
   (b) 3.0, 10.6, 21.7, 28.2, 21.7, 10.6, 3.0; (c) $\chi^2 = 2.22$; good fit.

Page 212

1. $F_{1/4} = 57.2$, $F_{1/2} = 68.5$, $F_{3/4} = 76.0$, $F_{1/10} = 49.1$, $F_{19/20} = 94.9$.
3. 45,250 and 45,750.   5. 0.297 and 0.294.
7. 2724 and 2785; $s = 2716$; 2558.   9. 0.069 and 0.0675.

Page 217

1. $z = -4.88$; reject null hypothesis.
3. The probability for 7 or more or less than 4 plus signs is 0.34; cannot reject null hypothesis.
5. Cannot reject null hypothesis.
7. $z = 0.14$; cannot reject null hypothesis.
9. $z = 3.44$; reject null hypothesis.
11. $H = 0.86$; no difference in effectiveness.

Page 223

1. $z = 2.59$; not random.   3. $z = 0.02$; cannot reject.
5. $z = 0$; not significant.
7. Maximum D is 0.24; cannot reject H_0.

Page 236

1. (a) $y' = 0.41 + 0.039x$; (b) 14.1.
3. $a = 3.01$ and $b = 14.14$; $11.26 < \beta < 17.02$.
5. $y' = 26.7 + 9.98x$; $14.2 - 39.2$.   7. (a) $47.6 - 57.4$.
9. (a) $\dfrac{\Sigma\, xy}{\Sigma\, x^2}$; (b) 14.8.   11. $x' = -2.44 + 0.10y$.

Page 249

1. $a = 30.0$ and $b = 0.0000375$.   3. (b) $a = 12.7$ and $b = 41.9$.

5. (a) 1.49; (b) $1.38 - 1.60$.   7. 1.002.

9. (a) A third degree polynomial; (b) dip at 652 feet and crest at 303 feet.

13. $y = 162.2 + 32.5x_1 - 0.0863x_2$.

Page 258

1. (a) $r = -0.60$; (b) $z = -2.86$; significant correlation.

3. -0.82 to -0.22.   9. $r' = -0.28$.

Page 270

3. 184, 48, and 136.   5. $F = 11.3$; significant at 0.01 level.

7. (a) $F = 20.7$; differences are significant;
   (b) $\hat{\mu} = 51.80$, $\hat{\alpha}_1 = -4.55$, $\hat{\alpha}_2 = -2.22$, $\hat{\alpha}_3 = 6.80$, $\hat{\sigma}^2 = 13.88$.

9. Estimated means are 73.5, 69.8, and 80.4; $F = 2.96$; differences are not significant.

13. $\displaystyle \sum_{i=1}^{k} \sum_{j=1}^{n_i} (y_{ij} - \bar{y}_.)^2 = \sum_{i=1}^{k} \sum_{j=1}^{n_i} (y_{ij} - \bar{y}_i)^2 + \sum_{i=1}^{k} n_i(\bar{y}_i - \bar{y}_.)^2$

Page 281

1. For displays $F = 55.2$; significant at the 0.01 level.

3. For days $F = 4.3$ and for shifts $F = 5.6$; both significant at the 0.05 level.

5. Error mean square is reduced from 0.2375 to 0.0742. For treatments $F = 47.2$, significant at the 0.01 level; for blocks $F = 9.8$, significant at the 0.05 level.

7. (a) $\displaystyle \sum_{i=1}^{a} \sum_{j=1}^{b} \sum_{k=1}^{r} (y_{ijk} - \bar{y}_{...})^2 = \sum_{i=1}^{a} \sum_{j=1}^{b} \sum_{k=1}^{r} (y_{ijk} - \bar{y}_{i..} - \bar{y}_{.j.} - \bar{y}_{..k} + 2\bar{y}_{...})^2$

$\displaystyle \qquad + br \sum_{i=1}^{a} (\bar{y}_{i..} - \bar{y}_{...})^2 + ar \sum_{j=1}^{b} (\bar{y}_{.j.} - \bar{y}_{...})^2 + ab \sum_{k=1}^{r} (\bar{y}_{..k} - \bar{y}_{...})^2$

(b) $C = T_{...}^2/abr$, $SST = \displaystyle \sum_{i=1}^{a} \sum_{j=1}^{b} \sum_{k=1}^{r} y_{ijk}^2 - C$, $SS(Tr) = \sum_{i=1}^{a} T_{i..}^2/br - C$,

$SS(Bl) = \displaystyle \sum_{j=1}^{b} T_{.j.}^2/ar - C$, $SSR = \sum_{k=1}^{r} T_{..k}^2/ab - C$,

$SSE = SST - SS(Tr) - SS(Bl) - SSR$

(c) $abr - a - b - r + 2$.

9. (a) Gain in degrees of freedom for SSE is $ab - b$; (b) Gain in degrees of freedom for SSE is $ab - 1$.

13. A B C
     47.2   49.6   58.6

15. C A B D
     7.33   10.67   12.33   15.00

Page 290

1. For fuels $F = 56.8$ and for mechanics $F = 21.5$, both significant at the 0.01 level; the Duncan test for fuels (with $\alpha = 0.01$) yields

$$C \qquad A \qquad B$$
$$15.67 \quad 20.11 \quad 24.67$$

3. For threads $F = 30.7$ and for technicians $F = 8.3$, both significant at the 0.01 level; the Duncan test for threads (with $\alpha = 0.01$) yields

$$E \qquad C \qquad D \qquad B \qquad A$$
$$22.46 \quad 22.64 \quad 22.72 \quad 23.08 \quad 31.68$$

5. For money spent on newspaper ads $F = 17.5$ and for locations in store $F = 99.4$; both significant at the 0.01 level.

Page 307

1. (a) For treatments $F = 51.0$; significant at the 0.01 level;

(b)

Source of variation	Degrees of freedom	Sum of squares	Mean square	F
Replicates	1	6	6	<1
Designs	3	1,457,408	485,803	92.6
Vibrations	2	1,345,912	672,956	128.3
Interaction	6	138,332	23,055	4.4
Error	11	57,696	5,245	
Total	23	2,999,354		

(c) Main effects are significant at the 0.01 level and interaction is significant at the 0.05 level.

3. For hull designs $F = 8.1$ and for days $F = 22.9$; both significant at the 0.01 level.

5. (a) $SST = 3,305$, $SS(Tr) = 3,188$, $SSR = 14$, $SSE = 103$;
   (b) If A represents detergents, B represents washing time, and C represents water temperature, $SSA = 645.5$, $SSB = 324$, $SSC = 1,936$, $SS(AB) = 10$, $SS(AC) = 108.5$, $SS(BC) = 161$, and $SS(ABC) = 3$.

(c)

Source of variation	Degrees of freedom	Sum of squares	Mean square	F
Replicates	2	14	7	1.50
Main effects:				
A	2	645.5	322.75	69.0
B	1	324	324	69.1
C	1	1,936	1,936	413.7
Two-factor interactions:				
AB	2	10	5	1.1
AC	2	108.5	54.25	11.6
BC	1	161	161	34.4
Three-factor interaction:				
ABC	2	3	1.5	<1
Error	22	103	4.68	
Total	35	3,305		

All main effects as well as the AC and BC interactions are significant at the 0.01 level.

7. $\mu = \frac{1}{4}(\mu_{111} + \mu_{121} + \mu_{211} + \mu_{221})$, $\alpha_1 = \frac{1}{4}(\mu_{111} + \mu_{121} - \mu_{211} - \mu_{221})$,
$\beta_1 = \frac{1}{4}(\mu_{111} - \mu_{121} + \mu_{211} - \mu_{221})$, $(\alpha\beta)_{11} = \frac{1}{4}(\mu_{111} - \mu_{121} - \mu_{211} + \mu_{221})$.

Page 318

1. (a) $SST = 110.44$, $SS(Tr) = 103.94$, $SSR = 1.56$, $SSE = 4.94$;
   (b) $[A] = -1$, $[B] = -13$, $[AB] = 3$, $[C] = -25$, $[AC] = 3$, $[BC] = -29$, $[ABC] = 3$;
   (c) $SSA = 0.06$, $SSB = 10.56$, $SS(AB) = 0.56$, $SSC = 39.06$, $SS(AC) = 0.56$, $SS(BC) = 52.56$, $SS(ABC) = 0.56$;
   (e) B, C, and BC are significant at the 0.01 level; the corresponding values of F are 14.9, 55.0, and 74.0.

3. For the B effect $F = 8.1$ and for the ABC interaction $F = 5.6$, which are both significant at the 0.05 level; for replicates $F = 9.1$, which is significant at the 0.01 level.

5. (a) $= r[\mu - \alpha_0 + \beta_0 + \gamma_0 - (\alpha\beta)_{00} - (\alpha\gamma)_{00} + (\beta\gamma)_{00} - (\alpha\beta\gamma)_{000}] + \sum\limits_{l=1}^{r} \epsilon_{100l}$

7. $\epsilon_A = \sum\limits_{l=1}^{r} [-\epsilon_{000l} + \epsilon_{100l} - \epsilon_{10l} + \epsilon_{110l} - \epsilon_{001l} + \epsilon_{101l} - \epsilon_{011l} + \epsilon_{111l}]$

Page 331

1. (a) *Block 1: a, b, c, abc, d, abd, acd, bcd; Block 2: 1, ab, ac, bc, ad, bd, cd, abcd;*
   (b) *Block 1: a, b, acd, bcd; Block 2: c, abc, d, abd;*
   Block 3: ac, bc, ad, bd; Block 4: 1, ab, cd, abcd; CD also confounded.

3. *Block 1: abc, bd, ae, cde, cf, adf, bef, abcdef; Block 2: a, cd, abce, bde, bf, abcdf,*
   cef, adef; Block 3: b, abcd, ce, ade, af, cdf, abcef, bdef;
   Block 4: 1, acd, bce, abde, abf, bcdf, acef, def; Block 5: bc, abd, e, acde, acf, df,
   abef, bcdef; Block 6: ac, d, abe, bcde, bcf, abdf, ef, acdef;
   Block 7: c, ad, be, abcde. abcf, bdf, aef, cdef; Block 8: ab, bcd, ace, de, f, acdf,
   bcef, abdef; CDE, ADF, BEF, and *ACEF* are also confounded.

5. The intrablock *SSE* equals 4.39; *B, C,* and *BC* are significant at the 0.01 level
   with corresponding *F* values of 14.5, 53.5, and 72.0.

7. (a) *Block 1: 1, bc, abd, acd, abe, ace, de, bcde; Block 2: ab, ac, d, bcd, e, bce,*
   abde, acde; Block 3: b, c, ad, abcd, ae, abce, bde, cde;
   Block 4: a, abc, bd, cd, be, ce, ade. abcde;

   (b) The intrablock *SSE* equals 415.8; *A* and *E* are significant at the 0.01 level
   with *F* values of 12.3 and 16.7; *B, C, AD, ACD,* and *BCD* are significant
   at the 0.05 level with corresponding *F* values of 5.5, 5.8, 6.1, 4.6, and 5.5.

11. (a) *A* and *BCD, B* and *ACD, C* and *ABD, D* and *ABC, AB* and *CD, AC* and
    BD, AD and *BC;*
    (b) *A* and *BCD* and *B* and *ACD, C* and *ABD* and *ABC* and *D, AC* and *BD*
    and *BC* and *AD.*

13. 1, *bc, adf, aeg, defg, abcdf, abceg, bcdefg, bdg, bef, cef, abfg, acfg, abde, acde,*
    cdg, ab, ac, bdf, beg, cdf, ceg, acdefg, abdefg, de, fg, adg, aef, bcde, bcfg, abcdg,
    abcef.

15. (a) 4920, −360, −420, −144, −84, −68, 12, −40, −374, 118, −126, 122, 22,
    2, −22, −22, −84, 16, −32, 64, −80, 44, −24, 120, −138, 70, −90, 42,
    −54, 18, −2, 82;
    (b) [*I*], [*A*], [*B*], [*AB*], [*C*], [*AC*], [*BC*], error, [*D*], [*AD*], [*BD*], error, [*CD*],
    error, error, [*EF*], [*E*], [*AE*], [*BE*], error, [*CE*], error, error, [*DF*], [*DE*],
    error, error, [*CF*] error, [*BF*], [*AF*], [*F*];
    (c) *MSE* = 123.41; *A, B,* and *D* are significant at the 0.01 level with *F* values
    of 32.8, 44.7, and 35.4, respectively; *AB* is significant at the 0.05 level
    with an *F* value of 5.2.

Page 345

1. (a) Central Line = 1.500, *UCL* = 1.513, *LCL* = 1.487;
   (b) Central Line = 0.0233, *UCL* = 0.0492, *LCL* = 0.

3. (a) Central Line = 58.10, *UCL* = 61.12, *LCL* = 55.08;
   (b) Central Line = 2.95, *UCL* = 7.60, *LCL* = 0;
   (d) *z* = −3.1, there is a significant trend; (e) Process is not in control.

5. (a) For $\bar{x}$ chart Central Line = 21.70, UCL = 24.44, LCL = 18.96; For σ chart Central Line = 1.16, UCL = 3.30, LCL = 0.

7. Central Line = 0.0024, UCL = 0.0068, LCL = 0.

9. (a) Central Line = 0.076, UCL = 0.187, LCL = 0.

11. Central Line = 4, UCL = 10, LCL = 0; in control.

Page 350

1. 34.9 − 50.1.

3. (a) 0.1274 − 0.1294; (b) 0.1283 − 0.1285.

Page 360

1. (a) c = 13; (b) 0.063.   3. (a) 0.03; (b) 0.13.

9. α = 0.15.   11. n = 80 and c = 3.

13. $a_n = -1.67 + 0.19n$, $r_n = 2.14 + 0.19n$; reject on 8th trial.

Page 370

1. 0.60.   3. 0.99963.

5. (a) $F(t) = \theta_1 + (1 - \theta_1 - \theta_2)\dfrac{t - \alpha}{\beta - \alpha}$ for $\alpha \leq t \leq \beta$.

7. (a) 0.632; (b) 0.368.   9. 141 hours.

11. (a) 0.301; (b) 0.9095; (c) 0.368.

13. (b) $F(x) = 1 - (1 - p)^x$ for $x = 1, 2, 3, \ldots$; (c) 0.189.

Page 380

1. (a) 206 − 2,412; (b) T_r = 2,600 < 4,575, cannot reject null hypothesis.

3. (a) 128 − 535; (b) T_r = 1,849 falls between 771 and 5,140, cannot reject null hypothesis.

5. (a) t^* = 63.3; (b) t^* = 12.1.   7. 166,917 < μ.

9. $\hat{\mu}$ = 500; using exponential model $\hat{\mu}$ = 746.

INDEX

$$B(x, m, p) - B(x-1, m, p)$$
$$5, 18, 20 - B(4, 18, 20$$

I am joint

1 on minimal approx   X > 0

$$1. \quad f(x) \begin{cases} e^{-x/2} \\ 0 \end{cases} \quad \text{optional}$$

$$\mu = \int_{-\infty}^{\infty} x \cdot f(x)$$